A-Level Year 1 & AS
Geography
Exam Board: AQA

AS Geography is like a day-trip to a British seaside town — one minute you're concerned with the nature and distribution of cold environments, the next you're seriously questioning the importance of place in human life and experience.

Unfortunately, you have to take exams at the end instead of going to the chip shop. That's where this fantastic book comes in — it has everything you need to make sure you're 100% prepared for anything the examiners might throw at you.

And since it's made by CGP, you can be sure it's going to be a whole lot more entertaining than anybody else's dreary Geography guide...

A-Level revision? It has to be CGP!

Contents

Exam Skills

Published by CGP

Based on the classic CGP style created by Richard Parsons.

Editors:
Claire Boulter, Joe Brazier, David Maliphant, Chris McGarry, Liam Neilson.

Contributors:
Matthew Boyle, Laura D'Henin, Paddy Gannon, Leanne Parr, Helena Richards, Sophie Watkins, Dennis Watts.

ISBN: 978 1 78294 647 2

With thanks to Nicholas Robinson, Krystyna Pasek-Corsar and Karen Wells for the proofreading.
With thanks to Jan Greenway for the copyright research.

Clipart from Corel®
Printed by Elanders Ltd, Newcastle upon Tyne.

Natural Systems

Nature is complicated... really complicated. So sometimes it's useful to cheat a little bit and imagine all those natural processes as a nice, well-ordered system. It's a simplification, but it makes things so much easier to understand...

Systems are Made Up of Stores, Flows, Boundaries, Inputs and Outputs

1) You need to **learn** what these **parts** of a **system** are:

- **Inputs** — when matter or energy (e.g. solar energy) is **added** to the system.
- **Outputs** — when matter or energy **leaves** the system.
- **Stores** (or components) — where matter or energy **builds up**.
- **Flows** (or transfers) — when matter or energy **moves** from one store to another.
- **Boundaries** — the **limits** of the system.

Matter is any physical substance involved in a system, e.g. water or carbon.

Example

In a **drainage basin system**, water enters as rain (**input**). The system's watershed is the **boundary**. Some water is **stored** in the soil and in vegetation. Water travels from the drainage basin to the river and then down the river (**flows**). It leaves the system where the river meets the sea (**output**).

Natural systems like drainage basins often have multiple inputs, outputs, stores etc. See pages 6-7 for more on drainage basin systems.

2) Systems can be **open** or **closed**:

Open Systems

- Both **energy** and **matter CAN enter** and **leave** an open system — there are inputs and outputs of both.
- Example: **drainage basins** (see p.6) are **open systems** — energy from the Sun enters and leaves the system. Water is input as precipitation, and output as river discharge into the sea.

Systems can also be isolated (neither matter nor energy can enter or leave) but these aren't found in nature.

Closed Systems

- **Matter CAN'T enter** or **leave** a closed system — it can only cycle between stores.
- **Energy CAN enter** and **leave** a closed system — it can be input or output.
- Example: the **carbon cycle** (see p.10) is a **closed system** — energy is input (e.g. from the sun by photosynthesis) and output (e.g. by respiration), but the **amount** of carbon on Earth stays the **same** because there are **no inputs** or **outputs** of matter.

Systems are Affected by Feedbacks

1) If the inputs and outputs of a system are **balanced**, the system is in **equilibrium** — flows and processes continue to happen, but in the same way at all times, so there are no overall changes to the system.

2) However, in reality there are lots of small **variations** in the inputs and outputs of a system (e.g. the amount of precipitation entering a drainage basin system constantly varies). These variations are usually small, so the inputs and outputs remain about **balanced** on average. The system is said to be in **dynamic equilibrium**.

3) **Large, long-term** changes to the balance of inputs and outputs can cause a system to change and establish a **new** dynamic equilibrium.

4) Changes can trigger **positive** or **negative** feedback:

1 Positive Feedback

- **Positive feedback** mechanisms **amplify** the change in the inputs or outputs.
- This means the system responds by **increasing** the effects of the change, moving the system even **further** from its **previous state**.
- **Example:**

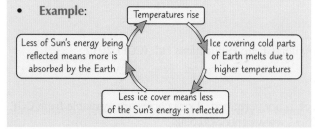

2 Negative Feedback

- **Negative feedback** mechanisms **counteract** the change in the inputs or outputs.
- This means that the system responds by **decreasing** the effects of the change, keeping the system **closer** to its **previous state**.
- **Example:**

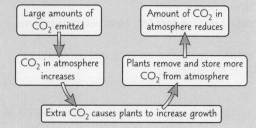

Natural Systems

The **Earth** Can be Seen as **One System** Made Up of **Lots** of **Subsystems**

1) The Earth can be seen as a **closed system** — energy is **input** from the **Sun** and **output** to **space**, but **matter** is **not input or output** to space (except for the odd space probe).

2) The whole Earth system can be **broken down** into **smaller** parts called **subsystems**:

"No outputs of matter to space?" scoffed Sam. "We'll see about that."

① Cryosphere

The cryosphere includes all the parts of the Earth system where it's **cold** enough for water to **freeze**, e.g. **glacial landscapes** (see pages 36-37).

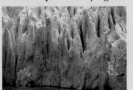

② Lithosphere

The lithosphere is the **outermost** part of the Earth. It includes the **crust** and the **upper parts** of the **mantle** (see p.56).

③ Biosphere

The biosphere is the part of the Earth's systems where **living** things are found. It includes **all** the living parts of the Earth — plants, animals, birds, fungi, insects, bacteria etc.

④ Hydrosphere

The hydrosphere includes all of the **water** on Earth. It may be in **liquid** form (e.g. in lakes and rivers), **solid** form (ice stored in the cryosphere) or **gas** form (e.g. water vapour stored in the atmosphere). It can also be **saline** (salty) or **fresh**.

⑤ Atmosphere

The atmosphere is the layer of **gas** between the **Earth's surface** and **space**, held in place by **gravity**.

3) These subsystems are all **interlinked** (connected together) by the cycles and processes that keep the Earth system as a whole running as **normal** (e.g. the water cycle and carbon cycle).

4) **Matter** (e.g. water and carbon) and **energy move between** the subsystems — the output of one cycle is the input of the next, then the output of that cycle is the input of the next, and so on...

5) Because of the way that matter and energy move from one subsystem to the next, the Earth system is said to be a **cascading system**.

6) **Changes** that occur in one subsystem can **affect** what happens in the **others**.

See pages 4-5 for how water moves through the subsystems and pages 10-11 for how carbon moves through the subsystems.

Practice Questions

Q1 What is meant by the term 'store' in a system?

Q2 What is meant by the term 'boundary' in a system?

Q3 What does it mean when a system is said to be in 'dynamic equilibrium'?

Q4 What is 'negative feedback'?

Q5 Name the five subsystems of the Earth.

Exam Questions

Q1 Outline the differences between open and closed systems. [3 marks]

Q2 Outline what is meant by 'positive feedback'. [3 marks]

And lastly, there's the examosphere...

...which is where knowing about all those other -spheres might come in useful. Not to be confused with the examofear, which is that feeling you get as you walk into the exam hall if you haven't revised as well as you could have. Luckily, you have a book in your hands right now (put that comic down and pick this book up) that can help avoid that. You just have get on with it.

The Water Cycle

Okay, I know you'll have studied the water cycle umpteen times before... but you can't have too much of a good thing.

Water is Stored in **Solid**, **Liquid** and **Gas** Forms

The hydrosphere contains 1.4 sextillion litres of water (that's 1, 4, then twenty 0s).

1) Most of this is **saline** water in the **oceans**. **Less than 3%** is **freshwater** (which most species, including humans, need to survive).

2) Of the Earth's **fresh water**:

- **69%** is frozen in the **cryosphere**.
- **30%** is **groundwater** (water stored underground in the lithosphere).
- **0.3%** is **liquid freshwater** on the Earth's surface in lakes, rivers etc.
- **0.04%** is stored as **water vapour** in the **atmosphere**.

3) Water must be **physically** and **economically accessible** for humans to be able to use it (e.g. groundwater is hard to access, so it may not be cost effective to extract it). As a result, only a **small** amount of water on the planet can be used by humans.

4) Water can change between solid, liquid and gaseous forms. For water to boil or melt, it has to gain **energy** (e.g. from the Sun). For water to **condense** or **freeze**, it has to lose energy.

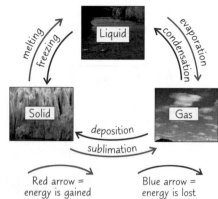

Red arrow = energy is gained

Blue arrow = energy is lost

Water is **Constantly Cycling** Between **Stores**

1) Water is continuously **cycled** between **different stores**. This is known as the **global hydrological cycle**.

2) The global hydrological cycle is a **closed system** — there are no **inputs** or **outputs** of water.

There's more on the processes shown here below and on the next page.

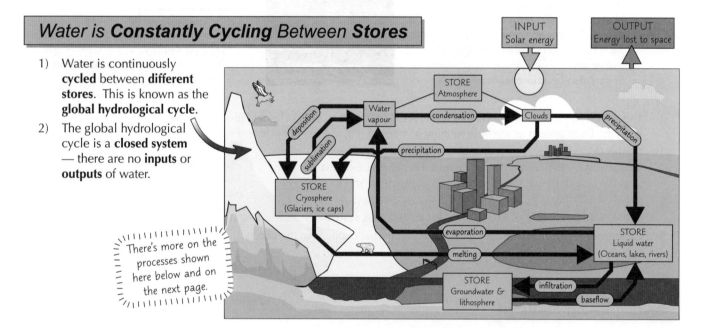

The **Magnitude** of the Stores Varies Over **Time** and in **Space**

1) The **amount** of water present in each store varies over a range of scales from **local** (e.g. an individual hillslope) to **global**.

2) The **magnitude** of each store depends on the **amount** of water **flowing between** them.

3) Different flows occur at a range of **spatial** and **temporal** (time) scales:

Evaporation

- Evaporation occurs when **liquid** water changes state into a **gas**, becoming **water vapour** — it **gains** energy, normally from **solar radiation**. Evaporation **increases** the amount of water stored in the **atmosphere**.

  Long-term changes in the climate can also affect the magnitude of evaporation. E.g. during the last glacial period, temperatures were lower, so evaporation was lower.

- The **magnitude** of the evaporation flow varies by **location** and **season**. If there is lots of **solar radiation**, a large supply of **water** and **warm, dry air**, the amount of evaporation will be **high**.

- If there is **not much** solar radiation, little available liquid water and **cool** air that is already **nearly saturated** (unable to absorb any more water vapour), evaporation will be **low**.

Topic One — Water and Carbon Cycles

The Water Cycle

Condensation

1) Condensation occurs when **water vapour** changes state to become a **liquid** — it **loses** energy to the **surroundings**. It happens when air containing water vapour **cools** to its **dew point** (the temperature at which it will change from a gas to a liquid), e.g. when temperatures fall at **night** due to heat being **lost** to **space**.

2) Water droplets can stay in the atmosphere or **flow** to other subsystems, e.g. when water vapour condenses, it can form **dew** on leaves and other surfaces — this **decreases** the amount of water **stored** in the atmosphere.

3) The **magnitude** of the condensation flow depends on the **amount** of water vapour in the atmosphere and the **temperature**. For example, if there is **lots** of water vapour in the air and there's a **large or rapid drop** in temperature, **condensation** will be **high**.

Cloud Formation and Precipitation

1) Cloud formation and precipitation are **essential** parts of the water cycle — precipitation is the **main flow** of water from the atmosphere to the ground.

2) Clouds form when **warm** air **cools down**, causing the **water vapour** in it to **condense** into **water droplets**, which gather as **clouds**. When the droplets get **big** enough, they fall as **precipitation**.

3) There are several things that can cause **warm air** to **cool**, leading to **precipitation**:

- **Other air masses** — warm air is **less dense** than cool air. As a result, when warm air meets cool air, the warm air is forced up **above** the cool air. It cools down as it rises. This results in **frontal precipitation**.
- **Topography** — when warm air meets **mountains**, it's forced to **rise**, causing it to cool. This results in **orographic precipitation**.
- **Convection** — when the sun **heats up** the **ground**, moisture on the ground **evaporates** and rises up in a column of warm air. As it gets higher, it cools. This results in **convective precipitation**.

4) Water droplets caused by condensation are **too small** to form clouds **on their own**. For clouds to form, there have to be **tiny particles** of other substances (e.g. dust or soot) to act as **cloud condensation nuclei**. They give water a **surface** to **condense** on. This encourages clouds to form, rather than allowing the moist air to **disperse**.

5) Cloud formation and precipitation can vary **seasonally** (e.g. in the UK there's normally more rainfall in winter than in summer) and by **location** (e.g. precipitation is generally higher in the tropics than at the poles).

Cryospheric Processes

1) Cryospheric processes such as **accumulation** and **ablation** (see p. 38) change the **amount** of water **stored** as ice in the **cryosphere**. The **balance** of accumulation and ablation varies with **temperature**.

2) During periods of global cold, **inputs** into the cryosphere are **greater** than **outputs** — water is transferred to it as snow, and less water is transferred away due to melting. During periods of warmer global temperatures, the magnitude of the cryosphere store **reduces** as losses due to melting are **larger** than the inputs of snow.

3) The Earth is **emerging** from a **glacial period** that reached its maximum **21 000 years ago**. There are still extensive stores of ice on **land** in Antarctica and Greenland, as well as numerous alpine glaciers. There is also a large volume of **sea ice** in the Arctic and Antarctic.

4) **Variations** in cryospheric processes happen over **different timescales**. As well as the changes in global temperature that occur over **thousands** of years, variations can also occur over shorter timescales. For example, **annual** temperature fluctuations mean that more snow falls in the winter than in summer.

Practice Questions

Q1 What percentage of Earth's water is freshwater?

Q2 Describe one change that can cause water vapour to condense.

Exam Question

Q1 Outline the importance of condensation to the water cycle. [3 marks]

With all this cycling, water could win gold at the Olympics...

There's plenty to learn here. At least it's all exciting stuff. Oh no, wait... Anyway, you've got to know it all, so you'd best crack on with safely storing it in your noggin. There are quite a lot of technical words in this section and it's well worth making sure you understand them all — examiners love it when you use the right technical terms in your answers.

Drainage Basins

And now, bandage raisins. Sorry, got my letters in the wrong order there — I meant drainage basins...

Drainage Basins are Natural Systems

Drainage basins can be viewed as **open**, **local** hydrological cycles:

1) A river's **drainage basin** is the area **surrounding** the river where the rain falling on the land **flows** into that river. This area is also called the river's **catchment**.

2) The **boundary** of a drainage basin is the **watershed** — any precipitation falling **beyond** the watershed enters a **different drainage basin**.

3) Drainage basins are **open systems** with **inputs** and **outputs**.

4) Water comes **into** the system as **precipitation** and **leaves** via **evaporation**, **transpiration** and **river discharge**.

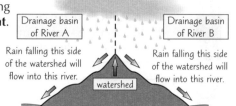

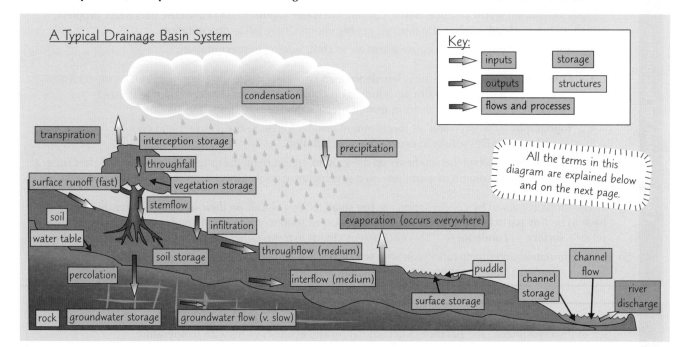

Drainage Basins Have Inputs, Stores, Flows and Outputs

Stacey seemed surprisingly upbeat about atmospheric moisture inputs.

Inputs — Water Coming into the System

Precipitation includes **all** the ways moisture **comes out** of the atmosphere.
Precipitation is mainly **rain**, but it also includes other types like **snow**, **hail**, **dew** and **frost**.

Storage — Water Stored in the System

1) **Interception** is when some precipitation **lands on vegetation** or other structures, like **buildings** and **concrete** or **tarmac** surfaces, before it reaches the soil. Interception creates a **significant store** of water in **wooded areas**. **Interception storage** is only **temporary** because the collected water may **evaporate** quickly, or fall from the leaves as throughfall (see next page).

2) **Vegetation storage** is water that's been **taken up** by **plants**. It's all the water **contained** in plants at any one time.

3) **Surface storage** includes water in **puddles** (**depression storage**), **ponds** and **lakes**.

4) **Soil storage** includes **moisture** in the **soil**.

5) **Groundwater storage** is water stored in the ground, either in the **soil** (**soil moisture**) or in **rocks**. The **water table** is the top surface of the **zone of saturation** — the zone of **soil** or **rock** where **all** the **pores** in the soil or rock are **full of water**. **Porous rocks** (rocks with lots of **holes** in them) that hold water are called **aquifers**.

6) **Channel storage** is so obvious that it's often overlooked — it's the **water** held in a **river** or **stream channel**.

Drainage Basins

Flows — Water Moving from One Place to Another

1) **Infiltration** is water **soaking** into the soil. **Infiltration rates** are influenced by **soil type, soil structure** and how much water's **already in** the soil.

2) **Overland flow** (also known as **runoff**) is water **flowing over** the **land**. It can flow over the **whole surface** or in **little channels**. It happens because rain is falling on the ground **faster** than infiltration can occur.

3) **Throughfall** is water **dripping** from one **leaf** (or other plant part) to **another**.

4) **Stemflow** is water running down a plant **stem** or a **tree trunk**.

5) **Throughflow** is water moving slowly **downhill** through the **soil**. Throughflow is **faster** through **"pipes"** — things like **cracks** in the **soil** or **animal burrows**.

6) **Percolation** is water **seeping down** through soil **into the water table**.

7) **Groundwater flow** is water flowing **slowly below** the **water table** through **permeable rock**. Water flows **slowly** through most rocks, but rocks that are **highly permeable** with lots of **joints** (gaps that water can get through) can have **faster** groundwater flow, e.g. limestone.

8) **Baseflow** is groundwater flow that **feeds** into rivers through river **banks** and river **beds**.

9) **Interflow** is water flowing **downhill** through **permeable rock above** the water table.

10) **Channel flow** is the water flowing in the **river** or **stream** itself. This is also called the **river's discharge**.

Outputs — Water Leaving the System

1) **Evaporation** is water turning into **water vapour** (see p.4).

2) **Transpiration** is **evaporation** from within **leaves** — plants and trees **take up** water through their roots and **transport** it to their **leaves** where it evaporates into the atmosphere.

3) **Evapotranspiration** is the process of evaporation and transpiration **together**.

4) **River discharge**, or **river flow**, is another **output**.

> **Potential evapotranspiration (PET)** is the amount of water that **could** be lost by evapotranspiration. **Actual evapotranspiration** is what **actually** happens. For example, in a **desert** potential evapotranspiration is **high** (because **heat increases evaporation**) but actual transpiration is **low** (because there **isn't** much moisture).

The **Water Balance** Shows the Balance Between **Inputs** and **Outputs**

Water balance is worked out from **inputs** (precipitation) and **outputs** (channel discharge and evapotranspiration). The water balance affects how much water is **stored** in the basin. The general water balance in the **UK** shows **seasonal patterns**:

1) In **wet seasons**, precipitation **exceeds** evapotranspiration. This creates a **water surplus**. The ground stores **fill** with water so there's **more surface runoff** and **higher discharge**, so **river levels rise**.

2) In **drier seasons**, precipitation is **lower than** evapotranspiration. **Ground stores** are **depleted** as some water is **used** (e.g. by plants and humans) and some flows into the **river channel**, but **isn't** replaced by precipitation.

3) So, at the **end** of a dry season, there's a **deficit** (**shortage**) of water in the ground. The ground stores are **recharged** in the next **wet season** (i.e. autumn).

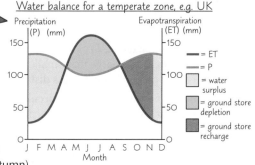

Water balance for a temperate zone, e.g. UK

Practice Questions

Q1 List three stores of water in drainage basin systems.

Q2 Water vapour evaporates from the leaves of plants. What is this process called?

Exam Question

Q1 Outline seasonal changes in the water balance. [3 marks]

If your basin takes an age to drain, you'll probably want to get a plumber in...

There are loads of words to remember on these pages. It might seem like a pain, but if you learn them all now it'll mean the rest of the section will make a lot more sense. And you thought geography was just about colouring in maps...

Topic One — Water and Carbon Cycles

Variations in Runoff and the Water Cycle

If you like runoff, the water cycle and variation (and who doesn't), these pages are going to blow your mind.

Hydrographs Show River Discharge Over a Period of Time

1) **River discharge** is the **volume** of water (in cubic metres, **m³**) that **flows** in a river **per second**. Unsurprisingly, it's measured in **cubic metres per second (m³/s)** — this is a bit of a mouthful, so it's usually just shortened to **cumecs**.

2) High levels of **runoff** (water flowing on the surface of the land) **increase** the discharge of a river because more water makes it into the river, increasing its volume.

3) **Hydrographs** are graphs of river **discharge** over **time**. They show how the **volume of water** flowing at a certain point in a river **changes** over a **period of time**. **Flood hydrographs** (also called storm hydrographs) show river discharge around the time of a **storm event**. They only cover a relatively **short time period** (hours or days, rather than weeks or months).

1 Peak discharge — this is the **highest** point on the graph, when the **river discharge** is at its **greatest**.

2 Lag time — this is the delay between **peak rainfall** and **peak discharge**. This delay happens because it takes **time** for the rainwater to **flow** into the river. A **shorter** lag time can **increase peak discharge** because more water reaches the river during a **shorter period of time**.

3 Rising limb — this is the part of the graph **up to** peak discharge. The river discharge **increases** as rainwater flows into the river.

4 Falling limb — this is the part of the graph **after** peak discharge. **Discharge** is **decreasing** because **less water** is flowing into the river. A **shallow** falling limb shows water is flowing in from **stores** long after it's **stopped raining**.

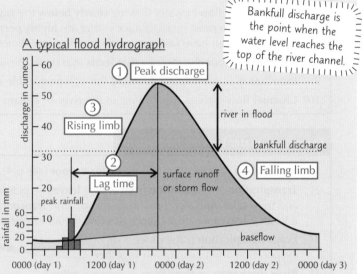

4) A basin with **rapid runoff** and not much **storage** capacity gives a hydrograph with a **short lag time** and **high peak discharge**. This is called a "**flashy**" hydrograph — the graph has **steep**, roughly **symmetrical** rising and falling limbs.

Runoff and Hydrograph Shape Are Affected by Numerous Factors

The **amount** of runoff and the **shape** of the hydrograph depends on various factors, e.g.:

Runoff is also affected by precipitation, seasonal changes and human activity (see below and next page).

- **Size of drainage basin** — **larger drainage basins** catch **more precipitation**, so they have a **higher peak discharge** than smaller basins. **Smaller basins** generally have **shorter lag times** because precipitation has **less distance** to travel, so it reaches the main channel more **quickly**.
- **Shape of drainage basin** — **circular** basins are more likely to have a **flashy** hydrograph than **long, narrow** basins. This is because all points on the **watershed** are roughly the **same distance** from the point of discharge **measurement**. This means lots of water will reach the measuring point at the **same time**.
- **Ground steepness** — water flows **more quickly** downhill in **steep-sided** drainage basins, shortening **lag time**. This also means that water has **less time** to **infiltrate** the soil, so runoff is higher.
- **Rock and soil type** — **impermeable** rocks and soils don't **store** water or let water **infiltrate**. This **increases** surface runoff. Peak discharge also **increases** as **more water** reaches the river in a shorter period.

The Water Cycle Varies Due to Physical Factors...

Hydrographs, runoff and the water cycle in general are affected by **natural processes**, e.g. storms and seasonal changes:

Storms and Precipitation

- **Intense storms** generate **more precipitation** and **greater peak discharges** than **light rain showers**.
- The **larger input** of water causes flows, e.g. runoff, and stores, e.g. groundwater, to **increase** in size.
- Some flows, e.g. infiltration, may not be able to occur **rapidly enough** for the size of the input, increasing **runoff**.

Variations in Runoff and the Water Cycle

Seasonal Changes and Vegetation

- The **size** of inputs, flows and stores in the water cycle varies with the **seasons** — e.g. in the UK, summer is normally drier than winter.
- During the winter, temperatures may drop **below 0 °C**, causing water to **freeze**. This can **reduce** the size of flows **through** drainage basins, while the **store** of **frozen water** grows. When temperatures **increase** again, flows through drainage basins (and outputs) can be **much larger** as the ice **melts**.
- Most plants show **seasonal variation** (e.g. vegetation usually dies back in winter). Vegetation **intercepts** precipitation and **slows its movement** to the river channel. Interception is **highest** when there's **lots of** vegetation and **deciduous trees** have their **leaves**.
- The **more vegetation** there is in a drainage basin, the **more water** is **lost** (through **transpiration** and **evaporation** directly from the vegetation) before it reaches the river channel, **reducing runoff** and **peak discharge**.

...and Due To **Human Activities**

Human activities also **affect** the size of stores in the water cycle, and the size and speed of flows:

Farming Practices

Infiltration is a key part of the water cycle. When rain hits the surface, what can't infiltrate **runs off** instead. Farming practices can affect infiltration in several ways:

- **Ploughing** breaks up the surface so that **more** water can **infiltrate**, **reducing** the amount of **runoff**.
- **Crops increase infiltration** and **interception** compared to bare ground, reducing runoff. **Evapotranspiration** also **increases**, which can **increase rainfall**.
- **Livestock**, such as cattle, trample and compact the soil, **decreasing infiltration** and **increasing runoff**.
- **Irrigation** (artificially watering the land) can **increase runoff** if some of the water can't infiltrate. **Groundwater** or **river levels** can **fall** if water is extracted for irrigation.

Land Use Change

- **Deforestation reduces** the amount of water that is **intercepted** by vegetation, increasing the amount that reaches the **surface**. In forested areas, dead plant material on the forest floor helps to **hold** the water, allowing it to **infiltrate** the soil rather than **run off**. When forest cover (and dead material) is **removed**, the amount of **infiltration** that can take place **decreases**.
- Construction of new **buildings** and **roads** creates an **impermeable** layer over the land, **preventing** infiltration. This massively **increases runoff**, resulting in water passing through the system much more **rapidly** and making **flooding** more likely (see page 88).

Water Abstraction

- More water is **abstracted** (taken from stores) to meet **demand** in areas where **population density** is **high**. This **reduces** the amount of water in **stores** such as lakes, rivers, reservoirs and groundwater.
- During **dry seasons**, even more water is abstracted from stores (especially groundwater and reservoirs) for **consumption** and **irrigation**, so stores are **depleted** further.

Practice Questions

Q1 What is river discharge?
Q2 What is the unit of measurement for river discharge?
Q3 Give three factors that can affect the amount of runoff in a drainage basin.

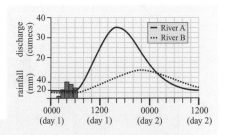

Exam Questions

Q1 The hydrograph on the right shows data for two rivers in the same area. Analyse the possible reasons for the differences between the two rivers. [6 marks]

Q2 Assess the causes of variations in the drainage basin-scale water cycle. [9 marks]

I ain't saying we like a bit of bling, but we love our flashy hydrographs...

Flood hydrographs can look quite confusing, but they're not so bad once you've got your head round them. And remember, at the end of the day, they're just fancy graphs — there's no need to runoff in the other direction whenever you see one...

The Carbon Cycle

It's not all about the water cycle you know (although water great cycle that is) — you also need to be clued up on the ins and outs, flows and stores of the carbon cycle. If only all this cycling counted as exercise — you'd be as fit as a fiddle.

Carbon is Found in **All** Earth's Systems

1) Carbon is an **element**, and a really **important** one at that.

2) It's found in both **organic** stores (living things) and **inorganic** stores (e.g. rocks, gases and fossil fuels).

3) Carbon can be found in **each** of the **Earth's systems** in some form or another:

Lithosphere
- Over **99.9%** of the carbon on Earth is stored in **sedimentary rocks** such as limestone.
- About **0.004%** of the carbon on Earth is stored in **fossil fuels**, such as coal and oil, in the lithosphere.

Atmosphere
- Carbon is stored as carbon dioxide (CO_2) and in smaller quantities as **methane** (CH_4) in the atmosphere.
- The atmosphere contains about **0.001%** of the Earth's carbon.

Hydrosphere
- **Carbon dioxide (CO_2)** is **dissolved** in **rivers**, **lakes** and **oceans**.
- The oceans are the **second-largest** carbon store on Earth, containing approximately **0.04%** of the Earth's carbon. The majority of carbon here is found **deep** in the ocean in the form of **dissolved inorganic carbon**.
- A small amount is found at the ocean **surface** where it is **exchanged** with the **atmosphere**.

Biosphere
- Carbon is stored in the tissues of **living organisms**. It is transferred to the **soil** when living organisms **die** and **decay**.
- The biosphere contains approximately **0.004%** of the Earth's total carbon.

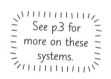

See p.3 for more on these systems.

Cryosphere
- The **cryosphere** contains **less than 0.01%** of Earth's carbon.
- Most of the carbon in the cryosphere is in the **soil** in areas of **permafrost** (permanently frozen ground) where **decomposing plants** and **animals** have **frozen** into the ground.

Carbon is **Transferred** Between **Different Stores**

1) The **carbon cycle** is the process by which carbon is **stored** and **transferred**.

2) The carbon cycle is a **closed system** (see p.2) — there are **inputs** and **outputs** of energy, but the **amount** of carbon in the system remains the **same**. However, some carbon is **locked away** (sequestered — see next page) in **long-term stores**, e.g. **rock** and **fossil fuels** deep underground. If these are **released** by e.g. burning fossil fuels, they are effectively **inputs**.

3) Make sure you know the major **stores** and **flows** in the carbon cycle:

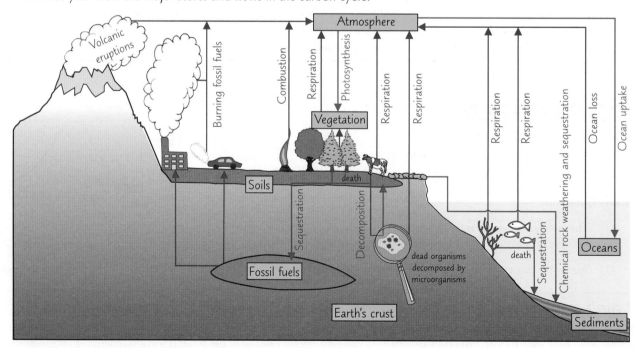

The Carbon Cycle

*Carbon Stores **Change** in **Size** Over **Time** Because of **Carbon Flows***

There are lots of **flows** of carbon between stores:

Photosynthesis
- Photosynthesis transfers carbon stored in the **atmosphere** to **biomass**.
- Plants and phytoplankton use energy from the Sun to change **carbon dioxide** and **water** into **glucose** and oxygen. This enables plants to **grow**.
- Carbon is passed through the **food chain** and released through **respiration** and **decomposition**.

Respiration
- Respiration transfers carbon from **living organisms** to the **atmosphere**.
- Plants and animals **break down glucose** for energy, releasing **carbon dioxide** and **methane** (a gas containing carbon) in the process.

Combustion
- Combustion transfers carbon stored in **living, dead** or **decomposed biomass** (including peaty soils) to the **atmosphere** by **burning**.
- **Wildfires** (see pages 72-73) cause carbon flow.

Decomposition
- Decomposition transfers carbon from dead **biomass** to the **atmosphere** and the **soil**.
- After **death**, bacteria and fungi **break** organisms down. CO_2 and **methane** are released.
- Some carbon is transferred to the **soil** in the form of **humus**.

Ocean uptake and loss
- CO_2 is directly **dissolved** from the **atmosphere** into the **ocean**. It is also transferred to the oceans when it is **taken up** by **organisms** that live in them (e.g. plankton).
- Carbon is also transferred from the **ocean** to the **atmosphere** when **carbon-rich water** from deep in the oceans **rises** to the surface and releases CO_2.

Weathering
- Chemical weathering transfers carbon from the **atmosphere** to the **hydrosphere** and **biosphere**.
- Atmospheric carbon reacts with water vapour to form **acid rain**. When this acid rain falls onto **rocks**, a chemical reaction occurs which **dissolves** the rocks. The molecules resulting from this reaction may be washed into the **sea**. Here, they **react** with CO_2 dissolved in the water to form **calcium carbonate**, which is used by **sea creatures**, e.g. to make shells.

Sequestration
- Carbon from the atmosphere can be **sequestered** (captured and held) in **sedimentary rocks** or as **fossil fuels**. Rocks and fossil fuels form over millions of years when **dead animal** and **plant** material in the ocean falls to the floor and is **compacted**.
- Carbon in fossil fuels is **sequestered** until we **burn** them (**combustion** — see page 12).

Sid the Herring's plans for a quiet burial had been scuppered.

*Carbon Flows Happen Over Different **Time** and **Spatial Scales***

1) **Fast** carbon flows quickly **transfer** carbon between sources. It only takes a matter of minutes, hours or days. **Photosynthesis**, **respiration**, **combustion** and **decomposition** are examples of fast carbon flows.

2) **Sequestration** is a **slow** carbon flow. It takes millions of years for carbon to be sequestered in sedimentary rocks.

3) The carbon flows taking place also depend on spatial **scale**. For example, at a **plant** scale, respiration and photosynthesis are the main flows. At an **ecosystem** scale, carbon flows such as combustion and decomposition also occur. At a **continental** scale, all of the carbon flows including sequestration occur.

Practice Questions

Q1 Draw a diagram showing the key processes within the carbon cycle.

Q2 What is carbon sequestration?

Exam Question

Q1 Outline the role of photosynthesis in the carbon cycle. [3 marks]

The world goes 'cos carbon flows...
You've probably gathered that the carbon cycle is really important. Make sure you know everything here before you move on.

The Carbon Cycle

The carbon cycle can be affected by lots of things. Some of them are natural, but surprise surprise, humans can play a big role too. There's lots to learn here, so get cracking or you'll never get to bed. Although this stuff might put you to sleep...

Natural Processes Can Change the Carbon Cycle

Natural events like **wildfires** and **volcanic eruptions** can alter the **magnitude** of the **carbon stores**:

Wildfires

- Wildfires rapidly transfer large quantities of carbon from **biomass** (or soil) to the **atmosphere**. Loss of vegetation decreases photosynthesis, so **less** carbon is **removed** from the atmosphere.
- In the longer term, however, fires can **encourage** the **growth** of new plants, which take in carbon from the atmosphere for photosynthesis. Depending on the **amount** and **type** of regrowth, fires can have a **neutral** effect on the amount of atmospheric carbon.

Volcanic Activity

- Carbon stored within the Earth in magma is released during **volcanic eruptions**. The majority enters the atmosphere as CO_2.
- Recent volcanic eruptions have released much less CO_2 than human activities. However, there is the **potential** for a very large eruption to disrupt the carbon cycle **significantly**.

Humans Can Also Impact the Carbon Cycle

1) Since the **industrial revolution**, the impact that humans have on the carbon cycle has increased hugely. We're currently causing **carbon flows** from the lithosphere and biosphere to the atmosphere to happen **much faster** than they would naturally.

2) The main **human causes** of change are:

Hydrocarbon (fossil fuel) extraction and use

- **Extracting** and **burning** (**combustion**) of fossil fuels releases CO_2 into the atmosphere.
- Without human intervention, the carbon would remain **sequestered** in the lithosphere for **thousands** or **millions** of years to come.

Deforestation

- Forests may be cleared for **agriculture**, **logging**, or to make way for **developments**.
- Clearance **reduces** the size of the **carbon store** and, if the cleared forest is **burned**, there is a **rapid flow** of carbon from the biosphere to the atmosphere.

Farming practices

Agricultural activities release carbon into the atmosphere:
- Animals release CO_2 and methane when they **respire** and **digest** food.
- **Ploughing** can release CO_2 stored in **soil**.
- Growing **rice** in rice paddies releases a lot of **methane**.

As the world's population has **risen**, so has food production. As a result, carbon emissions from **farming practices** have increased. **Mechanisation** of farming has also increased CO_2 emissions.

Land use changes

As well as deforestation (see above), the change of land use from natural or agricultural to **urban** is a major source of carbon:
- **Vegetation** is **removed** to make way for buildings — this reduces carbon storage in the biosphere.
- **Concrete production** releases lots of CO_2, and lots of concrete is used when urban areas expand.

The Carbon Budget is the Balance Between Carbon Inputs and Outputs

1) The **carbon budget** is the difference between the **inputs** of carbon into a subsystem and **outputs** of carbon from it.

2) For example, in the **atmosphere**, inputs of carbon come from **volcanic eruptions**, **burning fossil fuels**, **respiration** and **ocean loss**, and outputs occur through **photosynthesis**, **sequestration**, **decomposition**, **chemical weathering** and **ocean uptake**.

3) The **balance** of the inputs and outputs of a subsystem determines whether it acts as a **carbon source** (the outputs of carbon outweigh the inputs, so it **releases more carbon** than it **absorbs**) or a **carbon sink** (the **inputs** of carbon **outweigh** the **outputs**, so it **absorbs more carbon** than it **releases**).

The Carbon Cycle

The Carbon Cycle Affects the **Atmosphere**, **Land** and **Oceans**

The carbon cycle is **fundamental** to life on Earth. When there is a **change** to the carbon cycle, it can have a **significant impacts** on the atmosphere, land and oceans.

Some impacts of carbon cycle change are linked — e.g. an impact on the atmosphere can have knock-on effects on the land and ocean.

Atmosphere and Climate

- The carbon cycle affects the **amount** of gases containing carbon (e.g. CO_2 and methane) in the atmosphere. These are **greenhouse gases** — they trap some of the Sun's energy, keeping some of the heat in and keeping the planet warm (see p.14).
- As the concentrations of greenhouse gases in the atmosphere **increase** (e.g. due to **changes** in the carbon cycle caused by human activities such as deforestation and the burning of fossil fuels) **temperatures** are **expected to rise**. This is **global warming**.
- Changes in temperature across the globe will affect **other aspects** of the **climate**, e.g. **more intense storms** are predicted.

Though they made gardening unpleasant, Marjorie's increasing greenhouse gas emissions sure deterred Bruce from meddling with the cabbages.

Land

- The carbon cycle allows **plants** to **grow** — if there was no carbon in the atmosphere, plants could not **photosynthesise**. If there was no **decomposition**, dead plants would remain where they fell and their nutrients would **never be recycled**.
- Changes in the carbon cycle can **reduce** the amount of carbon stored in the land, e.g. warmer temperatures caused by global warming are causing **permafrost** to melt. This **releases** carbon previously stored in the permafrost into the atmosphere.
- An increase in global temperatures could also **increase** the frequency of **wildfires** (see previous page).

Oceans

- As part of the carbon cycle, **carbon dioxide** is dissolved **directly** into the oceans from the **atmosphere**.
- CO_2 in oceans is used by organisms such as **phytoplankton** and **seaweed** during **photosynthesis** and by other marine organisms to form **calcium carbonate shells** and **skeletons**.
- Increased levels of CO_2 in the atmosphere can increase the **acidity** of the oceans because the oceans initially absorb more CO_2 (see p.11). This can have adverse effects on **marine life**.
- **Global warming** can also affect oceans. For example, organisms that are **sensitive** to temperature, e.g. phytoplankton, may **not** be able to **survive** at higher temperatures, so their numbers **decrease**. This means that **less** CO_2 is used by them for **photosynthesis**, so less carbon is removed from the atmosphere.
- Warmer water is also **less able** to **absorb** CO_2, so as temperatures rise the amount of CO_2 that could potentially be **dissolved** in the sea **decreases**.

Practice Questions

Q1 How does deforestation cause a change in the carbon cycle?

Q2 What is the carbon budget?

Q3 Give one effect of changes in the carbon cycle on the land.

Exam Question

Q1 Outline how changes to the carbon cycle can affect the oceans. [3 marks]

Carbon, carboff, carbon... my yo-yo dieting's got me stuck in quite a cycle...

Hooray — two more pages on the carbon cycle for you to learn. Make sure you have a crack at the practice questions to help you cement your new-found knowledge. Then just for good measure, go over the pages again until you remember it all.

Water, Carbon and Climate

The water and carbon cycles are a bit like Ant and Dec — sure, you can separate them, but to get the full effect you just have to put them together. The difference is, rather than adding life to Saturday night telly, these two add life to Earth...

The **Water** and **Carbon Stores** and **Cycles** are **Essential** for **Life**

1) Carbon is a **fundamental building block** of life — **all living things** contain carbon. **Water** is also **essential** for life — all living things need water to survive.

2) Plants form the **base** of most **food chains** — when photosynthesis occurs, they use energy from sunlight to convert CO_2 and water into biomass that gets **passed up** the food chain. Photosynthesis requires **inputs** of both **water** and **carbon**.

3) Water is present in the **atmosphere** as **water vapour** (and water droplets), and carbon exists as **carbon dioxide** and **methane**. These are **greenhouse gases** — they cause a **natural greenhouse effect** that prevents some energy from **escaping** into **space** and **reflects** it back to **Earth**. This causes temperatures on Earth to be **higher** than they would otherwise be — without the natural greenhouse effect the Earth would be **frozen** and **uninhabitable**.

4) Human activities are increasing the **concentration** of greenhouse gases in the atmosphere. Most scientists agree that this is causing an **enhanced greenhouse effect**. This is where the **additional** greenhouse gases reflect **more** energy back to the Earth than in the natural greenhouse effect, so **temperature increases** even further. This is thought to be causing **global warming** and other changes to the climate (see next page).

There are **Feedbacks Within** the Two Cycles...

The effects of a change to a system may be **amplified** by a **positive** feedback or **dampened** by a **negative** feedback (see page 2). Sometimes, the **same change** can cause **either** a positive or negative feedback, for example:

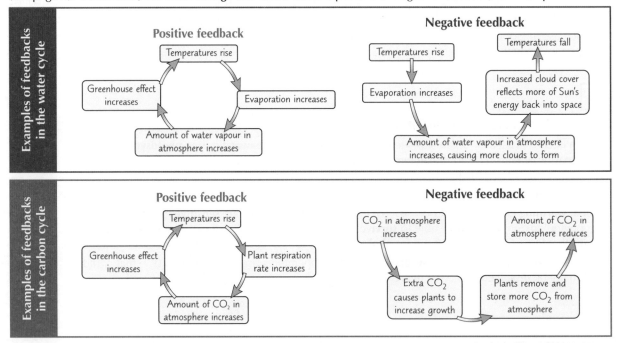

In these examples, the **positive** feedbacks would **increase** global warming because they're **amplifying** the temperature rise. The **negative** feedbacks would **cancel out** the temperature increase, so global warming wouldn't increase.

...as well as **Interactions** Between Them

The carbon and water cycles **depend** on each other. For example:

- **Carbon combines** with **water** in the atmosphere. This allows **chemical weathering**, which **removes** carbon from the atmosphere (see p.11).
- **Water** is needed for **photosynthesis**, which **removes** carbon from the atmosphere.
- The amount of CO_2 in the atmosphere affects **global temperatures**, which affect the amount of **evaporation** that can take place, which affects the amount of **precipitation**.

Nick loved interacting with the water cycle on the way to work.

Water, Carbon and Climate

Climate Change Affects Life on Earth

Climate change is predicted to have major impacts on plants, animals and people, for example:

1) The **pattern** of **precipitation** is expected to **change** — wet areas are expected to get wetter and dry areas are expected to get drier. This could cause **water shortages** in some areas, which could lead to **conflicts** in the future.

2) **Extreme weather events** (e.g. storms, floods and droughts) are expected to get **more frequent**. **Less developed** countries will probably be **worst** affected as they are **less able** to deal with the impacts.

3) **Agricultural productivity** will **decrease** in some areas, which could lead to **food shortages**.

4) **Sea levels** are expected to **rise** further. This will **flood** coastal and low-lying areas.

5) The geographical **range** of some species will change as climate changes. The arrival of new species in an area may **damage** the ecosystem, and some species may become **extinct**.

6) **Plankton** numbers may **decline** if temperatures increase, which will have a knock-on effect on **marine food chains**.

Humans are Trying to Influence the Carbon Cycle

1) Humans have **influenced** the carbon cycle for centuries, particularly by **extracting** and **burning fossil fuels**. There is now **40% more CO_2** in the atmosphere than there was in **1750**.

2) The **Intergovernmental Panel on Climate Change** (IPCC) is an international organisation set up by the UN to share knowledge about climate change. The IPCC states that countries need to **reduce** the amount of CO_2 emitted by **human activities** in order to prevent **large temperature rises**.

3) People are trying to mitigate the impacts of climate change by reducing transfers of **carbon** to the **atmosphere**. These measures can be at a range of **scales**, for example:

Individual
- People can choose to use their **cars less** and buy more **fuel efficient** cars.
- They can also make their **homes** more **energy efficient**, e.g. with double glazing, insulation and more efficient appliances.

Regional and National
- Governments can reduce **reliance** on **fossil fuels** for **heating** and **powering homes** by increasing the availability and reducing the cost of **renewable energy** sources such as **wind**, **tidal** and **solar**.
- **Afforestation** and **restoring degraded forests** can increase carbon uptake by the biosphere.
- Planners can **increase** the **sustainability** of developments by **improving public transport** (to reduce car use) and creating **more green spaces** (see p.95).
- Governments can invest in **carbon capture and storage** (CCS). CO_2 emitted from burning fossil fuels is captured and stored **underground**, e.g. in depleted oil and gas reservoirs.

Global
- Countries can work together to reduce emissions. For example, the **Kyoto Protocol** (1997) and the **Paris Agreement** (2015) are **international treaties** to control the total amount of greenhouse gases released. Participating countries agree to keep their emissions **within** set **limits**.
- There are also international **carbon trading schemes**. Countries and businesses are given a **limit** on the emissions they can produce — if they produce **less** they can **sell** the extra credits, if they produce **more** they need to **buy** more credits.

Practice Questions

Q1 Give an example of a negative feedback in the water cycle.

Q2 What is carbon capture and storage?

Exam Question

Q1 Assess the extent to which feedbacks in the carbon and water cycles may affect life on Earth. [9 marks]

How to influence the carbon cycle — everyone hold your breath...

There's a sure-fire way to influence your marks for questions on interactions between the water cycle, carbon cycle and climate, and it starts with you learning everything on these two pages, then having a crack at those practice questions...

The Amazon Rainforest — Case Study

Now, I know you probably studied the Amazon rainforest at GCSE and Key Stage 3, and quite possibly at least twice at primary school. But don't get too complacent — this time it's all about the water and carbon cycles within the Amazon...

The **Amazon** is a **Rainforest** in **South America**

1) The Amazon is the world's **largest** tropical rainforest and covers 40% of the South American landmass.

2) It has a **hot**, very **wet** climate and the **vegetation** is very **dense**.

3) Many groups of **indigenous people** live in the Amazon rainforest.

4) It's home to up to **1 million plant** species, over **500** species of **mammals** and over **2000** species of **fish**. The Amazon is also home to many **endangered species**, including the Amazonian manatee (an aquatic mammal), black caiman (a reptile) and the pirarucu (a fish).

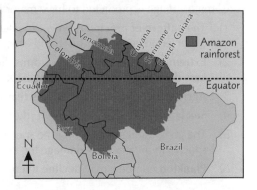

The **Water** and **Carbon Cycles** are **Important** to the **Amazon Environment**

The **water** and **carbon** cycles **affect** the **Amazon rainforest**, and the **Amazon rainforest affects** the **water** and **carbon** cycles:

Water Cycle

1) The water cycle causes the Amazon to be very **wet** — there is a lot of **evaporation** over the Atlantic Ocean, and the wet air is blown **towards** the Amazon. This contributes to the Amazon's very high rainfall.

2) **Warm temperatures** mean that **evaporation** is **high** in the rainforest itself, which increases the amount of precipitation.

3) The rainforest has a **dense canopy** — this means that **interception** is **high**. As a result, **less** water flows into rivers than might otherwise be expected, and it does so **more slowly**.

4) The water cycle affects the Amazon environment — it is populated by species that are **adapted** to **high humidity** and **frequent rainfall**.

Carbon Cycle

1) The Amazon rainforest **stores** lots of **carbon** in its **vegetation** and **soil**, so it's a **carbon sink** (see p.12).

2) The increasing concentration of CO_2 in the atmosphere has led to **increased productivity** in the Amazon rainforest because the vegetation is able to access more CO_2 for photosynthesis — the amount of **biomass** has been **increasing**.

3) As a result, the amount of CO_2 **sequestered** (see p.11) by the Amazon rainforest has **increased**, making it an even more important carbon store.

4) However, it has been suggested that although trees are **growing** more **quickly**, they're also **dying younger**.

5) As a result, we may **not** be able to **rely** on the Amazon rainforest to **continue** to be such an effective **carbon sink** in the **future**.

Human Activities in the Amazon are **Affecting** the **Water** and **Carbon Cycles**

The activities of people are **changing** the Amazon rainforest environment in various ways:

Deforestation

Lots of deforestation takes place in the Amazon, e.g. to exploit the **timber** or to use the land for **farming**.

<u>Effects on the water cycle:</u>

1) In **deforested areas** there is no tree canopy to intercept rainfall, so more water reaches the ground surface. There is too much **water** to soak into the soil. Instead the **water** moves to rivers as **surface runoff**, which increases the risk of **flooding**.

2) Deforestation reduces the **rate** of **evapotranspiration** (see p. 7) — this means less water vapour reaches the atmosphere, **fewer clouds form** and **rainfall** is **reduced**. This increases the risk of **drought**.

<u>Effects on the carbon cycle:</u>

1) Without **roots** to **hold the soil** together, heavy rain **washes away** the **nutrient-rich** top layer of soil, **transferring** carbon stored in the soil to the hydrosphere.

2) Deforestation means that there is **less leaf litter**, so humus isn't formed. The soil cannot support much new growth, which **limits** the amount of carbon that is **absorbed**.

3) Trees **remove** CO_2 from the atmosphere and store it, so fewer trees means more atmospheric CO_2, which enhances the greenhouse effect and global warming (see p. 14).

> Many of these effects limit vegetation growth, which can amplify changes to the water and carbon cycles. This is an example of positive feedback (see p. 2).

The Amazon Rainforest — Case Study

Climate Change

1) Climate change can severely impact tropical rainforests. In some areas **temperature** is increasing and **rainfall** is decreasing, which leads to **drought**. The **Amazon** had **severe droughts** in **2005** and **2010**.

2) **Plants** and **animals** living in tropical rainforests are adapted to **moist conditions**, so many species die in dry weather. **Frequent** or **long periods** of drought could lead to **extinction** of some species. **Drought** can also lead to **forest fires**, which can **destroy** large areas of forest, **releasing** lots of CO_2 into the atmosphere.

3) Scientists predict that a **4 °C** temperature rise could **kill 85%** of the Amazon rainforest. This would result in lots of **carbon** being **released** into the atmosphere as the dead material **decomposed**, and less carbon dioxide being taken in from the air by trees for **photosynthesis**.

There are Attempts to *Limit Human Impacts* on the Amazon

Selective Logging

1) Only **some trees** (e.g. just the oldest ones) are **felled** — most are left standing.

2) This is **less damaging** to the forest than felling **all the trees** in an area. If **only a few trees** are taken from each area the **forest structure** is kept — the canopy is still there and the soil isn't exposed. This means the forest is able to **regenerate**, so the impact on the carbon and water cycle is small.

Replanting

1) **New trees** are planted to replace the ones that are **cut down**. For example, **Peru** plans to restore **3.2 million hectares** of forest by 2020.

2) It's important that the **same types of tree** are planted that were cut down, so that the **variety of trees** is kept for the future and the local carbon and water cycles return to their initial state.

Environmental Law

Environmental laws can help **protect rainforests**. For example:

- Laws that **ban** the use of wood from forests that are not managed **sustainably**.
- Laws that **ban excessive logging**.
- Laws that control **land use**, e.g. the **Brazilian Forest Code** says that landowners have to keep 50-80% of their land as forest.

'Just keep smiling and back away slowly,' Stu told himself as he met the new head of environmental law for the first time.

Protection

1) Many countries have set up **national parks** and **nature reserves** to protect rainforests. For example, the **Central Amazon Conservation Complex** in Brazil was set up in 2003 and protects **biodiversity** in an area of 49 000 km² while allowing **local people** to use the forest in a **sustainable** way.

2) Within national parks and nature reserves, **damaging activities** such as logging can be monitored and prevented.

Practice Questions

Q1 How does the water cycle affect the environment of tropical rainforests?

Q2 Give an example of how human activities have affected the carbon cycle in tropical rainforests.

Q3 Give one way that people are attempting to limit human impacts on the water or carbon cycles in the Amazon.

Exam Question

Q1 To what extent is human activity affecting the water cycle in tropical rainforests? [9 marks]

Learn this lot and you're done...*

*with the first case study of the first section of the book, that is.

(The small print always has the bad news.) This Amazon case study is prime reading material, but you won't wake up to an exciting little package of knowledge on the doormat of your mind tomorrow unless you put the time into learning it (or the case study you did in class). Make sure you give the information a good review and you're sure to deliver the goods on schedule in the exam.

Topic One — Water and Carbon Cycles

The Eden Basin — Case Study

Pack your bags, we're off to a lovely spot in Cumbria. Unfortunately the water cycle likes to chuck a <u>LOT</u> of water at it from time to time — I'm sure the water cycle means well and just wants to make sure it stays hydrated, but it does cause issues...

The **River Eden** Flows Through **Cumbria**

1) The **Eden drainage basin** is in north-west England, between the **mountains** of the Lake District and the Pennines. The river drains the north-east Lake District fells and the north-west Pennines.

2) The River Eden's **source** is in the Pennine hills in south Cumbria. It flows north-west through **Appleby-in-Westmorland** and **Carlisle**. Its mouth is in the **Solway Firth** at the **Scottish border**.

3) The river basin is largely **rural**, although the River Eden does flow through the city of Carlisle.

4) The upland areas that drain into the River Eden experience **extreme weather** that can cause **flooding** downstream — Carlisle is particularly vulnerable as it's at the **confluence** of the **Eden**, **Petteril** and **Caldew** rivers, and is **fairly low-lying**.

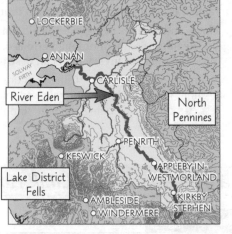

☐ Drainage basin   ▬ River   — Contour Line   — County Boundary

The **Characteristics** of the **Eden Basin** Affect the **Water Cycle**

1) **Rainfall** is **higher** than the national average in the Eden Basin, because of the **relief** of the area — the **mountainous** terrain encourages **orographic** rainfall (see p.5). High rainfall means that lots of water enters the river channels.

2) The Eden Basin is **long** and relatively **narrow**, which increases lag time (see p.8).

3) The **slopes** within the basin are **steep**. This reduces lag time and increases peak discharge.

4) The basin is made up of a number of different types of **rock**:

- The highest ground, to the west of the basin, is made of **igneous rocks**, which are **impermeable** (water won't soak into them). **Infiltration** is very **slow** and **surface runoff** is **high** in these areas, **reducing lag time**.

- Much of the basin, however, is made up of **limestone** and **sandstone**, which are **permeable**. When precipitation falls in these areas, **infiltration** is **quick** and there is **little surface run off**, increasing **lag time**. The amount of water in **ground stores** increases.

Changes in the Water Cycle have **Affected** the **Risk** of Flooding

Land use changes in the Eden Basin have affected the drainage basin's water cycle and **increased flood risk**:

Farming

1) More **intense** farming has caused soils to become **compacted**, e.g. by **heavy machinery** or **trampling** by **livestock**. Between 2000 and 2009, there was a 30% **increase** in the number of cattle in the Eden Valley, meaning that much more land is likely to have been trampled.

2) Compaction of soils reduces **infiltration**, so surface runoff is higher. This means water levels in rivers **rise quickly** during heavy rainfall, increasing the risk of **flooding**.

3) **Grazing** in upland areas, e.g. hill farming of sheep, has also reduced the **amount of vegetation** that can **intercept** rainfall, resulting in more water reaching rivers.

Construction

1) Although the majority of the Eden Basin is rural, built-up areas have **increased**. Many new **housing estates** have been built in and around Carlisle in recent years, e.g. the Eden Gate development to the north of the city, and there are plans to develop a huge 'garden village' to the south of the city, including up to 10 000 new homes.

2) Surfaces in built-up areas tend to be **impermeable**, which reduces the size of infiltration flows and greatly increases the **size** and **speed** of **surface runoff flows** (see page 88).

3) Some new developments, particularly near Carlisle, have been built on floodplains. This has created a **flood risk** to **property** and has required the construction of **flood defences** to protect homes. Building on floodplains can cause **flooding downstream** as water that would naturally infiltrate on the floodplains flows downstream instead.

The Eden Basin — Case Study

Deforestation

1) Deforestation has taken place in the basin for **thousands** of years, e.g. to provide timber, and land for farming. Much of the original forest cover in the Eden Basin has now been **removed**, giving way to large areas of open grassland and heathland.

2) Trees **increase infiltration** and **decrease runoff** (see page 9), so **fewer** trees means **more** runoff, **flashier** flood hydrographs and a **greater risk of flooding**.

Climate change is predicted to **change rainfall patterns** in the UK. For example, parts of the western UK could get up to 35% more winter rainfall by 2080. **Increased winter rainfall** in the Eden Basin would **increase runoff** and **flood risk**.

Storm Desmond Caused Severe Flooding in the Eden Basin

1) In **December 2015**, Storm Desmond caused devastating **flooding** in Cumbria. Some of the worst flooding occurred in the Eden Basin.

2) In some areas of Cumbria, there was **record rainfall**. In **Shap**, a village in the Eden Basin, **262.6 mm** of rain fell in **48 hours** between the 4th and 6th December. That's nearly **50 mm more** than the average rainfall for the **whole** of December.

3) **Appleby-in-Westmorland** and **Carlisle** were particularly badly affected. More than **2000** properties were flooded in Carlisle alone, leaving many people homeless.

4) The hydrograph shows the River Eden's response to **Storm Desmond**. The gauging station that recorded this information is located at **Linstock**, just upstream of Carlisle.

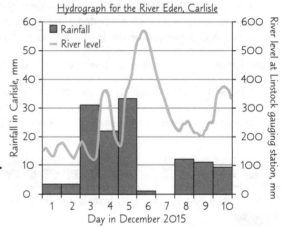

There are Fieldwork Opportunities in River Basins

There are loads of different things you could **investigate** in a convenient drainage basin. For example, you could look at **factors** affecting **flows** and **stores** in the water cycle:

- You could investigate how **rock type** and **land use** affect flows within a drainage basin.
- You might do this by measuring **soil saturation** in different parts of your drainage basin with different land uses or rock types.
- You could also measure the **response** of a river to precipitation. You could use **primary** or **secondary data** for this. In England, the **Environment Agency** regularly publishes **river flow** readings from its gauges on its website.

Dan and Kate hadn't expected fieldwork to be so enjoyable.

Practice Questions

Q1 Give an example of how the water cycle has changed over time in a drainage basin you have studied.

Q2 Give an example of a fieldwork investigation topic you could carry out in a local drainage basin.

Exam Question

Q1 Assess the extent to which changes in the water cycle have affected flood risk or sustainable water supply in a drainage basin that you have studied. [9 marks]

Too much water for the Eden basin? If only we'd had the Eden bath...

You might well have learnt about a different example instead. If you have, don't go thinking it gets you out of doing those practice questions. Oh no siree, you'd better give them a go — but please feel free to answer with a different example.

The Coastal System

Coastal systems are the areas where the land meets the sea. And they're almost as exciting as they sound...

Coasts are Natural Systems

Coasts are **systems** — they have **inputs**, **outputs**, **flows** and **stores** of **sediment** and **energy** (see p. 2):

> 1) **INPUTS** — e.g. **sediment** can be brought into the system in various ways (see next page). **Energy** inputs come from **wind**, **waves**, **tides** and **currents** (see below).
>
> 2) **OUTPUTS** — e.g. sediment can be **washed out to sea**, or deposited **further along** the coast.
>
> 3) **FLOWS/TRANSFERS** — e.g. processes such as **erosion**, **weathering**, **transportation** and **deposition** (see pages 22-23) can move sediment **within** the system (e.g. from beach to dune).
>
> 4) **STORES/COMPONENTS** — **landforms** such as **beaches**, **dunes** and **spits** (see p. 24-26) are stores of sediment.

Events such as storm surges give high energy inputs — this can increase sediment inputs or outputs.

Coastal systems are generally in **dynamic equilibrium** — inputs and outputs are **balanced**. A **change** in one input or output often causes **negative feedbacks** that **restore** the balance of the system:

> A **NEGATIVE FEEDBACK** is when a change in the system causes other changes that have the **opposite effect**. For example, as a beach is **eroded**, the cliffs behind it are exposed to **wave attack**. Sediment eroded from the cliffs is **deposited** on the beach, causing it to **grow in size** again.

Coastal systems also experience **positive feedbacks** that change the balance of the system, creating a **new equilibrium**:

> A **POSITIVE FEEDBACK** is when a change in the system causes other changes that have a **similar effect**. For example, as a beach starts to **form** it slows down waves, which can cause more sediment to be **deposited**, increasing the **size** of the beach. The **new** equilibrium is reached when **long-term growth** of the beach **stops**.

There Are Lots of Sources of Energy in Coastal Systems

In the coastal system, energy is **transferred** by **air** (as wind) and by **water** (as waves, tides and currents):

Wind

1) **Winds** are created by air moving from areas of **high** pressure to areas of **low** pressure. During events such as **storms**, the pressure gradient (the difference between high and low pressure) is high and winds can be very **strong**.

2) Strong winds can generate **powerful waves**. In some areas, wind consistently blows from the **same** direction (this is called a **prevailing wind**) — this causes **higher-energy waves** than winds that change direction frequently.

Waves

1) **Waves** are created by the **wind** blowing over the surface of the sea. The **friction** between the wind and the surface of the sea gives the water a **circular motion**.

2) The **effect of a wave** on the **shore** depends on its **height**. Wave height is affected by the **wind speed** and the **fetch** of the wave. The fetch is the **maximum distance of sea** the wind has blown over in creating the waves. A **high wind speed** and a **long fetch** create **higher** and more **powerful** waves.

3) As waves approach the shore they **break**. Friction with the sea bed **slows** the bottom of the waves and makes their motion more elliptical (squashed and oval-shaped). The **crest** of the wave rises up and then **collapses**.

4) Water washing **up** the beach is called the **swash**. Water washing **back** towards the sea is called the **backwash**.

5) There are **two types** of wave:

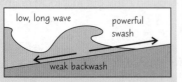

Constructive waves have a **low frequency** (only around **6-8** waves per minute). They're **low and long**, which gives them a more **elliptical** cross profile. The powerful swash carries material up the beach and **deposits** it.

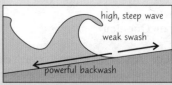

Destructive waves are **high** and **steep**, with a more **circular** cross profile. They have a **higher frequency** (**10-14** waves a minute). The strong backwash **removes** material from the beach.

Wave frequency is how many waves pass a point in a particular time.

6) The waves in an area are usually **mainly constructive** or **mainly destructive**.

The Coastal System

Tides

1) Tides are the periodic **rise** and **fall** of the **ocean surface**, caused by the gravitational pull of the **Moon** and the **Sun**.
2) Tides affect the **position** at which **waves break** on the beach (at high tide they break higher up the shore). The area of land between **maximum high tide** and **minimum low tide** is where most landforms are created and destroyed.

Currents

1) A **current** is the general flow of water in one direction — it can be caused by **wind** or by variations in water **temperature** and **salinity**.
2) Currents move material **along** the coast.

Currants — check. Salinity — check. Karen knew how to make her cake memorable.

Coasts can be **High Energy** or **Low Energy**

1) **High-energy** coasts receive high inputs of energy in the form of **large, powerful waves**. These can be caused by **strong winds**, **long fetches** and **steeply shelving** offshore zones. High-energy coastlines tend to have **sandy** coves and **rocky** landforms, e.g. cliffs, caves, stacks and arches (see p. 24). The rate of **erosion** is often **higher** than the rate of **deposition**.

2) **Low-energy** coasts receive low inputs of energy in the form of **small, gentle waves**. These can be caused by **gentle winds** (e.g. if the location is **sheltered**), **short fetches** and **gently sloping** offshore zones. Some coastlines are low energy because there is a **reef** or **island** offshore, which protects the coast from the full power of waves. Low-energy coastlines often have **saltmarshes** and **tidal mudflats**. The rate of **deposition** is often **higher** than the rate of **erosion**.

There Are Lots of **Sediment Sources** in Coastal Systems

1) There are lots of **inputs** of sediment into the coastal system:

- **Rivers** carry eroded sediment into the coastal system from **inland**.
- **Sea level rise** can flood river valleys, forming **estuaries**. Sediment in the estuary becomes part of the coastal system.
- Sediment is **eroded** from **cliffs** by waves, weathering and landslides.
- Sediment can be **formed** from the crushed **shells** of marine organisms.
- Waves, tides and currents can transport sediment into the coastal zone from **offshore deposits** (e.g. sandbanks).

2) The **difference** between the amount of sediment that enters the system and the amount that leaves is the **sediment budget**. If **more** sediment **enters** than leaves, it's a **positive sediment budget** and overall the coastline **builds** outwards. If **more** sediment **leaves** than enters, it's a **negative sediment budget** and overall the coastline **retreats**.

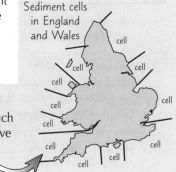

Sediment cells in England and Wales

Sediment Cells

- The coast is divided into **sediment cells** (also called **littoral cells**).
- These are lengths of coastline (often between two headlands) that are pretty much entirely **self-contained** for the movement of sediment (i.e. sediment doesn't move between cells). This means that **processes** going on in **one cell** don't affect the movement of sediment in **another** cell — each cell is a **closed coastal system**.

Practice Questions

Q1 Draw a table to show the main inputs, flows, outputs and stores of a coastal system.

Q2 Describe the differences between high-energy and low-energy coasts.

Exam Questions

Q1 Describe the characteristics of constructive waves. [3 marks]

Q2 Outline the sources of energy in a coastal system. [3 marks]

What did the sea say to the beach — nothing, it just waved...

Lots of technical terms on these pages, but it's worth learning them — they'll really help you understand the rest of this topic. So make sure it's all as familiar as your favourite pair of socks (you know the ones — with the holes and the sausage-dog print).

Coastal Processes

Coasts are affected by two types of processes — marine processes <u>are</u> caused by the sea (erosion, transport and deposition), and sub-aerial processes <u>aren't</u> directly caused by the sea (weathering, runoff and mass movement). Confused? Read on...

There are **Six** Main Ways **Waves Erode** the **Coastline**

Waves don't just erode beaches — they also erode **rocks** and **cliffs**. Here are the six main ways they do it:

1) **Corrasion (abrasion)** — Bits of rock and sediment transported by the waves **smash** and **grind** against rocks and cliffs, **breaking** bits off and **smoothing** surfaces.

2) **Hydraulic action** — **Air** in cracks in cliffs is **compressed** when waves crash in. The pressure exerted by the compressed air breaks off rock pieces.

3) **Cavitation** — As waves **recede**, the compressed air **expands violently**, again exerting **pressure** on the rock and causing pieces to **break off**.

4) **Wave quarrying** — The energy of a wave as it breaks against a cliff is enough to detach bits of rock.

5) **Solution (corrosion)** — **Soluble rocks** (e.g. limestone, chalk) get gradually **dissolved** by the seawater.

6) **Attrition** — Bits of rock in the water smash against **each other** and break into smaller bits.

Transportation is the Process of **Eroded Material** Being Moved

The **energy** provided by waves, tides and currents **transports eroded material**. There are **four** main processes:

Solution
Substances that can **dissolve** are carried along **in the** water. E.g. **limestone** is dissolved into water that's slightly **acidic**.

Suspension
Very fine material, such as **silt** and **clay** particles, is whipped up by **turbulence** (**erratic swirling** of water) and carried along in the water. **Most** eroded material is transported this way.

Saltation
Larger particles, such as **pebbles** or **gravel**, are **too heavy** to be carried in suspension. Instead, the **force** of the water causes them to **bounce** along the sea bed.
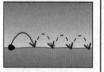

Traction
Very large particles, e.g. **boulders**, are **pushed** along the sea bed by the force of the water.
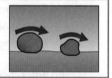

These processes can transport sediment **along** the shore — this is called **longshore drift** (or **littoral drift**):

1) **Swash** carries sediment (e.g. shingle, pebbles) **up** the beach, **parallel** to the prevailing wind. **Backwash** carries sediment back **down** the beach, at **right angles** to the shoreline.

2) When there's an **angle** between the prevailing wind and the shoreline, a few rounds of swash and backwash move the sediment **along** the shoreline.

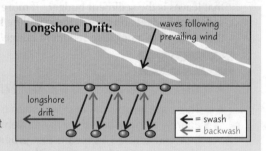

Longshore Drift:
waves following prevailing wind
longshore drift
← = swash
← = backwash

Deposition is the Process of **Dropping Eroded Material**

1) Deposition is when **material** being transported is **dropped** on the coast:
   - **Marine deposition** is when sediment carried by **seawater** is deposited.
   - **Aeolian deposition** is when sediment carried by **wind** is deposited.

Deposition forms landforms such as beaches, spits and dunes (see pages 25-26).

2) Both marine and aeolian deposition happen when the **sediment load** exceeds the ability of the water or wind to **carry** it. This can be because sediment load **increases** (e.g. if there is a landslide), or because wind or water **flow slows down** (so it has **less energy**). Wind and water slow down for similar reasons:
   - **Friction increases** — if waves enter **shallow** water or wind reaches **land**, **friction** between the water/wind and ground surface increases, which **slows down** the water or wind.
   - **Flow becomes turbulent** — if water or wind encounters an **obstacle** (e.g. a current moving in the opposite direction, or an area of vegetation), flow becomes **rougher** and overall speed **decreases**.

3) If the wind drops, wave height, speed and energy will decrease as well.

Coastal Processes

Sub-aerial Weathering Occurs Along the Coastline

Sub-aerial weathering is the gradual break down of rock by agents such as ice, salt, plant roots and acids. Weathering **weakens cliffs** and makes them **more vulnerable** to **erosion**. There are several types of weathering that affect coasts:

Salt Weathering

1) **Salt weathering** is caused by **saline (salty) water**.
2) This saline water **enters pores** or **cracks** in rocks at high tide.
3) As the tide goes out the rocks dry and the **water evaporates**, forming **salt crystals**.
   As the salt crystals **form** they **expand**, exerting **pressure** on the rock — this causes **pieces** to **fall off**.

Freeze-thaw Weathering

1) **Freeze-thaw** weathering occurs in areas where **temperatures** fluctuate **above** and **below freezing**.
2) Water enters the **joints** and **crevices** in rocks.
3) If the temperature drops **below 0 °C**, the water in the cracks **freezes** and **expands**.
4) Over time, **repeated** freeze-thaw action **weakens** the rocks and causes pieces to **fall off**.

ice expands → rock breaks off

Wetting and Drying

1) Some rocks contain **clay**.
2) When clay gets **wet**, it **expands** and the **pressure** caused by this **breaks fragments off** the rock.

clay expands → rock breaks off

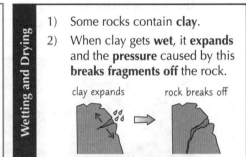

Chemical Weathering

1) **Chemical weathering** is the breakdown of rock by **changing** its **chemical composition**.
2) For example, **carbon dioxide** in the atmosphere dissolves in rainwater, forming a **weak carbonic acid**. This acid **reacts** with rock that contains **calcium carbonate**, e.g. carboniferous limestone, so the rocks are gradually **dissolved**.

Biological weathering — e.g. plant roots growing into cracks in the rock and widening them — can also cause rocks to break down.

Mass Movement is when Material Moves Down a Slope

1) Mass movement is the **shifting** of **material** downhill due to **gravity**. In coastal areas, it is most likely to occur when cliffs are **undercut** by wave action — this causes an unsupported **overhang**, which is likely to collapse.

2) Types of mass movement include **landslides**, **slumping** (a type of landslide), **rockfalls** and **mudflows**. Material can also move gradually downwards by **soil creep**.

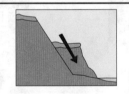

Slides — material shifts in a **straight line**

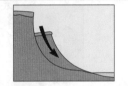

Slumps — material shifts with a **rotation**

Rockfalls — material **breaks up** and **falls**

Mudflows — material flows downslope

3) **Unconsolidated** rocks (e.g. clay) are prone to collapse as there's **little friction** between particles to hold them together.
4) **Heavy rain** can **saturate** unconsolidated rock, further reducing friction and making it more likely to **collapse**.
5) **Runoff** (the flow of water over the land) can **erode** fine particles (e.g. sand and silt) and **transport** them downslope.

Practice Questions

Q1 Describe two processes of coastal sediment transport.
Q2 Explain why water deposits sediment when it slows down.

Exam Question

Q1 Outline how sub-aerial weathering can cause breakdown of coastal rock.   [3 marks]

Mass movement — what happened when we spotted a spider in the office...

Seriously, it was a bad time — there was running, screaming, one man got trampled... Fortunately, mass movements at the coast aren't normally hazardous (unless you happen to be standing underneath a cliff at the wrong time — do try to avoid that).

Coastal Landforms

Walk this way for some coastal landforms... Geology and the amount of energy in the coastal system affect the type of landforms that occur — areas tend to be dominated by either erosional or depositional landforms, giving distinctive landscapes.

Some **Coastal Landforms** are Caused by **Erosion**

CLIFFS AND WAVE-CUT PLATFORMS

1) **Cliffs** are common coastal landforms — they form as the sea **erodes** the land. Over time, cliffs **retreat** due to the action of **waves** and **weathering**.

2) Weathering and wave erosion cause a **notch** to form at the high water mark. This eventually develops into a **cave**.

3) Rock above the cave becomes **unstable** with nothing to support it, and it **collapses**.

4) **Wave-cut platforms** are **flat surfaces** left behind when a cliff is eroded.

These cliffs and platforms are near Lannacombe Bay in South Devon.

HEADLANDS AND BAYS

1) **Headlands** and **bays** form where there are **bands** of alternating **hard rock** and **soft rock** at **right angles** to the shoreline.

2) The **soft rock** is **eroded quickly**, forming a **bay**. The **harder rock** is **eroded less** and sticks out as a **headland**.

These headlands and bay are on the Cape of Good Hope, South Africa.

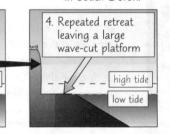

- ⟶ = Waves
- ☐ = Beach
- Ⓗ = Headland
- Ⓑ = Bay

CAVES, ARCHES AND STACKS

1) Some landforms are found in cliffs — these are called **cliff profile features**.

2) Weak areas in rock (e.g. joints) are **eroded** to form **caves**.

3) Caves on the opposite sides of a narrow headland may eventually join up to form an **arch**.

4) When an **arch** collapses, it forms a **stack**.

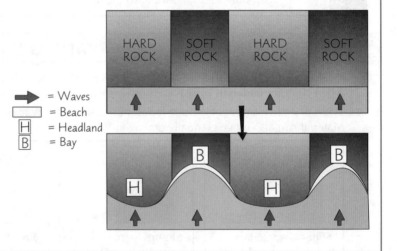

An arch, caves and stacks on the shore of Loch Bracadale, Scotland.

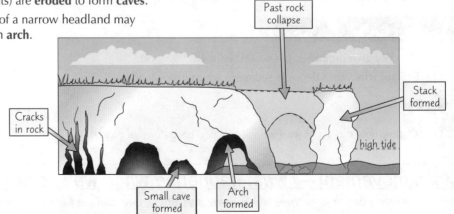

Topic Two — Coastal Systems and Landscapes

Coastal Landforms

Some **Coastal Landforms** are Caused by **Deposition**

BEACHES

1) **Beaches** form when **constructive** waves **deposit sediment** on the shore — they are a **store** in the coastal system.

2) **Shingle** beaches are **steep** and **narrow**. They're made up of **larger** particles, which pile up at steep angles. **Sand** beaches, formed from **smaller** particles, are **wide** and **flat**.

3) Beaches have distinctive features. **Berms** are **ridges** of sand and pebbles (about 1-2 metres high) found at **high tide** marks. **Runnels** are **grooves** in the sand running **parallel** to the shore, formed by **backwash** draining to the sea. **Cusps** are **crescent-shaped indentations** that form on beaches of mixed sand and shingle.

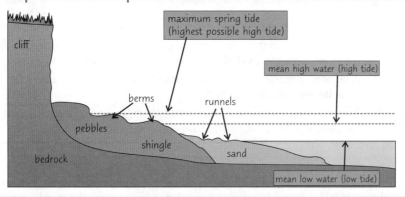

Berms on a beach in
Parque Tayrona, Colombia.

SPITS

Spits tend to form where the coast suddenly **changes direction**, e.g. across river mouths.

1) **Longshore drift** (see p. 22) continues to **deposit** material across the river mouth, leaving a bank of **sand** and **shingle** sticking out into the sea. A **straight** spit that grows out roughly **parallel** to the coast is called a **simple spit**.

2) Occasional **changes** to the dominant wind and wave direction may lead to a spit having a **curved end** (the fancy name for this is a **recurved end**).

3) Over time, several recurved ends may be abandoned as the waves return to their **original direction**. A spit that has **multiple recurved ends** resulting from **several** periods of growth is called a **compound spit**.

4) The area **behind** the spit is **sheltered** from the waves and often develops into **mudflats** and **saltmarshes** (see p. 26).

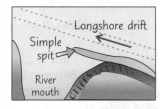 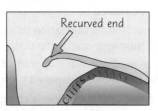  

OFFSHORE BARS AND TOMBOLOS

Bars are a type of barrier beach — see next page.

1) Bars are formed when a **spit joins two headlands together**. This can occur across a **bay** or across a **river mouth**.

2) A **lagoon** forms **behind** the bar.

3) Bars can also form off the coast when material moves **towards** the coast (normally as sea level rises). These may remain **partly submerged** by the sea — in this case they're called **offshore bars**.

The Slapton Sands bar at
Torcross, Devon.

Paul and Mary left
the bar to spend some
time enjoying the
lagoon...

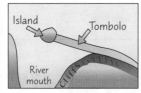 

4) A bar that **connects** the shore to an **island** (often a stack) is called a **tombolo**.

5) For example, **St Ninian's Isle** in the Shetland Islands is joined to a larger island by a tombolo.

Coastal Landforms

BARRIER ISLANDS

1) Barrier islands (also called barrier beaches) are long, narrow islands of sand or gravel that run **parallel** to the shore and are **detached** from it. They tend to form in areas where there's a good supply of **sediment**, a **gentle slope** offshore, fairly **powerful** waves and a **small tidal range**.

'Barrier beach' is a general term for any beach that shelters the coast, including barrier islands, spits and bars.

2) It's not clear exactly how barrier islands form, but scientists think that they probably formed after the **last ice age** ended, when ice melt caused rapid **sea level rise**. The rising waters **flooded** the

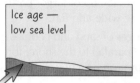
Ice age — low sea level

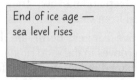
End of ice age — sea level rises

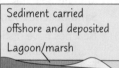
Sediment carried offshore and deposited
Lagoon/marsh

land behind beaches and **transported** sand offshore, where it was **deposited** in shallow water, forming islands.

3) Another theory is that the islands were originally **bars**, attached to the coast, which were **eroded** in sections, causing **breaches** in the bar.

4) A **lagoon** or **marsh** often forms behind the barrier island, where the coast is **sheltered** from wave action.

5) Barrier islands are found on many coastlines, including the **east coast** of the **USA**, e.g. Horn Island in Mississippi.

SAND DUNES

1) Sand dunes are formed when **sand deposited** by longshore drift is moved up the beach by the **wind**.

2) Sand trapped by driftwood or berms (see previous page) is colonised by **plants** and **grasses**, e.g. marram grass. The vegetation **stabilises** the sand and encourages **more sand** to accumulate there, forming **embryo dunes**.

3) Over time, the oldest dunes migrate inland as newer embryo dunes are formed. These **mature dunes** can reach heights of up to 10 m.

Sand dunes at Cape Hatteras in North Carolina.

ESTUARINE MUDFLATS AND SALTMARSHES

Saltmarsh, Huntington Beach State Park, South Carolina.

1) Mudflats and saltmarshes form in **sheltered**, **low-energy** environments, e.g. river estuaries or behind spits.

2) As **silt** and **mud** are **deposited** by the river or the tide, **mudflats** develop.

3) The mudflats are colonised by **vegetation** that can survive the **high salt levels** and long periods of **submergence** by the tide.

4) The plants **trap more mud** and **silt**, and gradually they build upwards to create an area of saltmarsh that remains **exposed** for longer and longer **between tides**.

5) **Erosion** by tidal currents or streams forms **channels** in the surface of mudflats and saltmarshes. These may be **permanently flooded** or **dry** at low tide.

Practice Questions

Q1 Name four landforms of coastal erosion and four landforms of coastal deposition.

Q2 Describe where headlands and bays form.

Q3 Briefly describe how stacks are formed.

Q4 Where do saltmarshes form?

Exam Questions

Q1 Outline how a wave-cut platform is formed. [3 marks]

Q2 Outline how spits form and develop. [3 marks]

Man walks into a bar, gets his feet wet...

The landforms you have to know are pretty much the same ones you have to know for GCSE — you just need to know more detail about how they form. And you thought it was going to be all excitement and glamour once you left your GCSEs behind. Sorry.

Topic Two — Coastal Systems and Landscapes

Sea Level Changes

There's a fair bit to learn on these three pages. Just try and keep your head above the water...

Sea Level Changes are Eustatic or Isostatic

You need to know the difference between **eustatic** and **isostatic** changes in sea level, and the role that **tectonic processes** (processes related to movement of the Earth's **crust**) play in each:

EUSTATIC

Eustatic sea level change is caused by a change in the **volume of water** in the sea, or by a change in the **shape** of the **ocean basins**.

The effects are always **global** and the main **causes** are:

1) **Changes in climate.** Different changes affect sea level in different ways:

   - An **increase** in **temperature** causes **melting** of **ice sheets**, which **increases** sea level. It also causes water to **expand**, which **increases** sea level further.
   - A **decrease** in **temperature** causes more precipitation to fall as **snow**. This increases the volume of water **stored** in **glaciers** and so reduces the volume of the sea, which **decreases** sea level.

2) **Tectonic movements** of the Earth's crust that alter the shape (and so the volume) of ocean basins. E.g. sea floor spreading **increases** the **volume** of the basin and so **decreases** sea level.

ISOSTATIC

Isostatic sea level change is caused by **vertical movements** of the land **relative** to the sea.

Any **downward** movement of the land causes sea level to **rise** locally, while **uplift of land** causes sea level to **fall**.

The effects are always **local** and the main **causes** are:

1) **Uplift** or **depression** of the Earth's crust due to accumulation or melting of **ice sheets**. Slow uplift of land can continue for thousands of years after the weight of a **retreating glacier** has gone. **Accumulation of sediment**, mostly at the mouths of major rivers, can also cause **depression**.

2) **Subsidence** of land due to shrinkage after **abstraction of groundwater**, e.g. drainage of marshland.

3) **Tectonic** (crustal) processes, e.g. as one plate is forced beneath another at a plate margin (see p. 58).

"There's definitely sea down there somewhere. Nigel, you go first."

Isostatic uplift had caused problems for Chris, Steven and Nigel.

Sea Level Has Risen in the Last 10 000 Years

1) Sea level **varies** on a daily basis with the **tidal cycle**. **Onshore winds** and **low atmospheric pressure systems** also cause the sea surface to rise **temporarily**.

2) On a much **longer time scale**, global sea level has changed by a much **larger** amount:

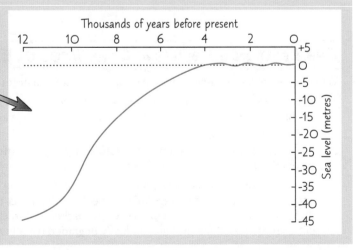

- During the **last glacial period** (from roughly 110 000 to 12 000 years ago), water was stored in **ice sheets**, so sea level was **lower** than present. At the **last glacial maximum** (around 21 000 years ago) sea level was about **130 m lower** than present.
- As temperatures started to **increase** (about 12 000 years ago), ice sheets **melted** and sea level **rose** rapidly. It reached its present level about **4000 years ago**.
- Over the **last 4000 years**, sea level has **fluctuated** around its present value.
- Since about **1930**, sea level has been **rising** (see next page).

Topic Two — Coastal Systems and Landscapes

Sea Level Changes

Climate Change Causes Changes in Sea Level...

1) Over the **last century**, **global temperature** has **increased rapidly**. This is called **global warming**. There's been a **sharp rise** in average temperature (**1.08 °C** between **1900** and **2016**).

2) The **temperature increase** over the last century has been **very fast**. There is a **consensus** among scientists that the **changes** in **climate** over the last century are a result of **human activities**, such as deforestation and burning fossil fuels.

3) These activities increase the concentration of greenhouse gases in the atmosphere — greenhouse gases absorb **outgoing long-wave radiation**, so less is **lost** to space. As their concentration increases, **more** energy is trapped and the planet **warms up**.

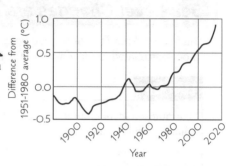

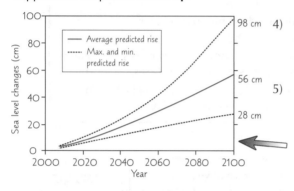

4) Increases in **temperature** are likely to cause increases in **sea level**, through **melting** of ice sheets and **thermal expansion** of water in oceans.

5) Global sea level is currently rising at almost **2 mm** each year. If greenhouse gas emissions remain very **high** during the 21st century, this is predicted to **increase** to **8** to **16 mm** a year by 2100.

The Watson brothers had a plan for dealing with sea level rise.

... and has Impacts on Coastal Areas

1) **Storms** are likely to become more **frequent** and more **intense** due to **changes in ocean circulation** and **wind patterns**. This would cause damage to coastal **ecosystems** and **settlements**.

2) If **sea level rise** continues as predicted, it will have major impacts on coastal areas:

   - **More frequent** and **more severe coastal flooding**. Flooding of low-lying areas has increased with sea level rise and it will increase more with further rises. For example, from 1995 to 2004, **Kings Point** in **New York** state, USA, flooded around **80 times**, but from 2005 to 2014 it flooded nearly **160 times**.

   - **Submergence of low-lying islands**. Lots of low-lying islands are **at risk** of disappearing. For example, if the sea level rises by just **0.5 m** from its current level then most of the **Maldives** will be submerged.

   - **Changes in the coastline**. As sea levels rise the coastline changes — islands are **created** and the **area** of **land** is **decreased**. E.g. if the sea level rises **0.3 m** from its current level, **8000 km²** of land in **Bangladesh** will be lost.

   - **Contamination of water sources and farmland**. Salt water may enter bodies of fresh water (e.g. lakes and rivers) near the coast, damaging **ecosystems** and making the water **unsuitable** for lots of uses. Salt water entering soils may **damage crops** and make land impossible to **farm**.

3) Sea level rise and increased storminess will increase **coastal erosion**, putting **ecosystems**, **homes** and **businesses** at risk.

Sea Level Fall Results in Coastlines of Emergence

When sea level falls relative to the coast, new coastline **emerges** from the sea. This creates different **landforms**:

1) **Raised beaches** are formed when the fall in sea level leaves beaches **above** the high tide mark. Over time, beach sediment becomes **vegetated** and develops into **soil**.

2) Sea level fall also exposes **wave-cut platforms** (**marine platforms**), leaving them **raised** above their former level.

3) The **cliffs** above raised beaches are no longer eroded by the sea, and slowly get covered by **vegetation**. They're called **relict cliffs**. It's not uncommon to see **wave-cut notches**, **caves**, **arches** and **stacks** within relict cliffs. These **raised features** are gradually **degraded** (weathered) over time.

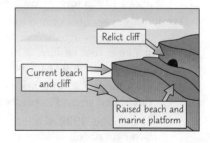

Topic Two — Coastal Systems and Landscapes

Sea Level Changes

Sea Level Rise Results in Coastlines of Submergence

When sea level rises relative to the coast, the sea **submerges** (drowns) the existing coastline. This creates different **landforms**:

RIAS are formed where **river valleys** are partially **submerged**, e.g. Milford Haven in South Wales is a ria. Rias have a **gentle** long- and cross-profile. They're **wide** and **deep** at their **mouth**, becoming **narrower** and **shallower** the further **inland** they reach.

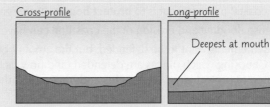

Cross-profile   Long-profile

Deepest at mouth

FJORDS

Cross-profile   Long-profile

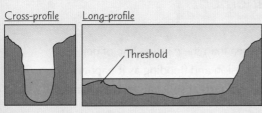

Threshold

FJORDS are a lot like rias, but they're **drowned glacial valleys** rather than drowned river valleys. They're relatively **straight** and narrow, with very **steep sides**. They have a **shallow mouth** caused by a raised bit of ground (called the **threshold**) formed by deposition of material by the glacier. They're very **deep** further **inland**, e.g. Sognefjorden in Norway is over 1000 m deep in places.

DALMATIAN COASTLINES

In areas where **valleys** lie **parallel** to the coast, an increase in sea level can form a **DALMATIAN COASTLINE**. Valleys are flooded, leaving **islands** parallel to the coastline. It's named after the Dalmatian coast in Croatia.

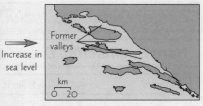

Increase in sea level

Former valleys

km
0   20

km
0   20

Processes Create and Alter Landforms and Landscapes Over Time

1) Individual **landforms** (e.g. spits, arches) **combine** to form **landscapes** — coastal landscapes can be dominated by processes of **erosion** or **deposition**, but most are formed by **both**.

2) Processes operating in coastal systems can **create new landforms** or **change existing landforms**. This means that coastal landscapes **change** over time. For example:
   - A change in **one factor** can lead to changes in **others**, e.g. a change in **wave direction** might increase **deposition** and eventually change a landscape dominated by **erosive landforms** to one dominated by **depositional landforms**.
   - **Relict** landforms can still experience coastal **processes**, e.g. a relict cliff may be **weathered** by salt and freeze-thaw.

3) Coastal landscapes are therefore often made up of a **mixture** of active and relict landforms that reflect **different periods** of **change**. E.g. a beach that is still being formed may be backed by a relict cliff from an **earlier time** of higher sea level.

4) Changes occur over a **range** of **spatial scales** and **temporal scales**. For example, changes can vary from **short** and **episodic** (e.g. storm waves that last for a few hours) to **long** and **gradual** (e.g. tectonic uplift over thousands of years).

Practice Questions

Q1 State two causes of eustatic sea level change and two causes of isostatic sea level change.

Q2 Give two examples of landforms that show there must have been a drop in sea levels.

Q3 Sketch a diagram showing the cross-profile of a fjord.

Exam Questions

Q1 Outline how coastal submergence can result in a range of landforms.   [3 marks]

Q2 Assess the likely impacts of climate change on coastal areas in the future.   [9 marks]

I'd start moving up onto high ground now...

You need to know how and why sea levels are rising, and the impacts this might have. Examiners love asking questions about current issues, and rising sea levels are a hot topic in the news at the moment — so make sure you're hot on all the details too.

Coastal Management

Coastal management is a complex thing. Fixing up one coastal area can have the unintended effect of messing up another area...

Only **Some Parts** of the **Coast** are **Defended**

1) The aim of coastal management is to **protect homes**, **businesses** and the **environment** from **erosion** and **flooding**.

2) This is because flooding and erosion of the coastline can have severe **social**, **economic** and **environmental impacts**.

3) All coastal settlements want to be defended, but the amount of **money available** is **limited** so not everywhere can be defended. Choosing which places are defended (and how) is based on a **cost-benefit analysis**. The money available is usually used to protect **large settlements** and important **industrial sites**, rather than isolated or small settlements.

There are **Four Options** for **Coastal Management**

1) **Hold the line** — maintain the **existing** coastal defences.

2) **Advance the line** — build **new** coastal defences **further out to sea** than the existing line of defence.

3) **Do nothing** — build **no** coastal defences at all, and deal with erosion and flooding **as it happens**.

4) **Managed realignment** — allow the shoreline to **move**, but **manage retreat** so it causes **least damage** (e.g. flooding farmland rather than towns). See next page.

Coastal Defences Include **Hard Engineering** and **Soft Engineering**

Hard Engineering Defences Involve **Built Structures**

Defence	How it works	Cost	Disadvantage
Sea wall	The wall reflects waves back out to sea, preventing erosion of the coast. It also acts as a barrier to prevent flooding.	Expensive to build and maintain	It creates a strong backwash, which erodes under the wall.
Revetment	Revetments are slanted structures built at the foot of cliffs. They can be made from concrete, wood or rocks. Waves break against the revetments, which absorb the wave energy and so prevent cliff erosion.	Expensive to build, but relatively cheap to maintain	They create a strong backwash, as above.
Gabions	Gabions are rock-filled cages. A wall of gabions is usually built at the foot of cliffs. The gabions absorb wave energy and so reduce erosion.	Cheap	Ugly
Riprap	Boulders piled up along the coast are called riprap. The boulders absorb wave energy and so reduce erosion.	Fairly cheap	Can shift in storms.
Groynes	Groynes are fences built at right angles to the coast. They trap beach material transported by longshore drift. This creates wider beaches, which slow the waves (reducing their energy) and so gives greater protection from flooding and erosion.	Quite cheap	They starve down-drift beaches of sand. Thinner beaches don't protect the coast as well, leading to greater erosion and flooding.
Breakwaters	Breakwaters are usually concrete blocks or boulders deposited off the coast. They force waves to break offshore. The waves' energy and erosive power are reduced before they reach the shore.	Expensive	Can be damaged in storms.
Earth bank	Mounds of earth act as a barrier to prevent flooding.	Quite expensive	Can be eroded.
Tidal barrier	Tidal barriers are built across river estuaries. They contain retractable floodgates that can be raised to prevent flooding from storm surges.	VERY expensive	Really, VERY expensive.
Tidal barrage	Tidal barrages are dams built across river estuaries. Their main purpose is to generate electricity. Water is trapped behind the dam at high tide. Controlled release of water through turbines in the dam at low tide generates electricity. They also prevent flooding from storm surges.	VERY expensive	They disrupt sediment flow, which may cause increased erosion elsewhere in the estuary.

Coastal Management

Soft Engineering Defences Involve Coaxing Natural Processes Along

1) **Beach nourishment** is where **sand** and **shingle** are added to beaches from elsewhere (e.g. **dredged** from offshore). This creates **wide** beaches, which **reduce erosion** of cliffs more than thin beaches.

2) **Beach stabilisation** can be done by **reducing the slope angle** and planting **vegetation**, or by sticking **stakes** and **old tree trunks** in the beach to stabilise the sand. It also creates **wide** beaches, which **reduce erosion** of cliffs.

3) **Dune regeneration** is where sand dunes are **created** or **restored** by either nourishment or stabilisation of the sand. and dunes provide a **barrier** between land and sea, **absorbing wave energy** and preventing flooding and erosion.

4) **Land use management** is important for dune regeneration. The vegetation needed to stabilise the dune can easily be **trampled** and destroyed, leaving the dune **vulnerable** to **erosion**. Wooden **walkways** across dunes, and **fenced-off areas** that prevent walkers, cyclists or 4×4 drivers from gaining access to the dunes, all **reduce vegetation loss**.

5) **Creating marshland** from mudflats can be encouraged by **planting** appropriate vegetation (e.g. glassworts). The vegetation **stabilises** the sediment, and the stems and leaves help **reduce the speed** of the waves. This **reduces** their **erosive power** and **how far** the waves reach **inland**, leading to **less flooding** of the area around the marsh.

6) **Coastal realignment** (also known as **managed retreat**) involves breaching an existing defence and allowing the sea to flood the land behind. Over time, vegetation will colonise the land and it'll become **marshland**.

Management Strategies for the Future Must be Sustainable

1) Coastal management has to be **sustainable** — this means that strategies shouldn't cause too much damage to the **environment** or to people's **homes** and **livelihoods**, and shouldn't **cost** too much.

- Hard engineering is often **expensive**, and it **disrupts natural processes**.

- Soft engineering schemes tend to be **cheaper** and require **less time** and **money** to **maintain** than hard engineering schemes. Soft engineering is designed to **integrate** with the natural **environment** and it creates areas like **marshland** and **sand dunes**, which are important **habitats**.

Some coastal engineering provides habitats for tiny kings and queens.

- So soft engineering is a **more sustainable management strategy** than hard engineering because it has a **lower environmental impact** and **economic cost**.

2) There are **two** important ideas involved in deciding how to **manage** coastal areas **sustainably**:

Shoreline Management Plans
1) The coastline is split into stretches by **sediment cells** (see p.21). For each cell, a **plan** is devised for how to manage different areas with the aim of **protecting important sites** without causing **problems elsewhere** in the sediment cell (e.g. starving an adjacent area of sediment could increase erosion).
2) For each area within a cell, authorities can decide to **hold**, **advance** or **retreat** the line, or to **do nothing**.
3) The **overall plan** for each sediment cell is called a **Shoreline Management Plan** (SMP). All the **local authorities** in one sediment cell **co-operate** in coming up with an SMP.

Integrated Coastal Zone Management
1) **Integrated Coastal Zone Management** (ICZM) considers **all** elements of the coastal system (e.g. land, water, people, the economy) when coming up with a management strategy. It aims to **protect** the coastal zone in a relatively **natural** state, whilst allowing people to **use** it and **develop** it in different ways.
2) It is **integrated** in various ways:
- The environment is viewed as a **whole** — the **land** and the **water** are **interdependent**.
- Different **uses** are considered, e.g. fishing, industry, tourism.
- **Local**, **regional** and **national** levels of authority all have an **input** into the plan.
3) It is a **dynamic** strategy — decisions are re-evaluated if the environment or demands on the area **change**.

Practice Questions

Q1 What is the aim of coastal management?

Q2 What are Shoreline Management Plans?

Exam Question

Q1 Distinguish between hard and soft engineering schemes in coastal management. [3 marks]

Do nothing? Retreat? Sounds like a lousy revision strategy to me...

Coastal management sounds like a difficult and unending job. Even after spending millions of pounds on a nice big concrete wall to keep the waves out, it can still go horribly wrong. These days, coastal managers try to use more sustainable methods instead.

Coastal Environment — Case Study

Time to put all the theory into practice — here's a bagful of juicy facts about Holderness in East Yorkshire.

The Holderness Coastline is **Eroding Rapidly**

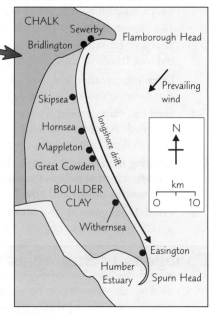

1) The Holderness coastline is **61 km long** — it stretches from Flamborough Head to Spurn Head.

2) Most of the cliffs are made of **till** ('**boulder clay**'), and the coast is exposed to powerful **destructive waves** from the North Sea during storms.

3) There are a number of **coastal processes** operating in the area:

- **Erosion** — the soft boulder clay is easily **eroded** by wave action. In some places, e.g. **Great Cowden**, the rate of erosion has been over **10 m/year** in recent years.

- **Mass movement** — the boulder clay is also prone to **slumping** when it's wet. Water makes the clay **heavier** and acts as a **lubricant** between particles, which makes it **unstable**.

- **Transportation** — prevailing winds from the northeast transport material **southwards**. These winds also create an **ocean current**, which transports material south by **longshore drift**. Rapid erosion means there is always plenty of sediment to be transported.

- **Deposition** — where the ocean **current** meets the **outflow** of the Humber River, the flow becomes **turbulent** and sediment is deposited.

Coastal Processes Have Created **Distinctive Landscapes**

See pages 24-26 for more on coastal landforms.

The coastal **landscapes** around Holderness **vary** — in the north are steep chalk **cliffs**, **wave-cut platforms** and sandy **beaches**. Further south there are less-steep boulder-clay **cliffs**, and around Spurn Head there are **depositional features**.

Headland and wave-cut platforms — to the **north** of the area, the boulder clay overlies **chalk**. The chalk is **harder** and **less easily eroded**, so it has formed a **headland** (**Flamborough Head**) and **wave-cut platforms**, such as those near **Sewerby**. Flamborough Head has features such as **stacks**, **caves** and **arches**.

Beaches — the area to the **south** of Flamborough Head is **sheltered** from wind and waves, and a **wide sand** and **pebble beach** has formed near **Bridlington**.

Sand dunes — around **Spurn Head**, material transported by the wind is **deposited**, forming **sand dunes**.

Slumping cliffs — frequent **slumps** give the boulder clay cliffs a distinctive shape. In some locations several slumps have occurred and not yet been eroded, making the cliff **tiered**. For example, slumps are common around **Atwick Sands**.

Spit — erosion and longshore drift have created a spit with a **recurved end** across the mouth of the Humber Estuary — this is called **Spurn Head**. To the **landward** side of the spit, estuarine **mudflats** and **saltmarshes** have formed.

The Holderness Coastline Needs to be **Managed**

1) The Holderness coastline has retreated by **around 4 km** over the past **2000 years**. Around **30 villages** have been **lost**.

2) Ongoing erosion could cause numerous **social**, **economic** and **environmental problems**, such as:

- **Loss of settlements and livelihoods** — e.g. the village of **Skipsea** is at risk and **80 000 m²** of good quality **farmland** is lost each year on the Holderness coast, which has a huge effect on **farmers' livelihoods**.

- **Loss of infrastructure** — the **gas terminal** at **Easington** is only **25 m** from the cliff edge.

- **Loss of Sites of Special Scientific Interest (SSSIs)** — e.g. **the Lagoons** near **Easington** provide habitats for birds.

Coastal Environment — Case Study

Hard Engineering has been Used Along the Holderness Coastline

A total of **11.4 km** of the 61 km coastline is currently protected by **hard** engineering:

- **Bridlington** is protected by a **4.7 km long sea wall** as well as **timber groynes**.
- There's a **concrete sea wall**, **timber groynes** and **riprap** at **Hornsea** that protect the village.
- **Two rock groynes** and a **500 m long revetment** were built at **Mappleton** in **1991**. They cost **£2 million** and were built to **protect the village** and the **B1242 coastal road**.
- A landowner in **Skipsea** has used **gabions** to help protect his caravan park.
- There are **groynes** and a **sea wall** at **Withernsea**. Some **riprap** was also placed in front of the wall after it was damaged in severe storms in 1992.
- **Easington Gas Terminal** is protected by a **revetment**.
- The **eastern** side of **Spurn Head** is protected by **groynes** and **riprap**.

Existing Schemes are Not Sustainable

1) The groynes **trap sediment**, increasing the **width** of the **beaches**. This **protects** the **local area** but **increases erosion** of the cliffs **down-drift** (as the material eroded from the beaches there isn't replenished). E.g. the Mappleton scheme has caused **increased erosion** of the cliffs **south** of Mappleton. **Cowden Farm**, just south of Mappleton, is now at risk of falling into the sea.

2) The **sediment** produced from the erosion of the Holderness coastline is normally washed into the **Humber Estuary** (where it helps to form **tidal mudflats**) and down the **Lincolnshire coast**. Reduction in this sediment **increases** the **risk of flooding** along the Humber Estuary, and **increases erosion** along the Lincolnshire coast.

3) The protection of local areas is leading to the **formation of bays** between those areas. As bays develop the wave pressure on headlands will increase and eventually the **cost** of maintaining the sea defences may become **too high**.

4) All these problems make the existing schemes **unsustainable**.

There are Challenges for All Possible Schemes

1) The **SMP** for Holderness for the next 50 years recommends '**holding the line**' at **some settlements** (e.g. at Bridlington, Withernsea, Hornsea, Mappleton and Easington Gas Terminal) and '**doing nothing**' along **less-populated stretches**. However, this is **unpopular** with owners of land or property along the stretches where nothing is being done.

2) **Managed realignment** has been suggested, e.g. relocating **caravan parks** further inland and allowing the land they are on to erode. This would be a **more sustainable** scheme as it would allow the coast to erode as normal without endangering businesses. However, there are issues surrounding how much **compensation** businesses will get for relocating. Also, relocation isn't always possible, e.g. there may be no land for sale to relocate buildings to.

3) In 1995, Holderness Borough Council decided to **stop** trying to protect Spurn Head from erosion and overwashing — **do nothing** became the new strategy. This **saves money** and allows the spit to function **naturally**, but overwashing may **damage marsh environments** behind the spit. A **coastguard station** on the spit may also be **at risk**.

4) **Easington Gas Terminal** is currently protected by **rock revetments**, and the SMP recommends that these defences are maintained for as long as the gas terminal is operating. However, the defences only span about **1 km** in front of the gas terminal, meaning that the **village of Easington** (with a population of about **700 people**) isn't protected. The defences may also **increase erosion** at legally-protected Sites of Special Scientific Interest (**SSSIs**) to the south.

Practice Questions

Q1 Briefly describe three impacts of coastal erosion in the Holderness area.

Q2 Briefly outline one challenge associated with coastal management along the Holderness coast.

Exam Question

Q1 To what extent do you agree that sustainable management of coastal areas is achievable? [20 marks]

Like easily eroded clay, I'll be gone when the morning comes...

Coastal environments offer loads of opportunities for fieldwork — you could measure beach or cliff profiles, measure sediment size, do vegetation transects, interview residents about their views on management, sun-bathe... OK, maybe not that last one.

Humans at the Coast — Case Study

Oh, I do love a day at the seaside. And I'm not the only one — around half the world's population live near the coast. Unfortunately, it's not all ice creams and donkey rides — life on the coast can bring some pretty serious risks, too.

The **Sundarbans** Region is in **Bangladesh** and **India**

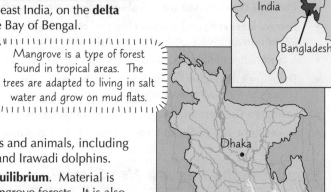

1) The Sundarbans region is in southwest Bangladesh and east India, on the **delta** of the **Ganges**, **Brahmaputra** and **Meghna** rivers on the Bay of Bengal.

2) Large parts of the region are protected as a National Park or forest reserve. It is part of the largest **mangrove** forest in the world.

> Mangrove is a type of forest found in tropical areas. The trees are adapted to living in salt water and grow on mud flats.

3) The land is very **flat** and **low-lying**. It is intersected by thousands of **channels**, many containing small sandy or silty **islands**.

4) The Sundarbans is home to many **rare species** of plants and animals, including orchids, white-bellied sea eagles, Royal Bengal tigers and Irawadi dolphins.

5) In its natural state, the coastal system is in **dynamic equilibrium**. Material is **deposited** by the rivers, allowing the growth of the mangrove forests. It is also **eroded** by the sea, so the size of the **sediment store** remains roughly the **same**.

The Sundarbans Region Brings **Opportunities**...

1) The Sundarbans region is home to more than **4 million people**. The area provides a range of **natural products**, which can be used by the people who occupy the area or sold to bring **economic benefits** to the region:

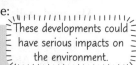

- The flat, fertile land of the river deltas is ideal for growing **crops**, particularly **rice**.
- The rich **ecosystem** of the mangrove forest provides the local population with **fish**, **crabs**, **honey** and **nipa palm leaves** used for roofing and basket-making.
- The mangrove forests provide **timber** for construction, firewood and furniture.

2) The Sundarbans also provides **services** for the people who live there:

- The mangrove forest provides a **natural defence** against **flooding** — it acts as a barrier against **rough seas** and absorbs **excess water** in the rainy (monsoon) season. This makes it easier to **live** and **grow crops**.
- The mangroves also protect the area against **coastal erosion** — their roots bind the soil together.

3) There are also opportunities for **development**, to increase the **wealth** of Bangladesh as a whole:

> These developments could have serious impacts on the environment.

- There are opportunities for **tourism** — visitors are attracted by the mangroves and **wildlife**.
- Since 2011, **cargo ships** transporting goods such as **oil** and food inland have been allowed to use the waterways. Some channels have been **dredged** to make passage easier for the ships.
- A **power plant** has been proposed just north of the national park, providing **energy** for people in the region.

... But Occupation Also Brings **Risks**

The location and nature of the Sundarbans create numerous **risks** for **occupation** and **development**:

1) There is a lack of **fresh water** for drinking and irrigation in much of the area. This is because fresh water is **diverted** from the rivers for irrigation of agricultural land further **upstream**.

2) The **growing population** has led to a need for more **fuel** and more **agricultural land**, so the mangrove forests are being **removed**. This increases the **risk** of flooding (e.g. during tropical cyclones) and coastal erosion.

3) Flooding can lead to **salinisation** (increased saltiness) of soil, making it hard to grow **crops**.

4) The Sundarbans is home to **dangerous animals** that attack humans, including tigers, sharks and crocodiles.

5) There is a lack of **employment** and **income** opportunities.

6) The low-lying land is at risk from **rising sea levels** due to global warming.

7) It is a relatively **poor** region, and only one-fifth of households have access to mains **electricity**. This makes **communication** by e.g. television and radio difficult, meaning that residents often don't receive **flood warnings**.

8) **Access** is difficult — there are **few roads**, and those that exist are of poor quality. This limits opportunities for development, and makes it harder for residents to receive **goods**, **healthcare** and **education**.

Humans at the Coast — Case Study

There are **Attempts** to **Overcome** These Risks

People can respond to risks through **resilience**, **mitigation** and **adaptation**.

Resilience

Resilience means being able to **cope** with the challenges the environment presents. There are attempts to **increase** the population's resilience, for example:

- The Public Health Engineering Department is increasing access to **clean water** and **sanitation**. This will improve **health** and **quality of life**.

- Better **roads** and **bridges** are being built in the region, improving **access** for residents and visitors. However, this can lead to **deforestation** and other environmental damage.

- Mains **electricity** is being extended to more areas, and subsidised **solar panels** are being made available in remote villages to allow them to generate their own power. This will make it easier for **flood warnings** to reach communities, and could create **employment** opportunities.

- There are efforts to **decrease poverty** and **increase food security** in the region, for example by providing **farming subsidies** to increase food production and provide jobs. However, there is a risk that some areas of land may be farmed too **intensively**, causing environmental damage.

- Some NGOs are offering **training** in **sustainable methods** of fishing and farming, to help prevent environmental damage from over-exploitation or poor practices.

> One issue with many of these strategies is that they are expensive. Much of the funding relies on non-governmental organisations (NGOs) such as charities, often based in other countries.

Steve wondered if he'd gone too far with the solar panels.

Mitigation

Mitigation means **reducing** the **severity** of hazards or other problems. For example:

- 3500 km of **embankments** were built to prevent flooding. However, the embankments are gradually being **eroded**, and around 800 km are vulnerable to being **breached** during storms and tsunamis.

- Coastal management projects aim to **protect** existing mangrove forests and **replant** areas that have been removed, to protect against flooding and erosion. However, it is difficult to prevent **illegal forest clearance** throughout the whole region, and it is unclear whether the mangroves will withstand **sea level rise**.

- There are attempts to mitigate the impacts of **extreme events**, e.g. cyclones. For example, the government and NGOs have provided funding for **cyclone shelters** and **early warning systems**, which should help people **shelter** or **evacuate**. However, many people may not have **transport** available to enable them to evacuate quickly.

Adaptation

Adaptation means **adjusting behaviour** to fit the environment. As the environment of the Sundarbans changes (due to e.g. climate change and sea level rise), people will need to adapt to it to **reduce risks** and **increase benefits**. For example:

- In some areas, **salt-resistant** varieties of rice are being grown — this could help residents cope with **flooding** and **sea level rise**. However, relying on a smaller range of crops can **reduce biodiversity** and may increase **vulnerability** to pests and diseases.

- Projects are underway to increase **tourism** to the area, providing **jobs** and **income**. For example, lodges have been built and tour operators run boat trips on the rivers. However, if not properly managed, tourism can cause **environmental damage**.

- People can adapt to sea level rise or flooding, e.g. by building houses on **stilts**. However, infrastructure such as **roads** cannot be protected as easily.

- **Sustainable** adaptations, e.g. using **non-intensive** farming practices and promoting **ecotourism**, will help ensure that the fragile environment remains relatively **undamaged** and **usable** for future generations.

Practice Questions

Q1 Briefly describe the location of the Sundarbans region.

Q2 Outline two ways in which the Sundarbans offer opportunities for human occupation.

Exam Question

Q1 For a coastal area beyond the UK, evaluate human responses to the challenges the region presents. [9 marks]

Cup of tea, cake, comfy chair — yep, I'm adapted to my environment...

Resilience, mitigation and adaptation are all interlinked — if you adapt to a threat, you become more resilient and mitigate its impacts. So really this page should just be one big box, called something like 'resilimitigadaptation'. But that would be silly.

Cold Environments

You're probably thinking that all cold environments are the same — they're all just, well, cold. Well it turns out that there are different types of cold environment, and it's not quite as simple as chilly, cold and blimmin' freezing.

There are **Four** Main Types of **Cold Environments**

Glacial

1) Glacial environments are areas of land permanently **covered by ice**. Land can be covered by **glaciers** or **ice sheets**:
    *   Glaciers are masses of **ice** that flow **downhill**. There are two main types — **valley** glaciers and **corrie** glaciers. Valley glaciers **fill valleys** and can be **several kilometres long** (e.g. the Franz Josef Glacier in New Zealand is 12 kilometres long). Corrie glaciers are **smaller** glaciers that are found in bowl-shaped hollows high up in **mountains** (e.g. the Lower Curtis Glacier in Washington State, USA).
    *   Ice sheets are **domes of ice** covering **huge areas** of land, e.g. the Antarctic Ice Sheet.
2) **Climate** — temperatures are cold enough for ice to be present **all year round**, but may be warm enough in summer for **meltwater** to affect glaciers. Most glacial environments have **high snowfall**, but in **extremely cold** areas (e.g. parts of Antarctica), ice sheets and glaciers can persist even when snowfall is very **low**.
3) **Soil** and **vegetation** — glacial environments are **covered by ice permanently**, so there is **no exposed soil**. There are very **few plants**, though **algae** and **moss** may grow on the glacier surface during summer.

Polar

1) Polar areas **surround** the **North** and **South Poles**.
2) Much of the Arctic polar environment is made up of the **northern land areas** of Asia, **North America** and **Europe**. The land-based polar environment can include **glacial** environments, e.g. the Greenland Ice Sheet, and **periglacial** environments, e.g. northern Russia.
3) **Climate** — polar areas are very cold — temperatures are **never** normally above 10 °C. Winters are **normally** below **–40 °C** and can reach **–90 °C**. Precipitation is **low** (no more than **100 mm** a year). There are **clearly defined** seasons — **cold summers** and **even colder winters**.
4) **Soil** — much of the ground is covered by ice. Where soil is exposed, it tends to be **thin** and **nutrient-poor**. There is normally a layer of **permanently frozen ground** called **permafrost** beneath the soil.
5) **Vegetation** — there are **very few** plants in polar areas — some **lichens** and **mosses** are found on rocks, and there are a few **grasses** in warmer areas, e.g. on the **coast** of Antarctica and in some parts of the Arctic.

Periglacial

1) **Periglacial** environments are places where the temperature is frequently or constantly **below freezing**, but which are **not covered by ice**.
2) **Climate** — periglacial areas are **cold** and precipitation is fairly **low** — 380 mm or less (mainly in the summer). There are **clearly defined** seasons (**brief, mild summers** and **long, cold winters**).
3) **Soil** — soil is **thin, acidic** and **not very fertile**. There is normally a **permafrost layer**, topped with a layer of soil that **melts in the summer** (see p.46).
4) **Vegetation** — plants grow **slowly** and **don't** grow **very tall** — grasses are the most common plants. Some **small, short** trees grow in **warmer, sheltered** areas. Nearer the poles, only **mosses** and **lichens** can survive.

Tribute act Katy Periglacial
received a frosty reception.

Alpine

1) Alpine environments are cold areas of land at an altitude **above the treeline** (the **limit** of the area where trees can grow — above this it's **too cold**).
2) Alpine environments may include areas of **glacial** conditions (at **higher** altitudes) and **periglacial** conditions (at **lower** altitudes).
3) **Climate** — winters are **cold**, but summers can be **mild**. **Temperature decreases** as altitude increases. **Snowfall** can be **high**.
4) **Soil** — when ice melts in the **summer**, soil is **exposed** in some areas. Higher up, the land is permanently covered by snow and ice, and lower down **periglacial** soils are present.
5) **Vegetation** — seasonally exposed soil means that **plants** can **grow**, e.g. grasses and alpine flowers.

alpine environment

glacial environment

periglacial environment

treeline

Cold Environments

Different Types of Cold Environment are Found in Different Places

1 Polar Environments

1) The Arctic polar environment can be defined either by the **Arctic circle (66° N)** or by the **10 °C July isotherm** (areas north of this line have an average temperature **below** 10 °C in **July**, the **hottest** month).

2) The polar environment around the South Pole is defined by the **10 °C January isotherm** (the hottest month in the southern hemisphere).

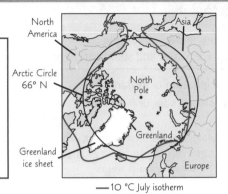

— 10 °C July isotherm   — 10 °C January isotherm

2 Periglacial Environments

Periglacial environments are found at:

- **High latitudes**, e.g. the northern parts of Asia, North America and Europe.
- **High altitudes** — periglacial conditions exist **around ice masses** in **mountain ranges**.

3 Alpine Environments

Alpine environments can be found at **high altitudes** at **any latitude**.

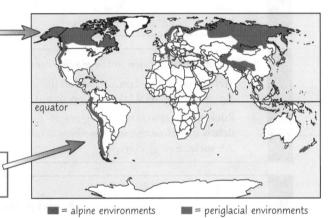

equator

Glacial environments can be found in polar and alpine settings.

■ = alpine environments   ■ = periglacial environments

There Were Several Periods of Glaciation in the Pleistocene

1) The Pleistocene lasted from **2.5 million years** ago to **11 700 years** ago.

2) During this time there were **fluctuations** in global temperatures which led to colder **glacials** (when glaciers advanced and sea levels fell) and warmer **interglacials** (when ice retreated and sea levels rose).

3) The **last glacial maximum** (the point when ice sheets were at their largest size) was about **21 000 years** ago — cold environments extended much further then than they do today, e.g. polar ice sheets covered much of the UK, and most of southern Europe was periglacial.

4) We're currently in an **interglacial** — glaciers are **retreating**.

Global Distribution of Cold Environments, Last Glacial Maximum (~21 000 years ago)

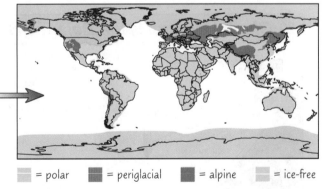

■ = polar   ■ = periglacial   ■ = alpine   ■ = ice-free

Practice Questions

Q1 What is the climate of polar areas like?

Q2 Where are alpine environments found?

Q3 What's the latitude of the Arctic circle?

Exam Question

Q1 Using the maps above, compare the distribution of cold environments today and 21 000 years before present. [6 marks]

So which is better — north or south? Let's take a poll...

It might not seem like it yet, but cold environments are actually pretty interesting. To really get yourself in the mood for these next few pages, try turning the heating off and opening all the windows, and read them with your scarf and gloves on.

Glacial Systems

Since plenty of cold environments contain glaciers, you need to know a fair bit about them. I do like a nice glacier...

Glaciers are **Systems**

The glacial system has **inputs**, **stores** and **outputs**.
There are **flows** (of **energy**, **ice**, **water** and **sediment**) **between** stores.

Inputs

1) **Snow** (from **precipitation** or **avalanches**).

2) **Condensation** of water vapour from the air (which then freezes).

3) **Sublimation** of water vapour from the air. This is when vapour turns directly to ice crystals, without passing through a liquid stage.

4) Bits of **rock** collected when the glacier carves away at the landscape, and rocks that have fallen onto the glacier from above.

Stores

1) The **main** store is **ice** in the **glacier** itself.

2) **Meltwater** is stored **on** and **within** the glacier, e.g. in **supraglacial lakes** on top of the glacier.

3) **Rock** is also stored in or on glaciers, e.g. **debris** from freeze-thaw weathering falls onto the **surface** of glaciers.

Flows

1) **Meltwater** flows through glaciers, e.g. from stores in supraglacial lakes to **channel storage** at the base of glaciers.

2) Debris flows through glaciers, e.g. from surface storage to **landforms**.

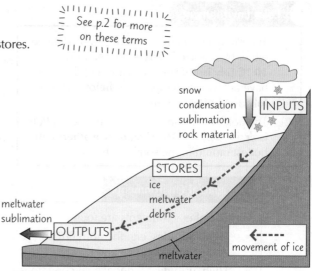

See p.2 for more on these terms

Outputs

1) Ice can **melt** and **flow out** of the glacier as **meltwater**.

2) Surface snow can **melt** and **evaporate**.

3) Ice and snow can **sublimate** to water vapour.

4) Snow can be **blown away** by strong winds.

5) With glaciers that end at the **sea** or a **lake**, blocks of ice fall from the **front** (the snout) of the ice mass into water to create **icebergs**.

A **Glacial Budget** is the **Balance** Between a Glacier's **Inputs** and **Outputs**

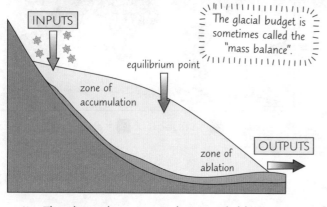

The glacial budget is sometimes called the "mass balance".

1) **Accumulation** is the **input** of snow and ice into the glacial system. Most accumulation is snow.

2) **Ablation** is the **output** of water from a glacier.

3) The **glacial budget** is the balance between accumulation and ablation over a year — it shows whether the mass of ice in the glacial system has **increased** or **decreased**. This determines whether the **front** of the glacier **advances** or **retreats**.

4) You get **more accumulation** than ablation in the **upper** part of a glacier — so it's called the **zone of accumulation**.

5) You get **more ablation** than accumulation in the **lower** part of a glacier — so it's called the **zone of ablation**.

6) The place where accumulation and ablation are **equal** is called the glacier's **equilibrium point**.

7) If there's **more accumulation** than ablation over a year, the glacier has a **positive regime** (or a positive mass balance). The glacier grows and **advances** (moves forward) in response to **high accumulation** in the upper zone.

8) If there's **less accumulation** than ablation over a year, this is a **negative regime** (or a negative mass balance). The glacier shrinks and **retreats** (moves back) in response to **low accumulation** in the upper zone.

9) If there's the **same amount** of accumulation and ablation over a year, the glacier stays the same size and the position of the snout **doesn't change** — the glacier is in **dynamic equilibrium** (see p.2). Dynamic equilibrium is when a system stays the same on **average**, despite **short-term variations** in e.g. inputs and outputs.

Glacial Systems

Feedbacks

When inputs or outputs change, there can be **negative feedbacks**. For example, if the size of the ice input increases, a glacier may speed up so that more water and ice are output and the mass of the glacier **remains constant.**

Glaciers can respond to a change in a way that makes the change **greater** — this is a **positive feedback.**
E.g. ice has a high **albedo** (it **reflects** lots of the Sun's **energy**). If glaciers **retreat** there is **less ice** — less of the Sun's energy is reflected and more is **absorbed**, so temperatures **rise** and glaciers **retreat further.**

The Glacial Budget **Changes** Throughout the **Year**...

1) You get **more ablation** during **warmer** times of the year — more ice melts when it's warm.

2) During the **colder** months, there's **more accumulation** than ablation.

3) Over the year, this might **balance out** — the glacier **advances** in winter but **retreats** in summer, so overall the mass in the glacier **stays the same.**

Glacial budget for a glacier in the northern hemisphere.

positive regime   negative regime

Mass of ice

accumulation
ablation

October   January   April   July   October

Hannah and Betty had a very positive regime.

...Over **Several Years**...

1) There is **variation** in the amount of accumulation and ablation from year to year. Even if the **overall** trend is for retreat, in some years there may be **advances** due to more accumulation or less ablation than usual.

2) For example, the **Kleinelend glacier** in the Austrian Alps **retreated** overall between 2000 and 2011, but recorded **advances** in **2001**, **2004** and **2008**.

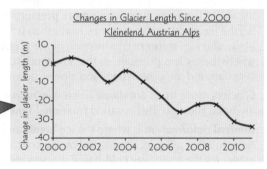

Changes in Glacier Length Since 2000
Kleinelend, Austrian Alps

Change in glacier length (m)

10
0
-10
-20
-30
-40

2000   2002   2004   2006   2008   2010

...and Over **Hundreds of Years**

Changes in **global temperature** over long periods of time affect the glacial budget. For example:

1) Temperatures in the **Little Ice Age** (a relatively cold period from about 1550 to 1850) were **colder** than the periods before and after it.

2) This meant that many glaciers **advanced** because they had a **positive regime** — the **Mer de Glace** in the French Alps advanced by over **1 km.**

3) Since 1850, global temperatures have **increased** so glaciers have tended to have a negative regime and **retreated** — the Mer de Glace has retreated by **nearly 2.4 km** since 1850.

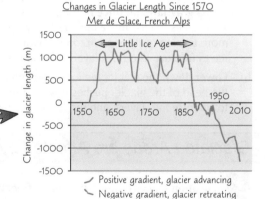

Changes in Glacier Length Since 1570
Mer de Glace, French Alps

Change in glacier length (m)

1500
1000
500
0
-500
-1000
-1500

Little Ice Age

1950

1550   1650   1750   1850   2010

Positive gradient, glacier advancing
Negative gradient, glacier retreating

Practice Questions

Q1 What are the main inputs, stores and outputs in a glacial system?

Q2 What are accumulation and ablation?

Q3 How does the glacial budget change throughout the year in the northern hemisphere?

Exam Question

Q1 Explain how a glacial budget shows whether a glacier is advancing or retreating. [3 marks]

Shouldn't have left the cage outside — now I've got a glacial budgie...

No, you're not reading an accountancy revision guide by mistake — glaciers have budgets too. If inputs are bigger than outputs, all is well and the glacier grows. If outputs are bigger than inputs, things aren't so rosy. Much like me with my salary.

Glacial Processes

Glaciers are moving all the time — they don't stop to think about the erosion they might be causing...

Glaciers can be **Cold-Based** or **Warm-Based**

Glaciers can be classified according to the **temperature** of their **base** (the bit where the ice touches the valley floor).

1) **Cold-based glaciers** are found in **very cold** areas, e.g. Antarctica — their bases are usually well **below** the ice's **melting point**, so there's very **little melting**. The ice is frozen to the base of the valley, so there's **very little movement**. There's hardly any melting at the surface either, even in summer. This means that cold-based glaciers **don't** cause very much **erosion** at all.

2) **Warm-based glaciers** occur in **milder** areas — their bases are **warmer** than the melting point of ice because of heat from **friction** caused by the glacier moving, or because of **geothermal heat** from the Earth. The ice at the bottom of the glacier melts, and the **meltwater** acts as a **lubricant**, making it easier for the glacier to move downhill. Ice at the **surface** also melts if the temperature reaches 0 °C, and meltwater moves down through the glacier, lubricating it even more. Lots of movement means **lots of erosion**.

Glaciers Move Downhill *under their Own* Weight

1) **Meltwater** underneath a glacier allows the glacier to **slide** over the ground. This is called **basal sliding**, and it's the main way that warm-based glaciers move.

2) There's **more melting** around bits of **rock protruding** from the valley floor, because there's **more pressure** on the ice (so the ice melts at temperatures lower than 0 °C). Meltwater can **refreeze** downstream of the obstruction where there's less pressure, so the flow tends to be faster around the obstruction, and slower downstream.

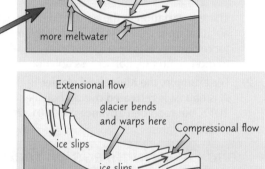

3) Glaciers move in an **arc shape** when they're in a **hollow** (by basal sliding). This is called **rotational flow**.

4) **Internal deformation** is where the ice **bends** and **warps** to flow downhill like a liquid. It's caused by ice crystals shifting past each other. It's the main way **cold-based** glaciers move.

5) At the **head** of a glacier the valley is steep, so there's a strong **gravitational force** pulling the ice downwards. This makes the ice **move quickly**. When ice moves quickly there's more **tension** (pulling apart forces), which causes the ice to **fracture** into thick layers. The **layers** then **slip downwards** — this is called **extensional flow**.

6) **Lower down** the glacier the ice is moving more **slowly** because the valley is less steep. The faster ice from the head of the glacier **pushes down** on the slower ice and **compresses it**. The **high pressure** causes the ice to **fracture** into layers, and the layers **slip forwards** — this is called **compressional flow**.

Glaciated Areas are Affected by **Nivation** and **Frost Action Weathering**

Nivation makes hollows **deeper** by **freezing** and **thawing**:

Nivation is especially common in periglacial areas where temperatures often fluctuate around 0 °C.

1) When snow gets into a **hollow** in the ground, it can **increase** the **size** of the hollow.

2) When temperatures **fluctuate** around **0 °C**, a lot of **freezing** and **thawing** happens — when the temperature's **above** 0 °C, the snow **melts**, and when it's **below** 0 °C, the water refreezes as **ice**.

3) Every time the ice **freezes**, it **expands**, so **frost shattering** eventually breaks bits off the rock at the base of the hollow. When the snow **melts**, the meltwater carries the broken bits of rock (debris) **away**.

4) Slopes **collapse** because they're **waterlogged** and they've been **eroded** — the material is **washed away** by meltwater.

5) Eventually the hollow becomes **deeper** and **wider**. The processes that cause this are collectively called **nivation**, and the hollows formed by nivation are called **nivation hollows**. Nivation hollows can be the beginning of a **corrie** (see p.42).

Nivation

Freezing

snow

frost shattering

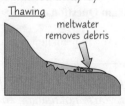

Thawing

meltwater removes debris

Glacial Processes

Frost Action

1) **Frost action** (**freeze-thaw** weathering) occurs in areas where there's **moisture** and **temperatures** that fluctuate **above** and **below freezing**.
2) Water from rainfall or melting **enters the joints** and **crevices** in **rocks** and **cliff faces**.
3) When the temperature **drops below 0 °C**, the water in the cracks **freezes** and **expands**.
4) Over time, **repeated** freeze-thaw action **weakens** the rocks and causes pieces to **fall off**.

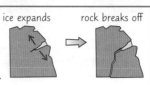

ice expands   rock breaks off

Glaciers **Erode** the **Surrounding Rock**

Glaciers erode the valley floor and sides by **plucking** and **abrasion**:

1) **Plucking** — ice in contact with rock surfaces can thaw slightly then **refreeze around rocks** protruding from the valley sides and floor. When the glacier **moves forward**, it **plucks** the rocks away from the valley sides and floor.
2) **Abrasion** — **debris** carried along by the glacier can **scrape** material off the valley walls and floor.

The **amount** and **rate** of erosion is increased in areas of **less resistant rock**, and if the glacier is **thick** or if it's **moving quickly**. It's also increased if there's **lots** of **debris** or if the debris is made of **resistant rock**.

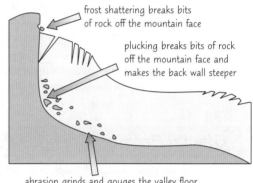

frost shattering breaks bits of rock off the mountain face

plucking breaks bits of rock off the mountain face and makes the back wall steeper

abrasion grinds and gouges the valley floor

Glaciers **Transport Debris**

1) Glaciers carry large loads of **debris** — this is material that the glacier has gathered by plucking, or bits of rock that have been broken off the back wall or valley sides and fallen onto (or into) the glacier. Debris ranges from **fine sediment** to **huge boulders**.
2) There are **three** main ways debris is transported. **Supraglacial** material is carried **on top** of the glacier's surface. **Englacial** material is carried **within** the body of the glacier. **Subglacial** material is moved along **at the base** of the glacier.

Glaciers **Deposit** their Load as they **Move** and as they **Melt**

1) The **unsorted** mixture of material **deposited** by the glacier is called **till** (it's sometimes called "boulder clay" too). It includes everything from massive boulders down to pebbles and clay. Glaciers drop any size of till anywhere.
2) **Lodgement till** is spread onto the valley floor beneath the ice by **moving** glaciers.
3) **Ablation till** is dropped by a glacier as it **melts**. The till is mainly deposited close to the glacier snout because this is where most ablation happens — the glacier drops debris as the ice around the debris melts.
4) Till **points** in the **direction** that the glacier is flowing.
5) Till is often **deposited** as landforms called **moraines** (see p. 43).

Practice Questions

Q1 What is rotational flow?
Q2 What is nivation?
Q3 What are the main ways that debris is transported by a glacier?

Exam Question

Q1 Outline how glaciers move by extensional flow. [3 marks]

Glaciers move r e a l l y s l o w l y — bit like me on a Sunday morning...

Alright, I'll admit that these two pages are slightly harder than the last two. It can be tricky at first to get your head around the different ways that glaciers move. Try reading over the first page a couple of times, then at least you'll know that rotational flow isn't a dance move. Don't forget that glaciers erode valleys in two different ways — by plucking and by abrasion.

Glacial Landforms

These pages are about the landscapes that glaciers leave behind them. Mountain climbers and geography teachers get very excited about the beauty of glacial landscapes. Whether or not they move you, you still need to learn about them.

Glaciers Create Basins called Corries (also called Cirques or Cwms)

1) Glaciers normally form on one side of a mountain peak — the side that gets **least sun** and the **coldest winds**. That's where there's **most accumulation** and **least ablation**.

2) Snow collects in hollows and turns to **ice**. **Basal sliding** (rotational flow) with **abrasion** and **plucking** deepen the hollow into a **corrie** (a bowl-shaped hollow).

3) When the ice in the hollow is thick enough, it **flows** over the lip and downhill as a glacier. Frost shattering and plucking **steepen** the back wall of the corrie.

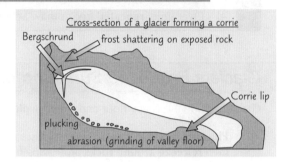

Cross-section of a glacier forming a corrie

Bergschrund — frost shattering on exposed rock
Corrie lip
plucking
abrasion (grinding of valley floor)

Glacial Erosion Changes the Landscape

Glaciers produce **erosional landforms**, which change the way the landscape **looks** after the ice has **gone**.

1) An **arête** is a steep-sided **ridge** — it's formed when two glaciers flow in parallel valleys. The glaciers erode the sides of the valley, which **sharpens** the mountain ridge **in between** them.

2) A **pyramidal peak** is a pointed mountain peak with at least **three sides**. It forms where **three** or more **corries** form **back to back** (their back walls make the mountain peak).

3) **Glacial troughs** (also called **U-shaped valleys**) are **steep-sided valleys** with **flat bottoms**. They're formed by the erosion of **V-shaped river valleys** by glaciers. As the glacier erodes through the V-shaped valley it makes it **deeper** and **wider**.

4) **Hanging valleys** are valleys formed by **tributary glaciers** — they erode the valley floor much less **deeply** because they're **smaller** than the main glacier. So, when the glaciers melt, the valleys get left at a **higher level** than the glacial trough formed by the main glacier. You get **waterfalls** from hanging valleys into the main glacial trough.

A tributary glacier is a smaller glacier that flows into the main glacier.

5) **Truncated spurs** are formed when **ridges of land** (spurs) that **stick out** into the main valley are **chopped off** (truncated) as the main valley glacier moves past.

6) **Tarns** are **lakes** that form in **corries** after a glacier has retreated.

7) A **roche moutonnée** is a **resistant** (hard) mass of rock on the valley floor. The **upstream** (stoss) side is **smooth**, because it was smoothed by **abrasion** as the glacier went over it. The **downstream** (lee) side is steep and **rough**, where the glacier **plucked** at it.

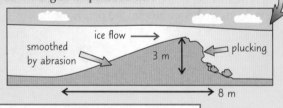

ice flow →
smoothed by abrasion
3 m
← plucking
← 8 m →

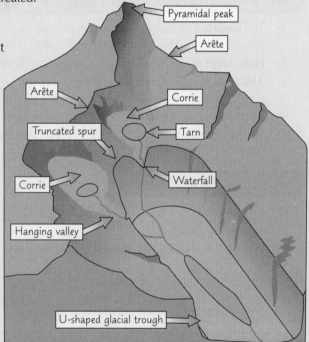

Pyramidal peak
Arête
Arête
Corrie
Truncated spur
Tarn
Corrie
Waterfall
Hanging valley
U-shaped glacial trough

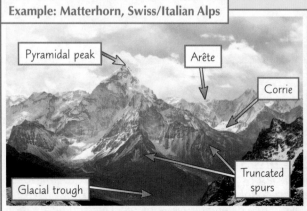

Example: Matterhorn, Swiss/Italian Alps

Pyramidal peak
Arête
Corrie
Truncated spurs
Glacial trough

Glacial Landforms

Glaciers Form *Moraines* and *Till Plains* by *Depositing Till*

Till is all the stuff that a glacier leaves behind — unsorted boulders, stones and clay (see p. 41). **Moraine** is the name given to particular formations of till:

1) **Lateral moraine** is deposited where the **sides** of the glacier were.

2) **Medial moraine** is deposited in the **centre** of the valley where two glaciers **converge** (the two lateral moraines join together).

3) **Terminal moraine** builds up at the **end** of the glacier, and is deposited as semicircular hillocks of till.

A **till plain** is a **large** expanse of gently rolling hills of till — it forms when an **ice sheet** melts where it is. Northern Ohio, USA is a large till plain.

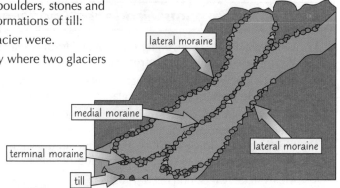

Till can also be Deposited as *Hills* called *Drumlins*

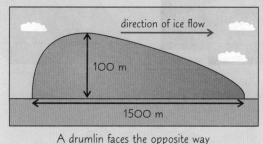

A drumlin faces the opposite way to a roche moutonnée.

1) **Drumlins** are **half-egg shaped hills** of till, up to 1500 m long and 100 m high. The **upstream** (stoss) end is **wide and tall**, and the **downstream** (lee) end is **narrow and low**.

2) Nobody's really sure **how** drumlins formed — it may be that till got stuck around a rock or a little hill sticking out into the glacier. It may be that an original mound of dropped till got streamlined when the ice **readvanced** over it.

3) Drumlins often form in **groups**. There are drumlins in the **Ribble Valley** in Lancashire. There are also a whole bunch of drumlins under the water level in Clew Bay, Ireland.

Erratics are *Boulders* that have been *Carried* a *Long Way* by *Glaciers*

1) Erratics are rocks that have been **picked up** by a glacier or an ice sheet, **carried along** and **dropped** in an area of **completely different geology**.

2) For example, in the Yorkshire Dales at Norber, loose black **Silurian** rocks sit on top of white **Carboniferous** limestone. They were deposited as ice **retreated** after the last glacial maximum, about 21 000 years go.

Practice Questions

Q1 What is the name of the ridge formed by two glaciers in parallel valleys?

Q2 Name three other landforms caused by glacial erosion.

Q3 What is an erratic?

Exam Questions

Q1 Explain the development of the landforms shown in the photograph above. [6 marks]

Q2 Outline how moraine is formed. [3 marks]

Corries? I'm more of an Emmerdale fan myself...

There are a fair few features to learn here, but don't let that get you down. You just need to learn the names of the features, what they look like and how they're formed. Even the names of the features are a bit tricky though — cirque, arête, roche moutonnée... anyone would think this was a French exam. At least you don't need to know how to pronounce them.

Fluvioglacial Processes and Landforms

The sad news for all you glacier fans is that glaciers don't always stay around forever. But don't worry, they don't go down without a fight — even when they're melting, they still manage to change the landscape.

Meltwater Streams Erode the Landscape

1) When glacial ice melts, water runs out and forms streams of **meltwater**. **Warm-based** glaciers and **retreating** glaciers produce **lots** of meltwater.

2) **Surface** meltwater **filters** through the glacier (e.g. through crevasses) and flows through **tunnels** underneath the glacier, before running out of the snout of the glacier.

3) Meltwater streams cause **erosion** in the same way as normal rivers (by hydraulic action, abrasion, attrition and solution) — but they cause **more** erosion than rivers of the same size. This is because the pressure of the ice means that meltwater streams flow very **quickly** — so they can carry **lots** of material that **erodes** the landscape.

4) Meltwater streams form deep **troughs** in the landscape called **meltwater channels**. Because meltwater streams have a lot of **erosive power**, the meltwater channels they produce are very **wide** and **deep**. After the glacier has **retreated**, the deep meltwater channels are left with very **shallow streams** running through them — e.g. Glen Valtos on the Isle of Lewis in Scotland.

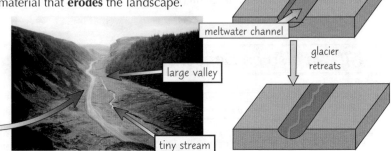

Fluvioglacial Deposits come from Glacial Meltwater

1) Glacial meltwater carries a **large load** of **sediment** of various sizes (from inside, on top of and underneath the glacier).

2) **Traction**, **saltation**, **suspension** and **solution** processes transport eroded material in glacial meltwater streams, just like in rivers.

3) Meltwater streams **deposit** their load on the **valley floor** as they flow away from the glacier.

4) Unlike glacial deposition features such as moraine, fluvioglacial deposits are **sorted** — the fine sediment is **separated** from the larger sand, which is separated from the gravel, and so on. This is because **fluvioglacial** deposition features are formed by meltwater **carrying debris** then **depositing** it **away** from the glacier. **Glacial** deposits form by glaciers **dropping material** as they **melt**.

Melting Glaciers leave Outwash Plains

1) An **outwash plain** (also called a sandur) is a layer of gravel, sand and clay that forms in **front** of where the snout of the melting glacier used to be. Meltwater flows out of the glacier, and carries the sediment with it.

2) Sediments on outwash plains are **sorted** into layers. **Gravel** gets dropped **first** because it's **heavier** than sand and clay, so it forms the **bottom layer** of the outwash plain. **Clay** is dropped **last** and gets carried furthest away from the snout because it's the lightest sediment — it forms the **top layer** of the outwash plain.

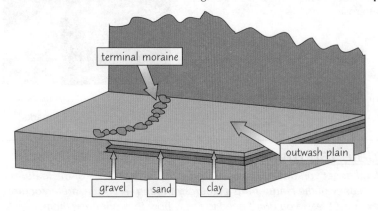

Satellite image of Skeiðarársandur, an outwash plain in southeast Iceland.

Topic Three — Glacial Systems and Landscapes

Fluvioglacial Processes and Landforms

Meltwater Streams Deposit **Kames** and **Eskers**

1) **Eskers** are long, winding **ridges** of sand and gravel that run in the **same direction** as the glacier. They're deposited by meltwater streams flowing in **tunnels** underneath the glacier — when the glacier retreats and the stream dries up, the load remains as an esker. Eskers show you where the glacial tunnel used to be.

2) **Kames** are **mounds** of sand and gravel found on the valley floor. Meltwater streams **on top of** glaciers collect in depressions and **deposit** layers of debris. When the ice **melts** the debris is dumped onto the valley floor.

3) **Kame terraces** are piles of deposits left against the **valley wall** by meltwater streams that run between the glacier and the valley sides. They look like lateral moraine, but they're **sorted** into layers — meltwater streams deposit their **heaviest** loads first, so kame terraces have **gravel** at the **bottom** and **finer sediment** on **top**.

The town of Pispala is built on Pyynikki ridge, an esker that divides two glacial lakes in Tampere, Finland.

4) Eskers, kames and kame terraces look a bit like this.

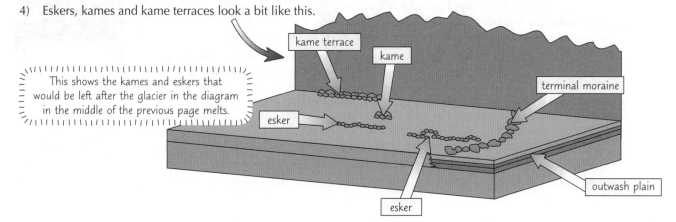

This shows the kames and eskers that would be left after the glacier in the diagram in the middle of the previous page melts.

5) Lakes (called **proglacial lakes**) can form in front of glaciers, e.g. when the flow from meltwater streams gets dammed by the terminal moraine. As meltwater streams flow into a proglacial lake, they **slow down** and **deposit** their sediment on the ice — these deposits are known as **deltas**. When the ice melts, these deltas are dumped on the valley floor, forming **delta kames**.

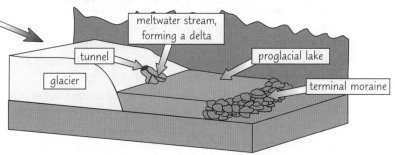

Practice Questions

Q1 What are meltwater channels?

Q2 What's the main difference between glacial deposits and fluvioglacial deposits?

Q3 What is an outwash plain?

Q4 What are eskers?

Exam Questions

Q1 Outline the role of meltwater in the formation of kames. [3 marks]

Q2 Outline how sediment becomes sorted in glacial outwash plains. [3 marks]

If you're pro-glacial, this section must be a dream come true...

Well, this is just typical of glaciers if you ask me. Not content with ripping bits of rock out of mountains and scattering them all over landscapes, glaciers then have to go and melt, and wash all kinds of bits of rock all over the place. If only they didn't have to be so, well, <u>messy</u> about it — then you wouldn't need to know what a kame or an esker is. Oh well, tough luck, eh.

Periglacial Processes and Landforms

Periglacial areas aren't covered in ice. There's usually ice in the soil though — I knew it'd be there somewhere...

Permafrost is Permanently Frozen Ground

1) **Periglacial** areas contain **permafrost** — **permanently frozen ground** with a top layer that can **melt** in the **summer** (called the **active layer**). **20-25%** of Earth's land surface is **permafrost**. Areas of permafrost can be **continuous** (**all** the ground is frozen), or **discontinuous** (only **patches** of the ground are frozen).

2) For **discontinuous** permafrost to form, the **mean annual temperature** needs to be **below 0 °C** for at least **2 years**. For **continuous** permafrost to form, the mean annual temperature needs to be **below –5 °C**.

3) **Mass movement** can occur in areas of permafrost. It can happen as the ground starts to **thaw**:

- The layer of permafrost is **impermeable** (water **can't** flow through it). If the temperature gets **above 0 °C** in the summer, the active layer **melts**, but the meltwater can't drain away.
- As a result, the active layer becomes **waterlogged** and **heavy**, and **flows easily**. This flow is called **solifluction** and it can occur **wherever** there's a gradient.
- Solifluction produces **lobe** formations — one section of soil **moves faster** than the soil around it, e.g. if it's on **steeper** ground, so it flows **further** and forms a **tongue** shape.

waterlogged active layer flows downhill

woomph

permafrost layer always stays frozen

Solifluction lobes in upland Alaska

4) Mass movement can also occur on slopes due to regular **freezing** and **thawing**:

- Water in soil **expands** when it **freezes**. This expansion causes soil particles to be forced upwards at **right angles** to the slope.
- When the ground **thaws**, the soil particles move **vertically** downwards.
- As a result, they end up **further down** the slope — this is called **frost creep**.

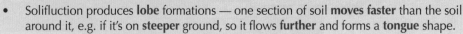

freezes | thaws

Ice Wedges Develop in Permafrost Soil

1) When temperatures **drop very low** in winter, the ground **contracts** and **cracks** form in the permafrost. This is called **frost contraction**.

2) When temperatures **increase** in spring, the active layer **thaws** and **meltwater seeps** into the **cracks**.

3) The permafrost layer is still frozen, so the water **freezes** in the cracks — the ice-filled cracks formed in this way are called **ice wedges**.

4) Frost contraction in following years can **re-open** cracks in the same place, **splitting** the ice wedge. More water seeps in and freezes, **widening** the ice wedge. The ice wedge gets **bigger** each time this happens.

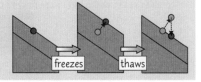

Pingo (see next page)

Ice wedges

Ice wedges and pingo, northern Canada

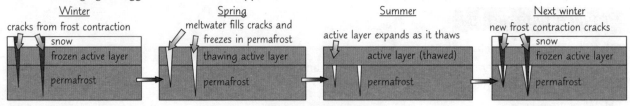

Winter
cracks from frost contraction
snow
frozen active layer
permafrost

Spring
meltwater fills cracks and freezes in permafrost
thawing active layer
permafrost

Summer
active layer expands as it thaws
active layer (thawed)
permafrost

Next winter
new frost contraction cracks
snow
frozen active layer
permafrost

Patterned Ground is Formed by Frost Activity

Sometimes **stones** on the surface of the ground are arranged in **circles**, **polygons** or **stripes** — this is called **patterned ground**. Patterned ground can be formed in two ways — by **frost heave** or by **frost contraction**:

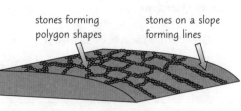

stones forming polygon shapes

stones on a slope forming lines

1) **Frost heave** happens when water underneath stones freezes and expands, forcing stones upwards. Once they reach the surface, they **roll down** to the **edges** of the **mounds** that have formed, so they form **circles** around them (**polygons** form when the mounds are **close together**). If the mounds are on a **slope**, the stones roll downhill and form **lines**.

2) **Frost contraction** causes the ground to **crack** in **polygon shapes**. The cracks get **filled in** with **stones**, forming polygon patterns on the surface.

Periglacial Processes and Landforms

There are Several Distinctive Periglacial Landforms

Pingos

1) A pingo is a **conical hill** with a **core** of **ice**. Pingos can be as large as 80 m high and about 500 m wide.

2) There are **two types** of pingo — **open-system** and **closed-system**.

3) **Open-system pingos** form where there's **discontinuous** permafrost. **Groundwater** is forced **up** through the **gaps between** areas of permafrost (from unfrozen layers lower down). The water **collects** together and **freezes**, forming a **core** of ice that **pushes** the ground above it **upwards**.

4) **Closed-system pingos** form in areas of **continuous** permafrost where there's a **lake** at the surface. The lake **insulates** the ground, so the area beneath it remains **unfrozen**. When the lake **dries up**, the ground is no longer insulated and the permafrost **advances** around the area of unfrozen ground. This causes water to **collect** in the centre of the unfrozen ground. The water eventually **freezes** and creates a **core** of ice that **pushes** the ground above it **upwards**.

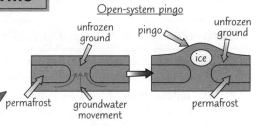

Open-system pingo

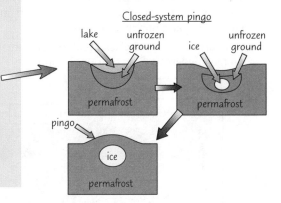

Closed-system pingo

Blockfields

Blockfields are expanses of **loose rocks**. They are formed **in place** by **frost shattering** of the **bedrock** layer due to repeated freezing and thawing.

Blockfield at top of Schiehallion, Scotland

Thermokarst

- A thermokarst landscape occurs when ice in the ground (e.g. pingos) **melts**, causing the ground to **collapse** and **holes** to form.
- These holes become **filled** with water, creating an **uneven**, **marshy** landscape.

Terracettes

- Terracettes form when **vegetation** interrupts soil moving down a slope due to **frost creep** or another mass movement process.
- This causes a **flatter** area to build up behind the **obstruction**, which leads to a series of **step-like terraces**.

Terracettes near Pen-y-ghent, North Yorkshire

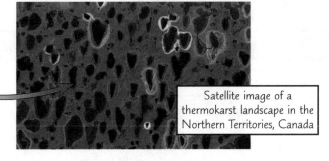

Satellite image of a thermokarst landscape in the Northern Territories, Canada

Practice Questions

Q1 What is permafrost?

Q2 How does patterned ground develop?

Q3 What's the difference between open-system pingos and closed-system pingos?

Exam Question

Q1 Outline how ice wedges form. [3 marks]

I always thought Pingo was one of the Beatles...

The trouble with this lot is that there are so many different processes going on, and all of them are to do with water freezing and then thawing. But you can sleep soundly now you know that patterned ground is caused by frost activity and not aliens.

Glacial Landscapes — Case Study

Mine's black, about 80 cm tall and has little spiny wheels that get clogged with mud whenever I take a shortcut through a field to the airport... oops, wrong sort of case study. Erm. Pack your bags, we're heading off to Snowdonia...

Snowdonia is a Glacial Landscape in North Wales

1) **Snowdonia** is an area in **north Wales**. It has been repeatedly covered by **ice** during **glacial periods**, including the **last glacial maximum** (see p.37).

2) The **upland areas** of Snowdonia (e.g. the **Glyders** — mountains to the north-east of Snowdon) show many of the **landforms** from pages 42-47. The area is no longer glaciated — since they formed, its landforms have been **modified** by periglacial processes and (more recently) fluvial action, weathering and human processes.

3) Here are some of the **glacial features** that are found on the **Glyders** and the surrounding area:

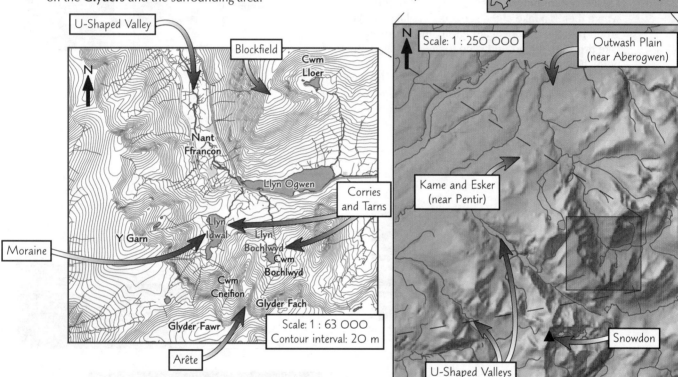

There are Lots of Glacial Landforms in Snowdonia

U-Shaped Valley — Nant Ffrancon

- **Nant Ffrancon** is a **glacial trough** formed by a glacier that flowed in a north westerly direction towards the coast at Anglesey.

- Today the **River Ogwen** flows in the valley, but it is much **too small** to have created it — it's a **misfit stream**.

Corries and Tarns

- **Llyn Bochlwyd** and **Llyn Idwal** are **tarns**. They sit above the Nant Ffrancon valley in corries (**Cwm Bochlwyd** and **Cwm Idwal**).

- They were formed by **tributary glaciers** that once flowed into the main glacier in Nant Ffrancon.

Glacial Landscapes — Case Study

Truncated Spur — Y Gribin

- Truncated spurs form when **ridges** of land (e.g. **arêtes**) stick out into the **path** of the main glacier and get **cut off** (truncated).
- The **Y Gribin arête** was cut off by the Nant Ffrancon glacier. There may once have been **interlocking spurs** in a **river valley** here, which were **bulldozed** by the glacier.

Arête — Y Gribin

- The **sharp ridge** between Cwm Bochlwyd and Cwm Cneifion, known as **Y Gribin**, is an **arête**.
- Glaciers formed in the corries on **either side** of the ridge and **eroded** the rock in between until it formed the **steep-sided arête**.

Arête   A rat

Moraine

A lot of **moraine** can be found around **Llyn Idwal**, where it was **deposited** by the melting glacier:

- **Terminal** moraine — at the mouth of the tarn.
- **Lateral** moraine — on the west side of the tarn.

These moraine formations have been **eroded** by other processes since being deposited — they are not as **obvious** as in **more recently** glaciated areas.

terminal

lateral

Kame and Esker — Pentir

- There's a **kame** and an **esker** near the village of **Pentir**. The esker is around **400 m long** and up to **10 m high**.
- They were probably formed by **meltwater** from the Nant Ffrancon glacier.
- Both features have been **eroded** by natural and human processes, so they are not easy to see.

Outwash Plain

- The glacier that once flowed in the Nant Ffrancon valley discharged into what is now **Conwy Bay**.
- There is a **flat expanse** of glacial till near **Aberogwen** — this was the outwash plain for the glacier shortly after the last glacial maximum.
- In places where the plain has been eroded to form cliffs, you can see a **clear layer** of glacial deposits.

Blockfields

There are **blockfields** formed by freeze-thaw weathering at the tops of many mountains in Snowdonia, e.g. at the summit of **Glyder Fach**.

Practice Questions

Q1 Give a brief description of the landscape of Snowdonia.

Q2 Give three examples of glacial landforms found in Snowdonia.

Exam Question

Q1 Analyse the processes that have affected the development of a glaciated landscape you have studied.   [9 marks]

I just tried to pronounce those place names. Please send wet wipes.

Don't worry, I won't be angry if you've Snow-done a different case study in class — there's no need to rePentir all your hard work. Just be Ffranc with yourself and make sure you've learnt one location well enough to cope if it cwms up in the exam.

Human Impacts on Cold Environments

Cold environments might not be great for beach holidays, but they've still got some great resources. There'll always be people who want to exploit those resources, even if it means damaging the environment in the process.

Cold Environments are Fragile

1) Environmental fragility refers to environments that are **easy** to **damage**, and which take a long time to **recover** from **damage**.

2) Cold environments are fragile because of the **harsh climate**:
   - The **short growing season** (when there's enough **light** and **warmth** for plants to grow) means that plants **don't have much time** to **recover** if they're **damaged**.
   - Plants are only able to **grow slowly**, so repairing damage can take a long time.
   - **Plants** and **animals** are **adapted** to the cold conditions, so they find it hard to survive if their **environment changes**.
   - **Decay** is **slow**, so **pollutants** are **broken down** very **slowly** (and so remain in the environment for a long time).

Human Activities have Changed over Time

1) For **centuries**, **indigenous people** like the **Inuit** have lived in cold environments. Their lifestyles are **adapted** to the **landscape** and the **climate**, and populations are **small**. This means their lifestyles are largely **sustainable** and cause minimal environmental damage.

The O742 to Kettering had also adapted to the cold conditions.

2) More recently, cold environments have been exploited on a **larger scale**. These activities can have **immediate** and **long-term effects** on the **local area** and the surrounding region, and tend to be **more damaging** to the fragile cold environment than small-scale occupation and use. For example:

Oil extraction

1) **Oil spills** can occur **during transport** of oil from the area. For example, in **1989** there was a huge **oil spill** off the coast of **Alaska** when the **Exxon Valdez oil tanker** crashed. Over **40 million** litres of oil spilled into the ocean, and over **250 000 birds** and **fish** were **killed**.

2) **Oil spills** can occur if **pipelines leak**. Between **1977** and **1994** there were, on average, **30 to 40** spills a year from the **Trans-Alaska pipeline**, which runs the length of Alaska. Some of these were caused by **intentional attacks** and **forest fires**.

Fishing

1) Fishing can **disrupt food chains**, e.g. large-scale **krill** fishing in the **Southern Ocean** is depleting food supplies for **whales** and **penguins**.

2) **Overfishing** of a species can severely **deplete** its **population**, sometimes beyond recovery. Overfishing of the **Patagonian Toothfish** in the **Antarctic** is currently a concern.

3) **Bottom trawling** catches fish by dragging nets along the sea-bed. This **disrupts** the **ecosystem** (by **reducing light levels** through increasing turbidity) and **catches other species** as well as the target one. It's carried out in the **Gulf of Alaska**, the **Greenland Sea** and the **Barents Sea**.

Tourism

1) Large **cruise ships** increase **pollution** in the area (from the ships and from tourists).

2) Tourists and tourism developments (e.g. roads, hotels) disrupt **wildlife** and **damage habitats**, leading to **reduced biodiversity**.

Hydroelectric power production

1) **Hydroelectric dams** can **block** the normal **migratory path** of fish. This can prevent them reaching **spawning grounds**, and so cause the fish **population** to **decrease**. Fish can travel **long distances** to spawn, so this can affect fish populations over a **large area**.

2) Hydroelectric dams also **heat up** the water, which can endanger **fish** that are adapted to **colder** temperatures.

Mining

1) Mining can lead to **ground** and **surface water contamination**, either by **chemicals** used **during mining** or by releasing the materials **being mined** into the environment. E.g. a lead-zinc mine in **Maarmorilik** (Greenland) was closed in 1990 but levels of **lead** and **zinc** pollution are **still high** in nearby fjords.

2) Mining produces both **solid waste** and **wastewater** that has to be disposed of. Some mines don't have the facilities required to deal with the quantities of waste produced, so the **waste is released** into the **environment**, polluting the local area.

3) Any development may require **additional infrastructure to** be built, e.g. support **buildings** and **access roads**. These can cause more damage to the environment, and improved access may open the area up to **further development**.

Human Impacts on Cold Environments

Climate Change is Causing Warming in Cold Environments

1) Most climate scientists believe that the climate is **warming**. There are **natural** reasons for this (e.g. changes in the **Earth's orbit**) and human reasons (e.g. increasing concentrations of **greenhouse gases** in the atmosphere).

2) Climate change has **current** and **predicted** impacts on cold environments:

Current Impacts

1) Melting glaciers and ice sheets, particularly those in Greenland and Antarctica, are causing **sea levels** to **rise**. **Globally**, most glaciers are **retreating** due to rising temperatures.

2) **Permafrost** is **melting**, e.g. in Alaska. This can cause **buildings** to **collapse** and **ice roads** (essential supply routes to remote settlements) to be usable for **less time** before they begin to thaw each year.

3) **Migration patterns** of some species, e.g. caribou, are **changing** due to changes in the seasons.

Predicted Impacts

1) **Sea level** will **rise** further as temperatures increase. This could **flood** low-lying coastal cold environments.

2) **Melting permafrost** could trigger a **positive feedback** as methane (a greenhouse gas) that is trapped in permafrost is **released**. More methane in the atmosphere will cause temperatures to rise, which will cause **further melting** of permafrost and the release of **even more** methane.

3) Plants and animals that are **adapted** to cold conditions may find it **harder** to survive. The range of **other** flora and fauna that prefer warmer temperatures may **extend into** cold environments.

Cold Environments are Managed but Under Pressure

1) There are various **management strategies** currently in place to protect cold environments:

- **Protected areas** — some countries have **protected** their cold environments by passing **laws** to prevent activities within them. E.g. some areas of Alaska are **designated wilderness areas**, where development is **forbidden** and access is **limited**.

- **International treaties** — some cold environments are **internationally important**, and there are global management strategies to protect them in the form of **treaties** signed by countries around the world. E.g. the **Antarctic Treaty** was signed by 12 countries in 1959 and now has 53 signatories. It states that Antarctica must only be used for **peaceful purposes**, including **science**.

- **Monitoring and regulation** — exploitation (e.g. number of visitors) can be monitored to assess its **impacts**. Activities can be strictly **managed**, e.g. visitors to Antarctica have to clean and **disinfect footwear** when they land to prevent the introduction of **non-native** species.

- **Fishing quotas** — in some areas, e.g. the Barents Sea, the number of fish that can be caught is **limited**.

2) Cold environments are increasingly under **pressure** — their **natural resources** (e.g. oil, minerals) offer opportunities for exploitation, and demand from **tourists** is increasing. This may influence how they are **managed** in future, for example:

- **Increased protection** — there are growing demands for cold environments to be **protected** from development and human activity. E.g. in 2015, the president of the USA proposed **extending** the wilderness area of Alaska, which would **prevent** oil exploration in that area.

- **Decreased protection** — as global population **increases** and reserves of oil and minerals in other areas are **depleted**, development of cold environments may become more of a **priority** than conservation. Areas that are currently protected (e.g. Antarctica) may be **opened up** for exploitation.

Practice Questions

Q1 What is environmental fragility?
Q2 How have human activities in cold environments changed over time?
Q3 What are the effects of melting permafrost?

Exam Question

Q1 Assess the extent to which management of fragile cold environments can prevent them being damaged. [9 marks]

Human impacts on cold environments — a big source of ski holiday injuries...

Ah, those pesky humans are getting in the way of things again. If only they'd manage without things like jobs, energy and houses. If you're itching for more on how humans use cold environments, you're in luck — we're off to Alaska next...

Humans in Glacial Landscapes — Case Study

Alaska is one example of a glaciated environment where the extreme climate creates challenges to development.

There are **Development Opportunities** in **Alaska**...

Alaska is a **glaciated environment** that's part of the **USA**. There are upland areas where **glaciers** still persist, and large areas of **periglacial landforms** in the northernmost parts of the state. The **northern** parts of Alaska are inside the **Arctic circle**.

Opportunities for economic development include:

1) **Oil and gas** — **over half** of Alaska's income comes from the **oil and gas industry**. Most oil fields are in the **tundra** in the north of the country. Oil reserves in **Prudhoe Bay** are currently exploited, but there are more reserves in more remote locations in the north of the state. The **Trans-Alaska oil pipeline** links the oil fields at Prudhoe Bay with **Valdez**, from where the oil can be **shipped** to customers.

2) **Mineral resources** — gold, silver, iron ore, lead, zinc and copper are mined, particularly in the **Tintina gold belt**. Mining in the Tintina belt contributed **$2.2 billion** to Alaska's GDP in 2013.

3) **Fishing** — salmon, crab and pollock are fished. Fishing employs **79 000** people and contributes over **$5bn** to Alaska's economy. The largest fishing ports are in the **Aleutian Islands** and **Kodiak Island**, both to the south-west of the state.

4) **Tourism** — tourists are attracted by Alaska's **wilderness scenery**. Around **2 million tourists** visit Alaska each year, bringing in **money** and creating opportunities for **employment**.

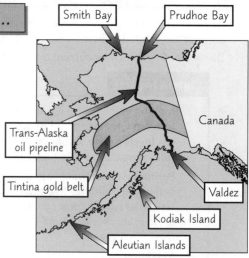

Smith Bay — Prudhoe Bay — Canada — Trans-Alaska oil pipeline — Tintina gold belt — Valdez — Kodiak Island — Aleutian Islands

Kodiak Island hadn't been the same since digital cameras came in.

...but there are also **Challenges** to **Development**

1) Alaska's state **population** is one of the **smallest** in the US, despite being the **largest state** by **area**. Most people live in the **south** and **southeast** of the state, near the **coast**, where it is **warmer** and **less remote**.

2) **Development** in Alaska can present **challenges** including getting **access** to resources and finding a **workforce** to exploit them, as well as providing **buildings**, **infrastructure** and protection from the **extreme weather**:

Environmental Conditions

- It's **really cold** — in **Prudhoe Bay** the mean annual temperature is around **–9 °C**. **Snow** and **strong winds** are common. **Exposure** to the extreme cold can cause **injury or death**, and **healthcare** may be a **long distance** away.

- In winter, it is **dark** nearly **all the time** in the north — this makes it hard to live and work there.

Inaccessibility

- Some areas of Alaska are **extremely remote**, and the **mountainous terrain** makes access **difficult** and **expensive**.

- In **winter**, the only way to get to some towns is by **air** or **ice roads**. In **summer**, the ground is **too soft** so there are **no roads** to some towns.

- Some development opportunities, e.g. oil reserves, are **hundreds** of kilometres from the nearest town — one proposed oil field in Smith Bay is **200 km** from the nearest **existing facilities**. This means it is **very difficult** and **expensive** to transport oil out.

- The population of Alaska is **small** and **scattered** — people in **small towns** may be a long way from **employment opportunities** or **services**.

3) Environmental conditions and inaccessibility create challenges for providing **buildings** and **infrastructure**:

- Most **construction work** can only take place in **summer**, when the days are **longer** and temperatures are **warmer**.

- Development takes a **long time** and is very **expensive**. For example, to exploit oil wells in northern Alaska, building materials have to be **shipped** to the area in **summer**, when seas **aren't frozen**. But prospecting for oil can only occur in **winter**, when the ground is **frozen** and able to support **temporary drilling rigs**.

- Permafrost provides a solid base to build on, but if it **melts** (e.g. due to warmth from buildings or pipelines) the ground becomes **unstable**. This can cause buildings to **collapse** or pipelines to **fracture**.

4) There can also be **conflict** between **development** and **conservation priorities** — the economic benefits of development may come at a high **environmental cost**, and conservation may **hinder** the **local economy**.

Humans in Glacial Landscapes — Case Study

Humans have **Responded** to the **Cold Conditions**

There are three main ways that people have responded to the **challenges** that Alaska presents — these responses have allowed them to **occupy** and **develop** the area.

1 Resilience

Resilience means being able to **cope** with the challenges the environment presents.

1) Electricity companies have **emergency generators** that can be started if the **power fails**, and emergency banks of **batteries** that can ensure electricity supplies are not **interrupted** while the generators are starting up. However, remote communities are still **very vulnerable** if there's a fault with their main generator as emergency generators can easily be **overloaded** and may **break down**, leaving the community with **no power at all**.

2) The Alaskan government has **emergency food supplies** to feed **40 000 people** for **seven days** in the event of a natural disaster cutting some people off from regular supplies.

3) When the only road to Prudhoe Bay, the **Dalton Highway**, is **damaged** by the weather, specially designed trucks called **rollagons** with wide, tube-like tyres can cross the tundra to deliver **fuel supplies**. But it's difficult to bring in enough for normal usage this way — this may mean that supplies are **limited** and **prices rise**.

Rollagons crossing snow-covered tundra to deliver fuel after flooding blocked the Dalton Highway in 2015.

2 Mitigation

Mitigation means **reducing** the **severity** of challenges.

1) Utilities such as water and sewage in towns are built in 'utilidors' — above-ground insulated corridors — to avoid **digging** into permafrost and prevent **melting**. However, they are **expensive** to build and maintain and may still freeze, causing damage and cutting off supplies.

2) Buildings are constructed on **thick** layers of **gravel** or on **stilts** to prevent them from **thawing** the permafrost below. Similarly, some sections of the **Trans-Alaska oil pipeline** are raised on stilts to prevent damage to the permafrost. However, this adds to the **cost** of construction.

3 Adaptation

Adaptation means **adjusting behaviour** to cope with the environment.

1) People **working** in the **cold**, particularly in the oil, gas and mining industries, burn lots of **calories**. Some employers make **food** available **24/7** to ensure employees have enough energy.

2) **Working practices** are **adapted** to the weather — employees may be made to take **warming-up breaks** to prevent **frostbite** and **hypothermia** as often as every **20 minutes** in extreme weather. However, this isn't a very **productive** way of working, so it may not be economically **viable** for some companies.

3) Many vehicles run their engines **continuously** all through winter, otherwise they would struggle to **start** in the cold.

Practice Questions

Q1 Name one important industry in Alaska.

Q2 Give one reason why it is difficult to construct buildings and infrastructure in Alaska.

Q3 Give one example of resilience to cold conditions in Alaska.

Q4 Give one example of a measure taken to mitigate the effects of the cold environment in Alaska.

Exam Questions

Q1 Outline the opportunities for development in a glaciated environment that you have studied. [3 marks]

Q2 "Challenges to development in glaciated environments can and should be overcome."
To what extent do you agree with this view? [20 marks]

Al ask ya again — read this case study until it's drilled deep into your brain...

I mean sure, breaks every 20 minutes and unlimited food sound great, but remember that it's dark all winter long and so absolutely blummin' freezing that even tyres on cars can freeze into shapes that aren't round. You may have studied a different example of human activities in glacial landscapes, which is fine — just make sure you've got one learnt.

Natural Hazards

Time for a bit of mayhem and disaster — it always makes Geography more interesting. Hazards come in all shapes and sizes, and when they happen in populated areas they can be pretty nasty things (as you can probably guess). I'm scared.

There are **Different Types** of Hazard

1) A **hazard** is something that's a **potential threat** to **human life** or **property**.

2) **Natural hazards** are caused by **natural processes**, e.g. a lava flow from a volcanic eruption.

3) Natural hazards can be divided into **three** types:

> **Geophysical hazards** (caused by **land** processes) — these include **earthquakes**, **volcanic eruptions**, **landslides** and **tsunamis**.

> **Atmospheric hazards** (caused by **climatic** processes) — these include **tropical cyclones**, **storms**, **droughts**, **extremes of hot or cold weather** and **wildfires**.

> **Hydrological hazards** (caused by **water** movement) — these include **floods** and **avalanches**.

4) Here are a few more useful terms:

   - **Disaster** — when a hazard actually **seriously affects** humans.
   - **Risk** — the **likelihood** that humans will be seriously affected by a hazard.
   - **Vulnerability** — how **susceptible** a **population** is to the damage caused by a hazard.

> *A tropical storm (see p. 68-71) is a hazard, but when it hits land and seriously affects people and property it's a disaster.*

5) Hazards can have significant **impacts** while they are **occurring**, and often need an **emergency response** (e.g. evacuating an area). The impacts can also go on for a **long time after** the hazard itself has passed.

People's **Circumstances** Affect Their **Perception** of Hazards

1) People view hazards in **different ways** — for example, some people believe they will **never experience** a particular hazard, others **adapt** their lifestyle to minimise risk, and others **accept** hazards as being beyond their control.

2) People's perception of hazards is affected by their **economic**, **social** and **cultural background**. For example:

"Hazards? Not a problem. I simply fly away in my platinum rocket."

   - **Wealth** — e.g. richer people may be able to afford to **move** to areas that are less prone to hazards, or to build their homes to **withstand** hazards, so they may perceive the risk as **smaller**.
   - **Religion** — e.g. some people view hazards as **acts of God**, sent to **punish** people.
   - **Education** — e.g. people with more **education** may have a better **understanding** of the risks of hazards, or they may believe that they are able to **reduce** the risks or **mitigate** the impacts.
   - **Past experience** — e.g. people who live in hazard-prone areas may have experienced hazards **before**, which may affect the perceived risk from **future hazards**.
   - **Personality** — e.g. some people **fear** hazards and others might think of them as **exciting**.

There are **Many Responses** to Hazards

Individuals and governments might respond to a hazard to try to **reduce** their **vulnerability**, or to **reduce its impacts**:

1) People might try to **prevent** a hazard or reduce its **magnitude**. For some hazards (e.g. volcanic eruptions), this isn't possible, but for others (e.g. floods) it may be, e.g. by building flood defences. **Risk sharing** involves sharing the **costs** of reducing a hazard, the **benefits** of preventing it or the **costs** of not preventing it — e.g. people buy **insurance** to help them repair their property after a disaster. Most people **won't** be affected by a particular event, so they won't **claim** on the insurance — this means **lots** of people **contribute**, so the cost is **shared**.

2) People might try to reduce (**mitigate**) the **impacts** of a hazard. This could be by **prediction** — working out **when** and **where** a hazard is likely to occur, which allows people to respond to it (e.g. by evacuating an area). It could also be by **adaptation** — e.g. adding earthquake-resistant features to buildings.

3) Governments may **coordinate** responses to a hazard to **manage** it effectively.

4) Some people believe that hazards **cannot** be avoided, so they must just be **accepted** — this is **fatalism**.

The **success** of attempts to manage hazards depends on **hazard incidence** (how often a hazard occurs), **magnitude** or **intensity** (how **powerful** the hazard is) and **distribution** (the **areal extent** of the hazard). Generally, hazards with **low incidence** and **high magnitude** are most destructive. **Level of development** is also important — less developed countries may lack the **wealth** and **technology** to manage hazards effectively.

Natural Hazards

The **Park Model** Shows How People **Respond** to Hazards

The Park model shows the different phases of **response** to a hazard:

1) **Pre-disaster** — **before** the event, the situation is **normal**.

2) **Disruption** — **during** and **directly after** the hazard event occurs, there is **destruction** of property, loss of life etc. before people begin to respond.

3) **Relief** — in the **aftermath** of the event, **rescue** efforts focus on **saving** people and **preventing** further damage.

4) **Rehabilitation** — once the immediate impacts are under control, people start to **resolve longer-term problems**, e.g. providing **temporary shelter** and **aid** for those affected.

Relief and rehabilitation often involve help from national or international sources, e.g. aid.

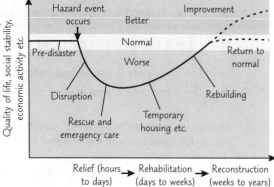

5) **Reconstruction** — this involves **rebuilding** permanent houses, infrastructure etc. This results in one of **two** outcomes:

- If buildings etc. are built to the **same standard** as before, the area returns to **normal**.
- If buildings etc. are built to a **higher standard** than before, the area **improves** (**vulnerability** to hazards **decreases**).

The Park model shows how responses **progress** during a disaster, which may help planners **predict** what resources will be needed at each stage. The model can also help planners to **prepare** for **future** hazard events. For example, the reconstruction phase of the model shows that conditions can be **improved** after a disaster (e.g. by designing hazard-resistant buildings or installing warning systems), which will help to **mitigate** the **impacts** of future hazard events.

There Are **Four Phases** in the **Hazard Management Cycle**

There are **four** stages that authorities go through in **managing** hazards:

1) **Mitigation** — this aims to **minimise** the **impacts** of future disasters. For example, building flood defences or adding fire-resistant roofs to buildings in areas prone to volcanic eruptions. Mitigation can happen **before** a hazard occurs or **afterwards**, when the area is recovering.

2) **Preparedness** — this is about **planning** how to respond to a hazard, e.g. making sure there are warning systems in place or educating people about how to evacuate safely if there is a cyclone.

3) **Response** — this is how people **react** when a disaster **occurs**, e.g. emergency services rescuing people who have been trapped or evacuating people from the danger zone.

4) **Recovery** — this is about getting the affected area back to **normal**, e.g. repairing or rebuilding houses and restoring services such as medical care and electricity.

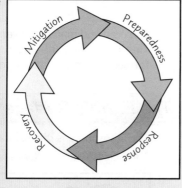

It's a **cycle** because hazard events **keep happening**, so efforts to prepare for them or mitigate their effects are **ongoing**.

Practice Questions

Q1 Name the three types of natural hazards, and give an example of each.

Q2 Explain the 'rehabilitation' stage of the Park model.

Exam Questions

Q1 Outline the stages of the Hazard Management Cycle. [3 marks]

Q2 Explain why different people may have different perceptions of natural hazards. [6 marks]

Disruption, relief, rehabilitation — the classic response to exams...

Some of this stuff might seem a bit woolly and theoretical at the moment, but if you can get your head round it it'll help you make sense of the rest of the section. Understanding all the different ways that people respond to hazards, and why, is a really important part of understanding why some disasters have much more severe impacts than others, so learn it well...

Plate Tectonics

The ground beneath your feet is moving all the time — but fear not, it's moving really, really, really slowly (about the same speed as your toenails grow. Yuk, toenails). Plate tectonics theory explains this movement...

Part of the Earth's *Mantle* is *Semi-molten*

1) At the **centre** of the Earth is the **CORE**, which is split into an **inner** core and an **outer** core:

   - The inner core is a **solid ball** containing lots of **iron and nickel**.
   - The outer core is **semi-molten** and also contains lots of **iron and nickel**.

2) Around the core is the **MANTLE**, which is mostly made of **silicate rocks** (rocks that have loads of the element silicon in them):

   - The part of the mantle **nearest the core** is **quite rigid**.
   - The **layer above** this, called the **asthenosphere**, is **semi-molten** (it can flow).
   - And the **very, very top bit** of the mantle is **rigid**.

3) The **outer layer** of the Earth is called the **CRUST**.

4) The **rigid top part** of the **mantle** and the **crust** together are called the **LITHOSPHERE**.

5) There are **two types** of crust — **CONTINENTAL** and **OCEANIC**:

   - **Continental** crust is **thicker** (30-70 km thick) and **less dense**.
   - **Oceanic** crust is **thinner** (6-10 km thick) and **more dense**.

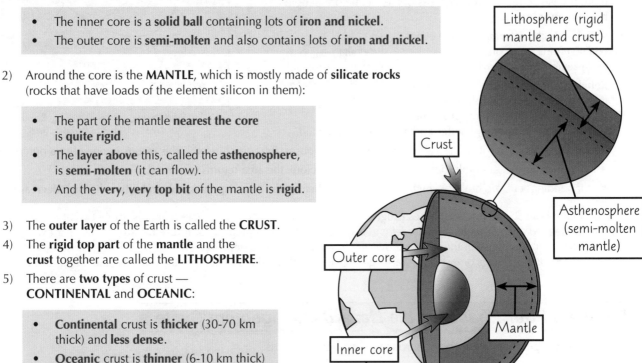

6) The core and mantle are **very hot** — the inner core is about **6000 °C** and the mantle is around **1000-3500 °C**. This heat is the Earth's main source of **internal energy**. Some of the heat energy is left over from when the Earth **formed**, and some comes from **radioactive decay** of elements such as uranium.

The **Earth's Surface** is **Separated** into **Tectonic Plates**

1) The lithosphere is **divided** into lots of slabs called **tectonic plates**, which **move** in relation to each other.

2) The places where plates meet are called **plate boundaries** or **plate margins**.

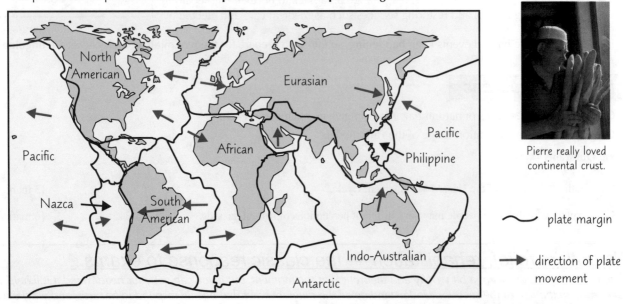

Pierre really loved continental crust.

~ plate margin

→ direction of plate movement

3) The idea that the Earth's lithosphere is made up of plates that move is called the **theory of plate tectonics**.

Topic Four — Hazards

Plate Tectonics

There Are Several **Theories** About How Tectonic Plates **Move**

Until recently, scientists thought that **convection currents** were the main process causing plate movement. Now, **slab pull** is thought to be the dominant process in most places, with **ridge push** happening in others.

Convection Currents

1) The Earth's mantle is **hottest** close to the **core**, so **lower parts** of the **asthenosphere heat up**, become **less dense** and slowly **rise**.
2) As they move towards the **top** of the asthenosphere they **cool down**, become **more dense** and slowly **sink**.
3) These **circular movements** of semi-molten rock are called **convection currents**.
4) They **create drag** on the **base** of the **tectonic plates**, causing them to **move**.

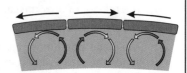

Slab Pull

1) At **destructive plate margins**, denser crust is forced **under** less dense crust (see p.58).
2) The **sinking** of the plate edge **pulls** the rest of the plate towards the boundary.

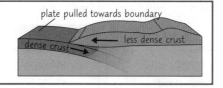
plate pulled towards boundary
less dense crust
dense crust

Ridge Push

1) At **constructive plate margins** (see p.58), magma rises to the surface and forms **new crust**, which is very **hot**. It heats the surrounding rocks, which **expand** and rise above the surface of the surrounding crust, forming a **slope**.
2) The new crust **cools** and becomes **denser**. Gravity causes the denser rock to move **downslope**, away from the plate margin.
3) This puts **pressure** on the tectonic plates, causing them to **move apart**.
4) Ridge push is also known as **gravitational sliding**.

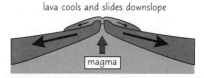
lava cools and slides downslope
magma

Sea-floor Spreading Happens When **Plates** Move **Apart**

1) As tectonic plates **diverge** (move apart), **magma rises up** to fill the gap created, then **cools** to form **new crust**.
2) Over time, the **new crust** is **dragged apart** and even **more new crust forms** between it.
3) When this happens at a plate margin under the sea the **sea floor gets wider**.
4) This **process** is called **sea floor spreading**... imaginative name.
5) It creates structures called **mid-ocean ridges** — ridges of higher terrain on either side of the margin.
6) A similar process of spreading occurs at **land margins** where the plates are moving apart.

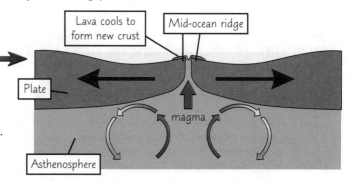
Lava cools to form new crust
Mid-ocean ridge
Plate
Asthenosphere
magma

Practice Questions

Q1 What is the asthenosphere?

Q2 What is the lithosphere?

Q3 Outline the main source of internal energy in the Earth.

Exam Questions

Q1 Outline how tectonic plates are moved by slab pull. [3 marks]

Q2 Outline how new crust is created by sea-floor spreading. [3 marks]

Plate tectonics — it's a cracking theory...

What a lovely couple of pages to ease you in to geophysical hazards, but don't think you can get away without knowing this stuff inside out. If you don't get the basics, the rest of this section will be more painful than stubbing your toe on a slab of oceanic crust. A bit of work now will help make the rest of plate tectonics a piece of Victoria sponge. Mmm, cake...

Types of Plate Margin

The next couple of pages build on some of the stuff you should have learnt at GCSE. It's not the most difficult of topics (I'm saving those for later...) but it's vital nonetheless — so put on your favourite revision hat and get ready to take it all in.

Earthquakes and Volcanoes Occur at Constructive Margins

1) A **constructive margin** occurs where two plates are moving **APART** (diverging).

2) The mantle is under **pressure** from the plates above. When they move apart, the pressure is **released** at the **margin**.

3) The release of pressure causes the mantle to **melt**, producing **magma**.

4) The magma is **less dense** than the plate above, so it **rises** and can **erupt** to form a **VOLCANO**.

5) The plates **don't** move apart in a **uniform way** — some parts move faster than others. This causes **pressure to build up**. When the pressure becomes **too much** the plate **cracks**, making a **fault line** and causing an **EARTHQUAKE**. **Further earthquakes** may also occur along the fault line once it's been created.

6) Constructive margins create **two different landforms**, depending on where they are:

> A fault line is where a plate has cracked under pressure.

OCEAN RIDGE

1) Where diverging plates are **underwater**, an **ocean ridge** forms (see page 57). For example, the **Mid-Atlantic Ridge** is where the **Eurasian plate** and **North American plate** are moving apart.

2) **Underwater volcanoes** erupt along mid-ocean ridges and they can **build up** to be above sea level. For example, **Iceland** has been formed by the build-up of underwater volcanoes along the Mid-Atlantic Ridge.

RIFT VALLEY

1) Where plates diverge **beneath land**, rising **magma** causes the continental crust to **bulge** and **fracture**, forming **fault lines**.

2) As the plates keep moving apart, the **crust** between parallel faults **drops down** to form a **rift valley**. For example, the **East African Rift System** is a series of rift valleys that stretches from **Mozambique** to the **Red Sea** — about 4000 km. It's formed because the **Nubian** and **Somalian** plates are diverging. Some parts of the system are hundreds of metres deep and thousands of metres wide.

3) **Volcanoes** are found around rift valleys. For example, **Mount Kilimanjaro** and **Mount Kenya** (the two highest mountains in Africa) are volcanoes in the **East African Rift System**.

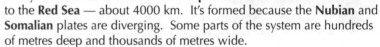

Earthquakes and Volcanoes Also Occur at Destructive Margins

A **destructive margin** occurs where two plates are moving **TOWARDS EACH OTHER** (converging). What happens at these margins depends on the **types of plates** converging:

Oceanic-Continental

1) Where continental crust and oceanic crust converge, the more dense oceanic crust is forced under the less dense continental crust (it's subducted). This forms a **DEEP SEA TRENCH** (a very deep trench in the sea — e.g. the Peru-Chile trench in the Pacific Ocean).

2) **FOLD MOUNTAINS** also form where the plates meet. They're made up of sediments that have accumulated on the continental crust, which are folded upwards along with the edge of the continental crust.

3) The oceanic crust is heated by friction and contact with the upper mantle, which melts it into magma.

4) The magma is less dense than the continental crust above and will rise back to the surface to form **VOLCANOES**.

5) As one plate moves under the other they can get stuck. This causes pressure to build up. When the pressure becomes too much the plates jerk past each other, causing an **EARTHQUAKE**.

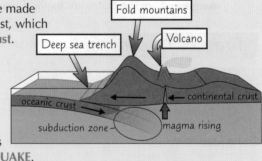

Oceanic-Oceanic

1) Most of the same processes occur where two plates of oceanic crust are moving towards each other — the denser of the two will be subducted, forming a **DEEP SEA TRENCH** and triggering **EARTHQUAKES** and **VOLCANIC ERUPTIONS**.

2) Volcanic eruptions that take place underwater (e.g. when two plates of oceanic crust converge) create **ISLAND ARCS** — clusters of islands that sit in a curved line, e.g. the **Mariana Islands**.

Types of Plate Margin

Continental-Continental

1) Where two plates of **continental crust** move towards each other, **neither** is subducted so there **aren't any volcanoes** — but the pressure that builds up between them can cause **EARTHQUAKES**.

2) **FOLD MOUNTAINS** form when continental crusts converge. E.g. the **Himalayas** were created in this way.

Only Earthquakes Occur at Conservative Plate Margins

1) A **conservative margin** occurs where two plates are moving **PAST EACH OTHER**.

2) The two plates get **locked together** in places and **pressure builds up**. As with destructive margins, this causes the plates to **jerk** past each other (or to **crack**, forming **fault lines**), releasing the **energy** as an **EARTHQUAKE**.

3) For example, the **Pacific plate** is moving past the **North American plate**. Many earthquakes occur along this margin and along its fault lines, e.g. along the **San Andreas fault** in **California**.

AERIAL PHOTOGRAPH OF THE SAN ANDREAS FAULT

This is the fault line

Movement of plates

©PETER MENZEL / SCIENCE PHOTO LIBRARY

Magma Plumes Can Form Volcanoes Away From Plate Margins

Most volcanic activity occurs at **plate margins**, but there are some areas of **intense volcanic activity** that **aren't** near any plate margins. These are caused by **magma plumes**:

The ground above a magma plume is called a hot spot.

1) A **magma plume** is a **vertical column** of **extra-hot magma** that **rises up** from the mantle.

2) **Volcanoes** form above magma plumes.

3) The **magma plume** remains **stationary** over time, but the **crust moves** above it.

4) Volcanic activity in the part of the crust that **was** above the magma plume **decreases** as it moves away.

5) **New volcanoes** form in the part of the crust that is **now above** the magma plume.

6) As the crust continues to move, a **chain of volcanoes** is formed.

7) The chain of islands that makes up **Hawaii** was formed by a magma plume.

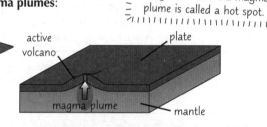

active volcano — plate — magma plume — mantle

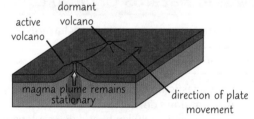

dormant volcano — active volcano — magma plume remains stationary — direction of plate movement

Practice Questions

Q1 Name the two landforms that are created at constructive margins.

Q2 At what type of plate margin do fold mountains form?

Q3 Explain what happens when two continental plates meet.

Q4 Give one example of each type of plate margin.

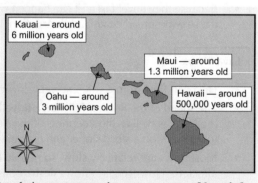

Kauai — around 6 million years old
Maui — around 1.3 million years old
Oahu — around 3 million years old
Hawaii — around 500,000 years old
N

Exam Questions

Q1 The diagram shows the names and estimated ages of some of the Hawaiian islands. Describe and explain the distribution of the islands in relation to magma plumes. [6 marks]

Q2 Outline how earthquakes are caused at conservative plate margins. [3 marks]

Tectonic plates are great — but they do have their faults...

Groan... Sorry — I'm running out of tectonics gags. It's not a good sign, since there are still eight pages left on geophysical hazards. I tell you what, you go back and have another read of these pages — make sure you know what happens at each type of plate boundary (and above a magma plume), and I'll see if I can find my sense of humour. See you on the next page...

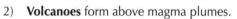

Volcanic Hazards

Volcanoes — I could talk about them all day. That's probably why I'm such a favourite amongst my friends and relatives.

Volcanic Hazards Usually Occur Near Plate Margins

1) Most volcanic eruptions occur near **constructive** and **destructive** plate margins:

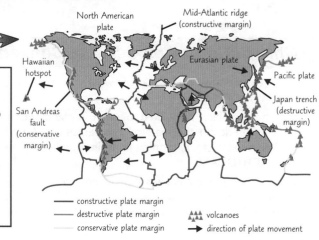

Constructive Margins

- **Basaltic lava** is formed here — it is very **hot** and has a **low viscosity** (it's runny), so it **flows** easily and quickly. Eruptions of basaltic lava are **frequent** and go on for a long time, but they're **not very violent**.
- If the margin is **underwater**, magma rises to fill the space left by plates moving apart, forming **ocean ridges**.
- If the margin is **on land**, as plates pull apart, forming **rift valleys**, they become thinner, and magma is able to break through at the surface.

Destructive Margins

- **Andesitic** and **rhyolitic** lavas are formed here — they are **cooler** and **more viscous** (less runny) than basaltic lava, so they flow **less easily**. Andesitic and rhyolitic lavas usually erupt **intermittently** (every once in a while) and the eruptions are **short-lived**.
- At **subduction zones**, where one plate is pulled beneath another, melting of the plate forms magma, which rises to the surface as volcanoes. Because the lava is viscous, it forms **blockages** in volcanic vents, causing **pressure** to build. The blockage is cleared by a **violent eruption**.

2) A few volcanoes occur **away** from plate margins at **hot spots** above magma plumes (see p.59). Most hot spots have **basaltic lava** that flows quickly, forming volcanoes with **gentle slopes** (shield volcanoes).

Volcanic Hazards Come in Lots of Different Forms

Volcanic eruptions can create **primary hazards** — hazards that come from the eruption itself, e.g.:

Pyroclastic Flows

A pyroclastic flow is sometimes called a nuée ardente.

- A **pyroclastic flow** is a mixture of **super-heated gas**, **ash** and **volcanic rock** that **flows** down the sides of a volcano. It travels at **high speed** (often more than 80 km/h) and flows a **long way** (generally around 10-15 km).
- Because they travel **fast** and can happen with relatively **little warning**, pyroclastic flows can cause widespread **death** and **destruction**, through e.g. burning and burial under debris.

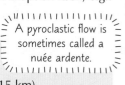

Pompeii and Herculaneum were buried by a series of pyroclastic flows from the eruption of Vesuvius in 79 A.D.

Lava Flows

- Lava can **flow** from a volcanic vent down the side of the volcano.
- The **speed** of the flow and **distance travelled** depend on the temperature and viscosity of the lava, as well as the steepness of the slope — **low viscosity** (runny) lava can flow at up to 10 km/h on a steep slope, and may travel tens of kilometres.
- Most flows are relatively **slow**, so people have time to **evacuate** areas that will be affected. However, lava flows **destroy** anything in their path, including buildings and vegetation, by **burning**, **burying** or **knocking it down**.

Volcanic Gases

- Lava contains **gases** such as **carbon dioxide** and **sulfur dioxide**, which are **released** into the atmosphere when a volcano erupts.
- Some of these gases can be **harmful** to humans and animals if they're breathed in, e.g. sulfur dioxide can cause breathing difficulties.

Volcanic Hazards

Pyroclastic and Ash Fallout

- **Pyroclastic fallout** is material that has been ejected from a volcano during an eruption and **falls back** to the ground. When fallout consists mostly of ash, it's called **ash fallout**.

Another name for pyroclastic material is tephra.

- Fallout consists of material of a **range of sizes** — from large pieces of rock weighing several tonnes to microscopic ash particles. Material can travel **thousands of kilometres** from the volcano. Heavier particles are deposited **earlier** than light ones, so material ends up being **well sorted**, with larger, heavier particles deposited **near** the volcano and smaller, lighter particles (e.g. ash) **further away**.

- Large pieces of falling tephra can **damage buildings** and **kill** or **injure people**. Finer material can form a layer up to several metres in thickness, which can **kill vegetation**, hinder road and rail **transport** and cause buildings to **collapse**. Ash can also be **harmful** to people if it is breathed in.

An ash cloud in Russia.

Eruptions can also create **secondary hazards** — hazards that are **caused by** the primary hazards, e.g.:

Mudflows (Lahars)

- Mudflows occur when volcanic material **mixes** with large amounts of **water** (e.g. from rainfall or from ice melted by the eruption). Flows move very **quickly** (over 80 km/h) and can travel for **tens of kilometres**.
- Mudflows can **bury** or **destroy** natural habitats, settlements and infrastructure (e.g. roads and bridges).

Acid Rain

- Volcanic **gases** can **react** with water vapour in the atmosphere, which then falls as **acid rain** — e.g. sulfur dioxide reacts with water to form weak **sulfuric acid**.
- This can **damage ecosystems**, and can also cause stone and metal to **deteriorate**, damaging buildings, bridges, statues etc.

Eruptions can cause other secondary hazards — e.g. if pyroclastic flows melt ice, it can cause flooding downslope, and if they enter the sea, they may generate a tsunami.

The *Magnitude* and *Frequency* of Volcanic Hazards *Varies*

There are a few more **terms** you need to know to understand volcanic hazards:

- **Magnitude** — volcanic events range from **small**, **slow** lava flows to **huge eruptions** of lava, ash and gas. Magnitude of eruptions can be measured using the **Volcanic Explosivity Index**, which grades volcanoes on a scale from 0 to 8 based on the **amount** of material ejected and **how high** the material is blasted.

- **Frequency** — some active volcanoes erupt only **once every 100 000 years** or so, whereas others erupt **every few months**. Generally, **less frequent** eruptions are **larger in magnitude** and more damaging.

- **Randomness vs. regularity** — some volcanoes erupt at very **regular** intervals, whereas others may be **dormant** for hundreds or thousands of years, then erupt **several times** in quick succession.

- **Predictability** — the regularity with which a volcano erupts can help scientists to **predict when** it might erupt again. They also monitor **tiny earthquakes** and changes in the **shape** of the volcano, which suggest that an eruption is imminent.

Practice Questions

Q1 Briefly summarise where active volcanoes are found

Q2 What is a pyroclastic flow?

Q3 What is meant by the predictability of a volcanic event?

Exam Question

Q1 Outline the role of lava type in determining the characteristics of volcanic eruptions. [3 marks]

The Nuée Ardente — sounds like the name of a pretentious synth pop band...

In fact, I might form a band of that name — my first track will be called 'I Will Survive (This Lava Flow by Walking Swiftly in the Opposite Direction)'. Anyway, back to volcanoes — turns out they're not just a great topic for a disaster movie, they're also the basis for some pretty tricksy exam questions. So make sure you know your lahars from your lava flows before you move on.

Volcanic Hazards — Impacts and Responses

So it turns out that volcanic eruptions don't just look scary, they also have some pretty scary impacts.
Nobody panic — there are lots of different ways of managing them, which can make them less damaging.

Volcanic Events Have **Primary** and **Secondary Impacts**

1) **Primary impacts** are a **direct result** of the eruption, e.g. people can be killed by falling tephra.

2) **Secondary impacts** occur as a **result** of the **primary impacts**, e.g. pyroclastic flows can melt glaciers and cause flooding.

3) Volcanic eruptions have **impacts** on people and the environment:

Have a look at pages 60-61 for the impacts of specific volcanic hazards.

Social
- People are **killed**, and buildings and infrastructure are **destroyed** by pyroclastic flows and fallout.
- Pyroclastic flows and lava flows can **start fires** that damage buildings.
- **Mudflows** and **flooding** from ice melt can cause further **damage** and **deaths**.

Environmental
- Ecosystems can be **damaged** or **destroyed** by flows and fallout of volcanic material.
- **Acid rain** can cause **acidification** of aquatic **ecosystems**, killing some plants and animals. It also damages the leaves of **trees** and **removes nutrients** from the soil, damaging forests.
- Volcanic gases contribute to the **enhanced greenhouse effect** and can add to **global warming**.
- Clouds of ash and volcanic debris can reduce the amount of **sunlight** reaching Earth, **decreasing temperatures** over large areas.

Economic
- Eruptions can **destroy businesses**, and ash clouds can prevent **aircraft** flying and damage **crops**. This damages the **economy** of the region and the country.
- Damage to buildings and infrastructure can be very **expensive** to repair.
- Eruptions and the scenery they form can **attract tourists**, boosting the economy.

Political
- Damage to agricultural land can cause **food shortages**, leading to **conflict** and political **unrest**.
- Governments may have to spend money on **repairing damage** to buildings and roads, rather than e.g. hospitals and schools, so countries may not develop as rapidly.

Volcanic Hazards Need **Short-term** and **Long-term Responses**

1) Hazard **mitigation** is anything that is done to **reduce** the **severity** or **impacts** of a hazard. This can be done through **short-term** or **long-term responses** to the volcanic hazard.

2) **Short-term responses** normally occur **immediately before**, **during** or **immediately after** the hazard begins — they include things like **evacuating** people from areas at risk from an eruption and providing **emergency food** supplies.

3) **Long-term responses** are designed to **reduce** the impacts of future eruptions by managing the **risks**.

4) Long-term responses fall into **three** main categories:

Mark wished the emergency food supplies had included something other than sprouts.

Prevention
- It's **not possible** to prevent a volcanic eruption.
- However, it is sometimes possible to prevent eruptions **posing a risk** to people — e.g. authorities can prevent the **land** around volcanoes from being **developed**.

Preparedness

Preparedness is about what happens **before** an eruption to **minimise risk** or **vulnerability**. For example:
- Authorities can install **monitoring systems** to predict **when** an eruption might occur, and make plans for how they will **evacuate** people if there is an eruption.
- If an eruption is imminent, authorities can **stop people** from **entering** the area around the volcano.
- **Individuals** can make sure they are prepared, e.g. by finding out where their nearest **emergency shelter** is, or making an **emergency kit** containing a torch, medicine, dust masks etc.
- **Communities** can set up **search and rescue** teams or **fire response units** to tackle the impacts of an eruption.

Adaptation

Adaptation is about how people **change** their behaviour or surroundings to **minimise** the **risks** and **maximise** the **benefits** of living near a volcano. For example:
- Buildings can be **strengthened** to reduce the chance of collapse if a layer of ash lands on them.
- People can capitalise on the **opportunities** of living near a volcano, e.g. by **farming** (volcanic ash makes soil very fertile) or by working in the **tourist industry**.

Volcanic Hazards — Impacts and Responses

The **Soufrière Hills** Volcano in **Montserrat** Erupted in **1997**

1) The **Soufrière Hills volcano** is in Montserrat, a small island in the Caribbean Sea. Montserrat is above a **destructive plate margin**, where the **North American plate** is being **forced under** the **Caribbean plate**.

2) Between June and September **1997** there was a series of **large eruptions**. In the largest eruption, about **4-5 million m³** of material was released over a **20 minute period**. **Pyroclastic flows** covered several square kilometres. The eruptions also produced **large ash clouds**.

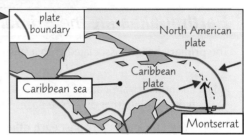

There were **Many Impacts**

ECONOMIC

1) The **total loss in value** of people's homes and investments was estimated to be about **£1 billion**.
2) Over **20 villages** and **two thirds of homes** on the island were **destroyed** by pyroclastic flows.
3) **Tourists stayed away** and **businesses** were **destroyed**, disrupting the **economy**. However, **tourism** on the island is now **increasing** as people come to **see the volcano**.
4) **Schools**, **hospitals**, the **airport** and the **port** were **destroyed**.

SOCIAL

1) **19 people died** and seven were injured.
2) **Hundreds** of people **lost** their **homes**.
3) **Fires destroyed** many buildings, e.g. local **government offices**, the **police headquarters** and **petrol stations**.
4) The **population has declined** — **8000** of the island's 12 000 inhabitants **left** after the eruption, and many still haven't returned.

ENVIRONMENTAL

1) **Large areas** were **covered** with **volcanic material** — the capital city **Plymouth** was buried under **12 m of mud and ash**.
2) **Vegetation** and **farmland** were **destroyed**.
3) **Volcanic ash** from the eruption has **improved soil fertility**.

Responses Included Help from the **Emergency Services** and **Aid**

The responses to the eruption were both short-term and long-term:

1) **People** were **evacuated** from the south to **safe areas** in the north.
2) **Shelters** were **built** to house evacuees.
3) Temporary **infrastructure** was also built, e.g. **roads** and **electricity supplies**.
4) The **UK** provided **£17 million** of **emergency aid** (Montserrat's an overseas territory of the UK).
5) **Local emergency services** provided support units to **search** for and **rescue** survivors.
6) A **risk map** was created and an **exclusion zone** is in place. The south of the island is **off-limits** while the volcano is **still intermittently active**.
7) The **UK** has provided **£41 million** of long-term aid to develop the north of the island — **new docks**, an **airport** and **houses** have been built with this.
8) The **Montserrat Volcano Observatory** has been set up to try and **predict** future eruptions.

Practice Questions

Q1 Describe the difference between short-term and long-term responses to a volcanic hazard.

Q2 Give two economic impacts of the Soufrière Hills eruption.

Exam Question

Q1 'It is possible to manage the impacts of volcanic eruptions, but the impacts cannot be prevented.' To what extent do you agree with this view?

[20 marks]

Maybe Caribbean islands aren't so idyllic after all...

The scientists at the volcano observatory take thermal images of the dome to see how hot it is, measure earthquakes and monitor how the ground is bulging. If things look like they're hotting up, they issue alerts so everyone knows to hightail it out of there.

Seismic Hazards

Now you're an expert on volcanic hazards, it's time to turn your attention to seismic hazards — that's earthquakes and all the other nasty hazards that they can cause. It's earth-shattering stuff.

Earthquakes are the Primary Hazard Caused by Seismic Activity

The **primary hazard** associated with a seismic event is an **earthquake**:

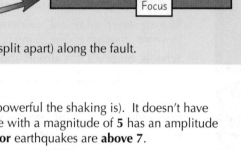

1) Earthquakes are caused by the **tension** that builds up at **all three** types of **plate margin** — see pages 58 and 59.

2) When the plates **jerk past each other** it sends out **shockwaves** (vibrations). These vibrations are the **earthquake**.

3) The shockwaves **spread out** from the **focus**. The focus doesn't have to be a single point — for example, it could be along a **fault line**. Near the focus the waves are **stronger** and cause **more damage**.

4) The **epicentre** is the point **on the Earth's surface** where the earthquake is **felt first**. It's **straight** above the **focus**.

5) Earthquakes cause the ground to **shake**, and sometimes to **rupture** (split apart) along the fault.

Earthquakes can be measured using three different scales:

1) The **Richter scale** measures the magnitude of an earthquake (how powerful the shaking is). It doesn't have an upper limit and it's **logarithmic** — this means that an earthquake with a magnitude of **5** has an amplitude (wave size) **ten times greater** than one with a magnitude of **4**. **Major** earthquakes are **above 7**.

2) The **moment magnitude scale** (MMS) is based on the total amount of **energy released** by an earthquake. Like the Richter scale, it is **logarithmic** and has **no upper limit**. It is **more accurate** than the Richter scale, especially for large earthquakes, so it's more widely used.

3) The **Mercalli scale** measures the **impacts** of an earthquake using **observations** of the event (e.g. reports and photos). The scale is between **1 and 12**, with **1** being an earthquake that's only detected by **instruments**, and **12** being an earthquake that causes **total destruction**.

Earthquakes Can Cause Other Seismic Hazards

Earthquakes cause a range of different **hazards**, including:

> Volcanic eruptions and landslides that slide into the sea can also displace large volumes of water and cause tsunamis.

Tsunamis

1) Tsunamis are **large waves** caused by the **displacement** of large volumes of **water**.

2) They can be triggered by **underwater earthquakes**. The earthquakes cause the seabed to move, which displaces water. Waves **radiate** out from the **epicentre** of the earthquake. The **greater** the **movement** of the sea floor, the greater the volume of water displaced, and the **bigger** the **wave** produced.

3) A tsunami will usually be **more powerful** if it starts **close to the coast**. This is because the waves **lose energy** as they travel towards land. So, the closer to the coast the waves start, the less energy they will lose.

4) The waves travel **very fast** in deep water so they can hit the shore **without much warning**. This means that they can cause a **high death toll**.

Landslides and Avalanches

1) **Shaking** of the ground can **dislodge** rock, soil or snow, causing landslides or avalanches that move **downslope** quickly.

2) Shaking can also loosen ground material, making it easier for **water** to infiltrate. The **weight** of the extra water may trigger a landslide even **after** ground shaking has stopped.

Soil Liquefaction

1) When soil is **saturated** with water, the vibrations of an earthquake can cause it to **act** like a **liquid**.

2) This makes the soil **weaker** and easier to **deform**, so it's more likely to **subside**, especially where it has a heavy **weight** on top of it (e.g. a building).

Seismic Hazards

Seismic Hazards Usually Occur Near Plate Margins

1) Most seismic hazards occur around **destructive** and **conservative** plate margins, but they can also occur around **constructive** margins.

2) The **nature** of an earthquake and its **magnitude** is affected by **three** main factors:

Margin Type

- The biggest earthquakes occur at **destructive** plate margins, where one plate is forced beneath another at the **subduction zone**. The subduction of a plate causes massive **pressure** to build up, causing a huge earthquake when it is released.

- Earthquakes at **constructive** margins tend to be **lower magnitude** than at destructive or conservative margins.

North American plate

Mid-Atlantic ridge (constructive boundary)

Eurasian plate

Pacific plate

San Andreas fault (conservative boundary)

Japan trench (destructive boundary)

—— constructive plate boundary   ·:· earthquakes

—— destructive plate boundary   → direction of plate movement

—— conservative plate boundary   ◗ highest tsunami risk

Rate of Movement

- Tectonic plates move in relation to each other at **different rates**, between about 1 and 15 cm per year.

- There's no clear **relationship** between rate of movement and earthquake **magnitude**.

Depth of Focus

- An earthquake's focus can be **close** to the Earth's **surface** or **deep** below it.

- **Deep** focus earthquakes tend to be **higher** magnitude than **shallow** focus earthquakes. However, deep focus earthquakes generally do **less damage** than shallow focus earthquakes — this is because shock waves generated deeper in the Earth have to **travel further** to reach the surface, which **reduces** their power.

The severity of the hazard also depends on where the event occurs, e.g. a mid-ocean earthquake may have fewer impacts than one on land.

Low Magnitude Seismic Hazards Occur Frequently

Just a few more bits to get your head round about seismic hazards:

- **Magnitude and frequency** — hundreds of **low magnitude** earthquakes happen around the world **every day**. Fortunately, earthquakes of very **high magnitude** occur much **less often**. The number of earthquakes that occur globally also **varies** from year to year.

- **Randomness vs. regularity** — earthquakes and other seismic hazards don't seem to follow any clear **pattern** or **trend** — their occurrence is largely **random**.

- **Predictability** — scientists can monitor the movement of tectonic plates to predict which **areas** are **at risk** from seismic hazards. However, it's currently impossible to tell **when** an earthquake will strike a particular place, and what **magnitude** it's likely to be.

Nigel's insistence on dressing as a mime was random, yet it happened with more regularity than his friends would ideally have liked.

Practice Questions

Q1 Describe what the focus of an earthquake is.

Q2 Briefly outline the differences between the Richter scale and the Mercalli scale.

Q3 Name two seismic hazards caused by earthquakes.

Exam Question

Q1 Outline the main controls on earthquake magnitude. [3 marks]

The Beach Boys' earthquake detector — great for picking up good vibrations...

The problem with not being able to predict earthquakes is that nobody knows to get out of the way before one happens. This means that they can have some pretty major impacts, which need to be managed. And that brings us neatly to the next page...

Seismic Hazards — Impacts and Responses

Unless you've been living in a cave, you'll probably be aware that seismic hazards have some pretty serious impacts. My response to this is to live as far away from the hazards as possible — funnily enough, in a cave.

Seismic Events Have **Primary** and **Secondary Impacts**

1) **Primary impacts** are a **direct result** of the hazard, e.g. people can be killed when a tsunami hits a coastal area.

2) **Secondary impacts** occur as a **result** of the **primary impacts**, e.g. earthquakes can break gas pipes, causing fires.

3) Seismic hazards have **impacts** on people and the environment:

Social
- Earthquakes can cause buildings to **collapse, killing** and **injuring** people, and leaving others **homeless**.
- Earthquakes and liquefaction can cause **gas lines** and **power lines** to break, starting **fires** that **kill** more people. Broken water pipes can cause **flooding**, and lack of water can make it hard to put fires out.
- Lack of clean water can cause **disease** to spread.
- Tsunamis can **flood** large areas, **killing** people and causing widespread **damage** to property.

Environmental
- Industrial units, including power plants, can be **damaged** by earthquakes and tsunamis, causing **leaks** of **chemicals** or **radioactive material** that damage the environment.
- **Fires** started by damaged gas and electricity lines can **destroy ecosystems**.
- Tsunamis can **flood** freshwater ecosystems, killing plants and animals and **salinising** water and soil.

Economic
- Earthquakes can **destroy business premises** through ground shaking and liquefaction. This damages the **economy** of the region and the country.
- Damage to **industry** may mean that the country has to rely on **expensive imports** of goods and energy.
- Damage to **buildings** and **infrastructure** can be very **expensive** to repair.

Political
- **Shortages** of food, water and energy can cause **conflict** and political **unrest**.
- Governments may have to **borrow** money to repair damage, putting the country in **debt**. Money that is earmarked for development may have to be spent on **repairing damage** rather than on development.

Seismic Hazards Need **Short-term** and **Long-term Responses**

1) Attempts to mitigate the effects of a seismic hazard can rely on short-term or long-term responses.

2) **Short-term responses** normally occur **immediately before**, **during** or **immediately after** the hazard — they include things like rescuing people from collapsed buildings after an earthquake, and **evacuating** people from areas at risk from a tsunami.

3) **Long-term responses** are designed to **mitigate** the impacts of future hazards by managing the **risks**.

Helen and Darren's tsunami response was ill-advised.

4) Long-term responses fall into **three** main categories:

Prevention
- It's **not possible** to prevent most seismic hazards.
- However, it's sometimes possible to prevent them **posing a risk** to people — e.g. authorities can prevent land that is prone to **liquefaction** from being built on, or build **giant sea walls** to prevent tsunamis hitting land.

Preparedness

Preparedness is about preparing an **area** and the **people** who live there for a future seismic hazard. E.g.:
- Authorities can install **earthquake warning systems** — these detect weaker seismic waves that may be a sign of a more powerful earthquake to come. The systems send out **warnings** by e.g. TV, radio and SMS.
- Individuals and businesses can have **plans** for how people should **respond** during an earthquake, e.g. **staying away** from buildings if possible, finding a strong door frame or desk to **shelter** under if inside.
- Authorities can develop **tsunami warning systems** and make sure **evacuation routes** are well signposted.
- **Communities** can set up **search and rescue** teams or **fire response units** to tackle the impacts of a hazard.

Adaptation

People can adapt their behaviour or surroundings to **minimise** the **risks** of seismic hazards. For example:
- Buildings can be **designed** to **withstand** earthquakes, e.g. by using strong or flexible materials, or by building special foundations that absorb an earthquake's energy.
- Buildings can also be designed to reduce vulnerability to **tsunamis**, e.g. **tall, strong** buildings allow people to **escape** the tsunami quickly, and buildings with **raised, open** foundations are less likely to be damaged.

Seismic Hazards — Impacts and Responses

The **Kashmir Earthquake** Happened on **8th October 2005**

1) The **Kashmir region** in north **Pakistan** sits on a **destructive plate margin** where the **Indian plate** is being forced under the **Eurasian plate**.

2) An earthquake measuring **7.6** on the Moment Magnitude Scale occurred in the Kashmir region on **8th October 2005**.

3) The earthquake caused **damage** to an area of **30 000 km²**.

4) Over the next few weeks there were nearly 1000 **aftershocks**.

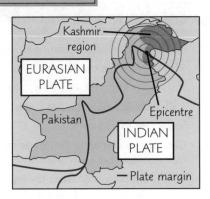

The **Earthquake** Had a Lot of **Impacts**

SOCIAL

1) Around **80 000 people died**, and **hundreds of thousands** were **injured**.

2) Around **3 million people** were made **homeless**.

3) **Water pipes** and **electricity lines** were **broken**, cutting off supplies.

4) **Landslides** buried **buildings** and **people**. They also **blocked roads** and destroyed **telephone lines**.

5) **Diarrhoea** and **other diseases** spread due to little **clean water**.

ECONOMIC

1) It's been estimated that the earthquake cost around **US $5 billion** in **total**.

2) **Whole villages** and **thousands of buildings** were **destroyed** or severely damaged. The **total cost of rebuilding** has been estimated to be **US $3.5 billion**.

ENVIRONMENTAL

1) **Landslides** and **rockfalls** occurred throughout the region, affecting habitats.

2) A landslide in Jhelum Valley was over **1 km wide** and over **2 km long**. The debris created a **dam** at the bottom of the valley that **blocked two rivers** where they joined.

People Tried to **Respond**, But the Response was **Delayed**

1) **International aid** and **equipment** such as helicopters and rescue dogs were brought in, as well as **teams** of people from **other countries**.

2) However, the poor roads meant that **help didn't reach** many areas for **days** or **weeks**. People had to be rescued without any equipment or help from emergency services.

3) **Tents**, **blankets** and **medical supplies** were distributed within a **month**, but **not to all areas** affected.

4) The Pakistani government set up the **Earthquake Reconstruction and Rehabilitation Authority** (ERRA) and the **Federal Relief Commission** (FRC) to **coordinate activities** with other international agencies and non-governmental organisations.

5) Around **40 000 people** were **relocated** to a **new town**, from the destroyed town of Balakot.

6) **Government money** was given to people whose homes had been destroyed so they could **rebuild them themselves**.

7) **Training** has been provided to help rebuild more buildings as **earthquake resistant**.

> About US $5.8 billion of foreign aid was provided by the international community in response to the disaster. Some of this was for long-term development.

Practice Questions

Q1 Give three possible environmental impacts of seismic hazards.

Q2 Give two possible ways of increasing preparedness for a seismic hazard.

Q3 Describe three social impacts of the Kashmir earthquake.

Exam Question

Q1 Assess whether the secondary impacts caused by seismic hazards are more dangerous than the primary impacts. [9 marks]

Nope, sorry — it's just not very funny...

So, you've reached the end of tectonic hazards. It's been quite a journey — almost to the centre of the Earth. Well, not quite, but 'a journey to a bit below the Earth's surface' sounds far less dramatic. And, let's face it, this section is all about drama.

Storm Hazards

The weather in tropical areas is generally a darn sight better than it is here, but things can get ugly...

Tropical Storms Form Over Warm Water in the Tropics

1) Tropical storms are **huge spinning storms** with **strong winds** and **torrential rain**.

2) They develop over **warm water**. As warm, moist air **rises** and **condenses**, it **releases energy** that increases wind speed.

3) Scientists don't know exactly **how** they're formed but they do know the **conditions needed**. These include:

   - A **disturbance** near the sea-surface that triggers the storm (e.g. an area of low pressure).
   - **Sea water** that's **warm** (above **27°C** to **at least 50 m** below the surface), so lots of water will evaporate.
   - **Convergence of air** in the **lower atmosphere** — either within the ITCZ or along the boundary between warm and cold air masses. This forces warm air to **rise**.
   - A location at least **5° from the Equator**. They **don't form 0-5° either side** of the Equator because the **Coriolis effect** isn't strong enough to make them spin.

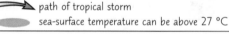

The Coriolis effect is a force caused by the Earth's rotation. It deflects the path of winds but it's weak at the Equator.

4) So tropical storms form in the **tropics** because the water there is **warm enough**.

5) They occur in the **Caribbean Sea** (where they're called **hurricanes**), in the **Bay of Bengal** (where they're called **cyclones**), in the **China Sea** (where they're called **typhoons**) and in **Northern Australia**.

6) Tropical storms **lose strength** when they move **over land** because their supply of warm, moist air is cut off.

7) They initially **move westwards** due to the **easterly winds** in the **tropics**, e.g. trade winds move cyclones west across the Atlantic Ocean.

8) They **move away** from the **Equator** because of the **Coriolis effect**.

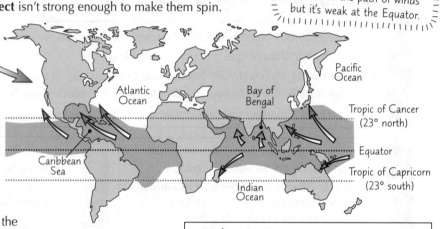

path of tropical storm
sea-surface temperature can be above 27 °C

Tropical Storms Are Circular

1) Tropical storms are **circular** in shape, hundreds of kilometres wide and usually last 7-14 days. They spin **anticlockwise** in the northern hemisphere, and **clockwise** in the southern hemisphere.

2) At the **centre** of the storm is an area of very **low pressure** called the **eye**.

3) **Rising air spirals** around the eye in the **eyewall**, causing strong winds.

4) Near the **top** of the storm, there is an **outflow** of moisture-laden air, so cloud cover extends for a long distance either side of the eye.

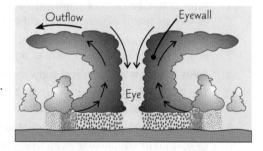

Storm Magnitude is Measured on the Saffir-Simpson Scale

1) Storms are classified using the **Saffir-Simpson Scale**, which is based on wind speed. Category 5 is the **strongest** (with winds over 250 km/h) and 1 is the **weakest** (with winds of 120-150 km/h).

2) The Saffir-Simpson Scale also estimates how much **damage** a storm of a given magnitude will do, from **limited** damage at Category 1 to **catastrophic** damage at Category 5.

3) Tropical storms are quite **frequent** — around one hundred occur each year. Some of these **never reach land**, so they never develop into a major **hazard**. Storms are more frequent in the **northern** hemisphere between June and November, and in the **southern** hemisphere between November and April.

4) There are lots of factors that affect **where** and **when** a tropical storm will form and where it will hit land, so the hazards created by storms are largely **irregular** (they follow no clear **spatial** or **temporal pattern**).

5) Certain cloud formations in tropical areas can be identified from **satellite imagery** and used to tell when a tropical storm is **forming**. The storm can then be **tracked** using satellite imagery and models, helping scientists to work out when and where it is likely to hit land. The path of a tropical storm can therefore be **predicted** fairly accurately.

Storm Hazards

Storms Bring **Strong Wind** and **Heavy Rain**

1) Storm hazards can take a number of forms:
   - **High winds** — wind speeds on the ground can reach more than **300 km/h**. Wind can **destroy** buildings, **uproot** trees, and carry debris (e.g. cars and trees) long distances before **smashing** them into other objects.
   - **Storm surges** — a storm surge is a **large rise** in sea level caused by **high winds** pushing water towards the coast, and by the **low pressure** of a storm.
   - **Heavy rain** — as warm, moist air rises it cools and condenses, causing torrential rain. E.g. in 1966, over **1000 mm** of rain fell in 12 hours at La Réunion (an island in the Indian Ocean) during Tropical Storm Denise.
   - **Flooding** — heavy downpours can cause **river discharge** to **increase** suddenly, causing rivers to overtop their banks and flood the surrounding area. Heavy rain and storm surges can also cause flooding in **coastal** areas.
   - **Landslides** — water infiltrates soil and rock, making it **less stable** and increasing the risk of landslides.

2) These hazards can have lots of **impacts**:

Social	Political
• People may **drown**, or be **injured** or **killed** by **debris** that's blown around or carried in flood water. • Houses are destroyed, so people are left **homeless**. • Electricity cables are **damaged** and supplies are **cut off**. • Flooding causes **sewage** overflows, **contaminating water**. • The **lack** of **clean water** can help **diseases** spread. • Damage to agricultural land can cause **food shortages**.	• People may blame the **authorities** for **shortages** of food, water and energy, leading to **conflict** and political **unrest**. • Expensive **repairs** to buildings, infrastructure etc. limit the amount of money that can be spent on **development**.

Economic	Environmental
• **Buildings** and **infrastructure** cost a huge amount to **rebuild**. • **Businesses** are **damaged** or **destroyed**, so they **can't trade**. • **Agricultural land** is **damaged**, affecting **commercial farming**.	• **Beaches** are **eroded** and **coastal habitats** (e.g. coral reefs) are **damaged**. Sediment deposited in aquatic ecosystems may damage fish breeding grounds. • **Environments** are **polluted**, e.g. by salt water, oil and chemicals spilled from damaged factories. • Landslides can **block watercourses**, so they change course.

Responses Aim to **Reduce the Impacts** of Storm Hazards

1) **Short-term responses** to a storm hazard normally occur **immediately before**, **during** or **immediately after** the hazard — they include things like **evacuating** people from areas at risk.

2) **Long-term responses** are often designed to **mitigate** the impacts of future storms by managing the **risks**. For example:
   - **Prevention** — storms **cannot** be prevented, but they can be **studied** to help scientists understand which areas are **most likely** to be affected. This means that future developments can be **planned** to **avoid high-risk areas**.
   - **Preparedness** — people and authorities can make sure they are **prepared** for a storm, e.g. **emergency services** can **train** and **prepare** for disasters, governments can plan **evacuation routes** to get people away from storms quickly and **educate people** about how to prepare for a storm (e.g. stockpiling water and food and boarding up windows).
   - **Adaptation** — buildings can be **designed** to **withstand** tropical storms, e.g. by using **reinforced concrete** or by **fixing roofs securely** so they're not blown off. Buildings can also be put on **stilts** so they're safe from floodwater. **Flood defences** can be built **along rivers** (e.g. levees) and **coasts** (e.g. sea walls).

Practice Questions

Q1 Briefly outline the characteristics of a tropical storm.

Q2 Give two social impacts and two environmental impacts of tropical storms.

Exam Question

Q1 Outline the conditions needed for a tropical storm to form. [3 marks]

My response to this page is aaaaaaaaaaaaagggggggggggghhhhh...

There's a whopping amount to learn on these two pages, so stop eyeing up the TV remote (I saw you) and get learning.

Storm Hazards — Case Studies

And now time for the inevitable case studies — first, a little madam called Katrina, and then a nasty chap called Nargis...

Hurricane Katrina *Struck the* South East USA *on* 29th August 2005

1) A storm hit the south east USA — one of the **wealthiest** countries in the world — in 2005. It **formed** over the **Bahamas** on the **23rd August**.

2) It moved **north west** and **strengthened** as it passed over the warm water of the Gulf of Mexico. By the time it struck Louisiana and Mississippi on the **29th August**, it was a **Category 3** hurricane.

3) It brought winds of around **200 km/h** and **200-250 mm** rainfall to **Louisiana**, and a **storm surge** of up to **8.5 m** in **Mississippi**.

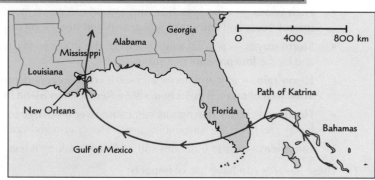

The Hurricane had a Huge Economic Impact

1) The coast of **Louisiana** and **Mississippi** bore the brunt of the hurricane, but south Florida and Cuba were also affected. The storm surge and heavy rainfall **overwhelmed levees** around New Orleans, causing over **80%** of the city to flood.

2) The **high winds**, **storm surge** and **flooding** had the following impacts:

SOCIAL
- **1836** people were **killed**.
- **300 000 houses** were **destroyed**, **hundreds of thousands** of people were made **homeless** and **3 million** people were left **without electricity**.
- One of the main routes out of New Orleans was closed because parts of the **I-10 bridge collapsed**.
- **Water supplies** were **polluted** with sewage and chemicals. **Five people died** from using contaminated water.
- **18 schools** in **New Orleans** were **destroyed** and **74** were badly **damaged**, disrupting **education**.

ECONOMIC
- **230 000 jobs** were **lost** from damaged businesses.
- **Industry** was disrupted — **30 oil platforms** in the Gulf of Mexico were **damaged** or **destroyed**, disrupting the oil industry. **Ports** such as **Gulfport** in Mississippi were **damaged**, affecting the **shipping industry**.
- **5300 km²** of **forest** was destroyed in **Mississippi**, causing around **$5 billion** lost income from logging.
- The total **cost of damage** was around **$300 billion**.

ENVIRONMENTAL
- **Coastal habitats** such as **sea turtle breeding beaches** were **damaged**.
- Some **coastal conservation areas** were **destroyed**, e.g. **Breton National Wildlife Refuge** in **Louisiana**.
- Flooding damaged oil refineries in Louisiana, causing massive **oil spills**.
- Flooding of **salt marshes** led to habitat loss.

Effective Warning Systems *Helped the USA* Respond Rapidly

1) The USA has a **sophisticated monitoring system** to **predict** if (and where) a hurricane will hit. On **August 26th** the **National Hurricane Center** (**NHC**) in Florida issued a **hurricane warning** for **Louisiana**, **Mississippi** and **Alabama**. It continued to track the hurricane, updating the government on where and when it would hit.

2) This helped the Federal Emergency Management Agency (**FEMA**) and other organisations to start preparing, e.g.:

- The **US Coast Guard** positioned **helicopters** and **boats** around the area likely to be affected.
- **FEMA** organised teams and supplies, e.g. **mortuary teams** with refrigerated trucks to deal with bodies.
- Some areas, including New Orleans, ordered **mandatory (compulsory) evacuation**. It's estimated that around **80%** of New Orleans' residents **were evacuated** before the hurricane reached land.

3) The response continued during the hurricane, and after it had passed. For example:

- **Emergency shelters** were set up for people who hadn't evacuated, e.g. the **Louisiana Superdome** in New Orleans sheltered **26 000 people** during the hurricane.
- The coastguard, police, fire service and army **rescued over 50 000 people** after the hurricane hit.
- Organisations sent **search and rescue** teams, **medical** teams and **supplies** into the area after the hurricane.
- **Charities** collected over **$4 billion** of donations from the public to provide aid (e.g. food) to victims.

Storm Hazards — Case Studies

Cyclone Nargis Struck Myanmar on 2nd May 2008

1) A storm **formed** in the **Bay of Bengal** during the **last week** in **April**.

2) As it approached the **coast of Myanmar** (one of the **least developed** countries in the world, sometimes called **Burma**) it strengthened to a **Category 4** cyclone.

3) On **May 2nd** it **hit** the coast of Myanmar with **wind speeds** of around **215 km/h** and a **storm surge** of **5 m** (storm waves added another 2 m on top of this).

The Cyclone had a Huge Social Impact

1) The **Irrawaddy Delta** in Myanmar was the hardest hit area because the cyclone hit it head on. A large proportion of it is only just above sea level and over **14 000 km²** of land was **flooded**.

2) **Sri Lanka** was also affected by heavy rainfall, **flooding** and **landslides**.

3) Across the region, the **high winds**, **storm surge** and **flooding** had the following impacts:

SOCIAL
- More than **140 000** people were **killed**.
- **450 000 houses** were **destroyed** and up to **2.5 million** people were left without **shelter**.
- **4000 schools** and **75%** of **health facilities** were **destroyed** or severely **damaged**.
- **43%** of **freshwater ponds** (valuable sources of fresh water for local people) were **damaged** by salt water. Almost **70%** of people **had no access** to **clean water**.
- A lot of people suffered from **diseases** caused by **poor sanitary conditions** and **contaminated water**, e.g. dysentery, diarrhoea.

ECONOMIC
- Over **6000 km²** of **agricultural land** was damaged, including rice paddies.
- **Agriculture** was affected — **crops** and **farm animals** were **lost** and over **40%** of **food stores** were **destroyed**.
- **Millions** of people **lost their livelihoods**, e.g. many **fishing boats** were destroyed.
- The **total cost** of damage was around **US $4 billion**.

ENVIRONMENTAL
- **380 km²** of **mangrove forests** were **destroyed**.
- Flooding caused **erosion** and **salinisation** (increased salt content) of land.

Mangrove forests protect the coast from flooding. Unfortunately loads had been chopped down to make rice paddies and shrimp farms, reducing the natural protection.

Myanmar Wasn't Prepared for Cyclone Nargis and Responded Slowly

1) Myanmar **doesn't have** a dedicated **hurricane monitoring centre**. **Indian** weather agencies **warned** Myanmar's government that Cyclone Nargis was likely to hit the country **48 hours before** it did, and **Myanmar's weather forecasters issued warnings** the cyclone was coming via **TV** and **radio**. However, it's claimed that they **didn't** say how **severe** it would be or give any advice about **how to prepare** or **evacuate**.

2) There were **no emergency preparation plans**, **no evacuation plans** and the country **didn't** have an **early warning system**.

3) After the cyclone, the **government** initially **refused** to accept any **foreign aid**. On the 9th May they decided to **accept aid donations** of things like food and tents, and organisations such as the **UN refugee agency** (UNHCR) and charities sent shelters, water purification tablets, first aid kits, blankets and food parcels.

4) At the time, Myanmar was ruled by the **military** — they **seized** some **aid**, and some was turned away. Aid workers were not allowed into the country until 19th May — more than two weeks **after** the disaster occurred. The delay in accepting international aid greatly **increased** the **number of deaths**.

Practice Questions

Q1 Give two social impacts, two economic impacts and two environmental impacts of Hurricane Katrina.

Q2 Give two social impacts, two economic impacts and two environmental impacts of Cyclone Nargis.

Exam Question

Q1 'The impacts of tropical storms are always more severe in less developed countries.'
To what extent do you agree with this view?   [20 marks]

Make sure you learn two case studies of tropical storms...

If you've studied different tropical storms, that's fine — just make sure you know the impacts and responses inside out.

Wildfires

Fires aren't just for sitting around, telling ghost stories and toasting marshmallows. Nope, when they get out of control they can be pretty devastating. Welcome to the text version of the latest rubbish documentary series... When Fires Go Bad.

Wildfires Normally Occur During **Hot**, **Dry** Periods

1) Wildfires are **uncontrolled fires** that destroy forests, grassland and other areas of vegetation. They usually occur in **rural** areas, but if they reach inhabited areas, they will also destroy **agricultural land** and **settlements**.

2) There are **three types** of wildfire:
   - **Ground fire** is where the **ground** itself (e.g. peat and tree roots) burns. It is a **slow**, smouldering fire with **no flame** and **little smoke**.
   - **Surface fire** is where **leaf litter** and **low-lying** vegetation burn. Fire can be **low** or **high intensity**.
   - **Crown fire** is where fire moves rapidly through the **canopy** (the top layer of vegetation). Fires are likely to be **intense** and **fast-moving**.

   All three types of fire can be present at once.

3) There are certain **conditions** that favour **intense** wild fires:

Vegetation Type	• **Thick undergrowth** or **closely spaced trees** allow fire to travel easily. • Some trees, such as eucalyptus and pine, contain a lot of **oil** and so burn very **easily**. • Eucalyptus trees **shed strips** of their bark which helps the fire to **spread** quickly.
Fuel Characteristics	• **Fine**, **dry** material (e.g. long grass, thin twigs) catch fire and burn most **easily**. • **Large amounts** of fuel that form a **continuous cover** will help the fire burn for longer and spread.
Climate and Recent Weather	• Rainfall must be **sufficient** for vegetation to **grow**, so there's plenty of **fuel**. • The area usually has a distinct **dry season** when rainfall is **low** for a **significant time**. **Warm**, **dry weather** causes water in the vegetation to **dry up**, so it's more **flammable**. • **Strong winds** provide more oxygen to help the fire **burn** and **spread** burning embers.
Fire Behaviour	• Fire burns in **different ways** — e.g. a **creeping** fire moves across the ground surface fairly slowly, whereas a **running** fire **spreads** rapidly and is more **intense**. • Fires can throw out **burning debris** (**firebrands**) that help the fire spread and become more intense.

Wildfires Can Have **Natural** or **Human Causes**

Fires need **fuel**, **oxygen** and a **heat source** to ignite the fire. Heat sources can be **natural** or **human**:

1) **Natural causes** — **lightning** is particularly likely to start a fire if it occurs **without much rain**. **Volcanic eruptions** can produce very hot lava, ash or gas, which can start fires.

2) **Human causes** — most fires are started by **people**. This can be **accidental**, e.g. by dropping **cigarettes**, allowing **campfires** and **barbecues** to get out of control, or if **fireworks** or **sparks** from machinery land in vulnerable areas. Fires can also be started **on purpose** (**arson**).

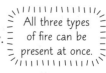

Jed hoped the boys' ability to control their campfire was better than their harmonies.

Wildfires Have a Range of **Impacts**

Wildfires have **primary impacts** — these occur as a **direct result** of the fire, e.g. houses burning down. They also have **secondary impacts** — these occur as a result of the primary impacts, e.g. people have to move. Some impacts are:

Social
- People may be **killed** or **injured** if they don't evacuate in time.
- Homes are **destroyed**, so people may be left **homeless**.
- Wildfire can destroy **power lines** and damage **reservoirs**, leaving people without **electricity** or **clean water**.
- Wildfires can cause **health problems**, e.g. inhaling smoke can cause long-term breathing difficulties.

Political
- Governments can face **criticism** when wildfires have severe impacts.
- Governments may have to **change** their **forest management practices** to reduce the risk of wildfire, e.g. by clearing vegetation to limit fuel.

Economic
- Wildfires destroy **businesses**, leading to loss of **jobs** and **income**.
- **Insurance** premiums increase dramatically after a wildfire.
- The **cost** of fighting wildfires is huge.
- Wildfires may **discourage tourists** from visiting an area, reducing income.

Environmental
- **Habitats** are destroyed. Some species may not return to the area after a fire, changing the **ecosystem**.
- **Soils** are damaged as the fire removes organic matter.
- Smoke causes **air pollution**, and water sources can be **contaminated** with ash.
- Some ecosystems **rely** on wildfires to **clear** dead vegetation, and some plant seeds need fire to **germinate**.

Wildfires

Responses to Wildfires Aim to Reduce Their Impacts

1) **Mitigation strategies** aim to **reduce** the **severity** of the wildfire's impacts. They can be **short-term** or **long-term**.

2) **Short-term responses** to a wildfire normally occur **during** or **immediately after** the hazard. For example:
   - Trying to put the fire out, **diverting** it away from settlements, **evacuating** people from areas at risk and **spraying water** onto the roofs of houses to prevent embers from setting them alight.

3) **Long-term responses** are often designed to **reduce** the impacts of future fires by managing the **risks**. For example:
   - **Prevention** — preventing fires from starting may involve public **education** about the risks of using campfires and barbecues in vulnerable areas. Authorities may also provide **fire beaters** to put small fires out before they spread.
   - **Preparedness** — being prepared for a wildfire may involve households having an **emergency plan** and emergency **supplies** of food, water and medicine, or authorities making **emergency shelters** available.
   - **Adaptation** — individuals and authorities can **change** the way they **live** to help them cope with wildfires, e.g. using **non-flammable building materials** and creating **fire breaks** (gaps in trees) around settlements to stop fire spreading.

Wildfires Hit South-east Australia in February 2009

1) In February 2009, severe wildfires burned for a **month** in the state of Victoria in south-east Australia. The **worst** fires occurred in **forested areas**.

2) **Environmental conditions** added to the intensity of the fires — they followed **ten years** of **drought**, recent temperatures had been **over 40 °C** and there were **strong winds**.

3) **Lack of management** (e.g. controlled burning of forest litter, such as branches and leaves), meant that there was a **large amount** of very dry oil-rich material to **fuel** the fire. Several of the fires were caused by **faulty power lines**.

4) Despite attempts to **manage** the fires, the impacts were **severe**:

Impacts
- **173** people were killed and around **400** injured. Many more suffered from **stress** and **depression**.
- **2000 houses** in 78 communities were destroyed.
- More than **60 businesses** were destroyed, causing loss of jobs and income to the region.
- The total estimated cost of the fire was more than **AUS $4 billion**.
- Around **4300 km²** of land was burned, including forest and national parks. Millions of **animals**, **birds** and **reptiles** were killed, including some **rare species** such as the sooty owl and spotted tree frog.

Responses
- The Australian Bureau of Meteorology **predicted** how the fires would spread and told residents that they could either **evacuate** or **stay** and **defend** their homes. Evacuation **reduced** the number of deaths, but many people were **put at risk** by choosing to stay in their houses.
- More than **20 000 firefighters** and **volunteers** helped to put out the fires and support victims.
- More than **AUS $400 million** was donated to help **rebuild** houses and community facilities. However, making new houses more fire-resistant **increased costs**, so not everyone could afford to finish building.
- Recommendations for **long-term responses** include building **fire shelters** in vulnerable areas, improving **warning systems** and improving the emergency **evacuation** strategy.

Practice Questions

Q1 Briefly describe three conditions that may lead to intense wildfires.

Q2 Give two natural causes of wildfires.

Exam Question

Q1 For a place you have studied, evaluate the impacts of a wildfire event and the effectiveness of responses to it. [9 marks]

Crown fire — the curse of royalty everywhere...

Phew, that's it for wildfires — a pretty hot topic, I think you'll agree. Those of you with sharp eyes may have spotted that similar impacts and responses crop up for a lot of different hazards — that's worth remembering for the exam. Just saying.

Multi-Hazard Environment — Case Study

If you like your surroundings to not try to kill you, the Philippines probably isn't the place for you...

The **Philippines** is a **Multi-Hazard Environment**

The Philippines is a group of islands in **south-east Asia.** The area is vulnerable to a **variety of hazards** with **social**, **economic** and **environmental impacts**, e.g.:

1) **Volcanoes** — the Philippines is near to a **destructive plate boundary**, where the **Philippine plate** is being **subducted** beneath the **Eurasian plate**. E.g. **Mount Pinatubo** erupted in 1991 — more than 700 people **died**, around 200 000 were left **homeless**, buildings **collapsed**, **crops** were **destroyed** and **agricultural land** was **ruined** by falling ash.

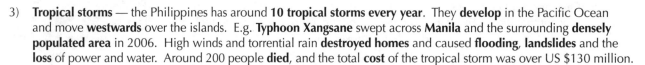

2) **Seismic hazards** — earthquakes occur along the plate boundary and at **fault lines** where the plate has **cracked** under pressure. E.g. an earthquake of **magnitude 7.8** occurred on **Luzon island** in 1990, killing over **1500 people**. Earthquakes in the surrounding oceans can cause tsunamis, e.g. in 1976, an earthquake of **magnitude 7.9** caused a tsunami that hit the coastline around the **Moro Gulf**. **Thousands were killed** and several cities were **devastated**.

3) **Tropical storms** — the Philippines has around **10 tropical storms every year**. They **develop** in the Pacific Ocean and move **westwards** over the islands. E.g. **Typhoon Xangsane** swept across **Manila** and the surrounding **densely populated area** in 2006. High winds and torrential rain **destroyed homes** and caused **flooding**, **landslides** and the **loss** of power and water. Around 200 people **died**, and the total **cost** of the tropical storm was over US $130 million.

Human Qualities and **Responses** Allow People to **Live** in the Area

1) Despite the risk of disasters, the Philippines is quite **densely populated**, with around 340 people per km².

2) Communities often **understand** the risks of hazards, having experienced them **before**. In many cases, people **prepare** for hazards **themselves**, e.g. by **widening rivers** near settlements to prevent flooding, and by **stockpiling food**. In this way, individuals and communities **increase** their own **resilience**.

3) In the past, funding for dealing with disasters was **only** available **after** the disaster occurred — this meant that the response focused on **reacting** to a disaster that had happened, rather than trying to **prevent** or **prepare** for future disasters.

4) From 2009 onwards, the Philippines' **policy** on disasters has changed — the country is now working to increase large-scale resilience to disasters by **adaptation**, **mitigation** and **management**. Strategies include:

- Preventing people **building** in areas at high risk of disaster.
- Adapting new and existing **buildings** and other **structures** to cope with earthquakes.
- Building **embankments** to reduce **flood risk** from tsunamis and tropical storms.
- Increasing **public awareness** of hazards and how to respond to them.
- **Monitoring** hazards and developing **early warning systems** so people in at-risk areas have time to prepare.

Practice Questions

Q1 Give one social impact that volcanic eruptions have on the Philippines.

Q2 Give one economic impact that tropical storms have on the Philippines.

Exam Question

Q1 Evaluate human responses to occupying places that experience a range of hazards. [9 marks]

Just add a swarm of locusts and it starts to look like an apocalypse...

As my geography teacher used to say, case studies 'put the meat on the bones'. However odd that sounds, the point is that it's all very well learning the theory, but it's really important that you know details of real-world examples if you want top marks.

Topic Four — Hazards

Hazardous Setting — Case Study

Italy — the home of pasta, pizza, Pisa... and a surprising number of earthquakes.

Central Italy has a **High Risk** of **Earthquakes**

1) **Fault lines** run **north-south** close to the **Apennine mountain range** and **east-west** across the centre of Italy. The fault lines are near the **destructive plate margin** between the **Eurasian** and **African plates**.

2) **Earthquakes** are common in the area, for example:
   - Three earthquakes up to magnitude 6.4 hit the area around **Assisi** in **1997**.
   - A 6.3 magnitude earthquake struck **L'Aquila** in April **2009**.
   - A series of earthquakes hit the area around **Amatrice** from August to October **2016**.

3) The **L'Aquila earthquake** was caused by movement along the **north-south fault line**. It **killed** around 300 people, made about 70 000 people **homeless** and **cost** Italy an estimated US $15 billion.

■ North-south fault line

■ East-west fault line

Assisi
Amatrice
L'Aquila

Earthquake Risk Has Affected the **Character** of the Area

1) Before 2009, L'Aquila itself **hadn't** suffered from a **major earthquake** for 300 years. The risks were known, and some steps were taken to mitigate hazards — e.g. there were **strict building regulations** to ensure that **newer buildings** were **designed** and **built** to withstand earthquakes. However, much of the city was very old, and some newer buildings didn't comply with regulations, so they were **severely damaged** or **destroyed** by the earthquake.

2) The **character** of L'Aquila reflects the **impacts** of the 2009 earthquake and the **risk** of future earthquakes:

Social
- Many historic buildings in the city centre were **destroyed**, and people were **rehoused** in newly built **earthquake-resistant** homes in suburban areas or in **new towns** outside the city. Many younger people **left** the area to look for jobs elsewhere. All these changes altered the **architectural** and **social** character of the city.
- Attendance at **social** and **religious** activities has **declined** — e.g. around 1000 people attended a Good Friday procession in 2016, compared with around 30 000 before the earthquake. People are **reluctant** to use the shops, bars and restaurants that were rebuilt in the town centre, and many have **closed down**.
- Some residents suffer from **mental health issues** as a result of the earthquake, and **fear** of more earthquakes occurring. However, others have developed **coping strategies** and increased their **resilience** to future hazards.

Economic
- University buildings in L'Aquila were badly damaged, making them **unusable**. The number of students enrolling **decreased**, which caused a major **economic loss** for the city.
- The Italian government plans to **reconstruct** the area to be economically **stronger** than before the disaster, for example by making the city more attractive to students. If successful, this would make L'Aquila a **busier**, more **affluent** place.

Political
- Officials and scientists have been blamed for not giving the public **adequate warning** about the earthquake risk. This has led to **tension** between residents and officials.
- The government has also been blamed for not **rebuilding** L'Aquila quickly enough or **involving residents** in decisions about how it would be rebuilt. This added to residents' feelings of **discontent** and **lack of support**.

3) **Communities** in and around L'Aquila have responded to earthquake **risk** in different ways. Some **accepted** homes in new towns or suburbs, possibly believing that risk would be **lower** there. Others took their own steps to **reduce risk** — e.g. some residents of Pescomaggiore, a village to the east of L'Aquila, worked with professional builders to create new **earthquake-resistant homes** using wood and straw, with **solar panels** to decrease reliance on mains power.

Practice Questions

Q1 Outline why central Italy is prone to earthquakes.

Q2 What magnitude was the 2009 L'Aquila earthquake?

Exam Question

Q1 Assess how the character of a place you have studied has been changed by its hazardous setting. [9 marks]

L'Aquila earthquake? L'Killer more like...

The L'Aquila earthquake killed hundreds of people and had profound physical and psychological effects on thousands more. It's a pretty downbeat end to a fairly depressing topic — unfortunately, we just haven't got that good at coping with hazards yet.

Urbanisation

Ahh cities, at last. This is a section you'll know a little bit about already. You might live in a city, or maybe you've visited a few on holiday. These first couple of pages will help you get to grips with the basics of urban areas...

The **Population** of **Urban Areas** is **Increasing**

1) Globally, the **number** and **proportion** of people living in **urban** areas has **increased** dramatically since 1945. In **1950**, **30%** of people **lived** in **urban areas**. In **2014**, just over **50%** lived in **towns** or **cities**.

2) In the developed world, the **majority** of people **live in cities**, but the **urban population** has only **increased slightly** since 1945. This is because urbanisation **began** much **earlier** in the **developed world** than in the **developing world** — during the **Industrial Revolution**, many people **moved** to cities in search of **work** in **mills** and **factories**. Although people are still **moving** to **cities** such as **London** and **New York**, **similar** numbers of people are leaving these cities.

3) In the developing world, **most people** currently live in **rural areas** — but this is **changing** fast. In many developing countries and emerging economies (countries with a rapidly growing economy), **old cities** are **growing** in size and **new cities** are **forming**. For example, in **Beijing, China**, the **urban population** increased from **4.4 million** in **1970** to **20.4 million** in **2015**.

With her cool new look and sassy attitude, Sam knew she'd fit in just fine in the city.

Four **Processes** Affect the **Populations** of **Cities**

There are **four processes** that involve the **movement of people** into and out of urban areas:

People move because of push factors (things that make them leave an area) and pull factors (things that attract them to an area).

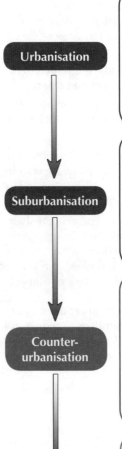

Urbanisation

- This is the **growth** in the **proportion** of people living in **urban areas**.
- It usually occurs because of **migration** (especially **rural-urban migration**) and **natural increase** (when birth rate is higher than death rate). People often migrate to cities for easier access to **schools** and **healthcare**, and because there are **more jobs** available.
- Many migrants are **young adults** — if they have **children**, the population increases further.
- In **developing countries**, urbanisation can result in **shanty towns** — **unplanned** and often **illegal** settlements made out of any material available.

Suburbanisation

- This is the migration of people from **city centres** to the **outskirts** of cities.
- As **urbanisation increases**, city centres become **overcrowded** and people desire **more space**. Improvements to **transport links** mean people can **live further away** and **commute** to work. Many people choose to move to the suburbs when they have **children** or **retire**.
- A **complex pattern** of **wealthy** and **poorer** areas develops. **Wealthier middle-class people** may move to the **suburbs** where there is a **better quality of life**. Those left behind are **poorer** and may include **foreign immigrants**. This can lead to economic and ethnic **segregation**.

Counter-urbanisation

- This is the movement of people **out of the city** into surrounding **villages** and **rural areas**.
- Improvements in **transport** mean people can **commute** to work and better **communications** (e.g. internet access) allow people to **work from home**.
- People leave cities because of **high property prices** and **overcrowding**. Some people may just **prefer quieter rural areas**.
- Counter-urbanisation can lead to new **housing estates** being built in rural areas. House prices may **increase**, meaning that some local people (e.g. young people) **can't afford** to live there. It can change the **age structure** of the area, e.g. average age may increase.

Urban Resurgence

- This is the **movement** of people **back** to the **city centre**.
- People may move back to city centres because of a **lack of jobs** in rural or suburban areas. People are also attracted by new developments (e.g. high quality housing).
- Urban resurgence is **common** in many **post-industrial countries**, like the UK and USA.
- New **shops** and **services** may open in the city as people move back, boosting the local **economy** and creating **jobs**. However, original residents may not be able to **afford** to live in the area any more, and may be forced to **move** to cheaper locations.

Urbanisation

Urbanisation has led to the Emergence of Megacities

Population growth in urban areas has **increased** the number of **big cities** in the world:

1) A **megacity** is an urban area with **over 10 million people** living there, e.g. Istanbul, Turkey.

2) In 1950 there were only **two** megacities — Tokyo and New York. By 2014 there were **28**, and this is predicted to rise to **41** by **2030**. More than **two-thirds** of megacities are in **developing nations**, e.g. Lagos, Nigeria.

3) Megacities develop because of **rural-urban migration** and **natural increase**. Migrants tend to move to **large** cities, and to cities that are experiencing **rapid economic growth**, so their population increases rapidly.

4) Megacities **dominate** the national and regional **economies** of countries. This is because companies choose to build their **headquarters** in cities with a **high number** of **skilled workers** and good **transport links**, e.g. international airports.

5) Megacities often have people living at **opposite extremes** — some are **really rich**, while others live in **extreme poverty**.

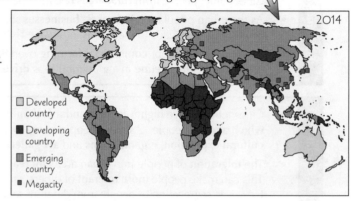

World Cities are Global Centres for Finance, Business and Culture

1) A **world city** is a city that has political and financial **influence** over the **whole world,** e.g. London and Sydney. Most are in the **developed world** but **some**, e.g. Dubai and Rio de Janeiro, are in **emerging economies**.

2) The **number** of **world cities** is **increasing**. In **1950**, the only world cities were London, Paris, Tokyo and New York. More recently, **economic growth** in **oil-rich countries** such as Nigeria has allowed cities such as **Lagos** to become **contenders** for **world city status**. These cities are **increasingly important** in **global economics** and **business**.

3) Since 1945, **world cities** such as London and New York have **emerged** as the **leaders** of **banking** and **finance**. Many **banking companies**, such as HSBC, Lloyds and RBS, have **headquarters** in these cities.

4) **World cities** usually **dominate** international **trade** and **regional economies** in their area. For example, **Tokyo** is extremely **influential** in international **trade** between the **East Asian nations**. World cities have good international **transport links**, which allow them to trade with the rest of the world.

5) World cities are generally home to world-renowned **universities**. They also tend to be centres for **science** and **innovation**, with high-quality **research and development** facilities.

6) They are also centres for **culture** — they are often home to large, globally influential **media** and **communications** corporations, as well as a range of theatres, museums and other cultural attractions.

7) They tend to attract high numbers of **people** from other countries, including **migrants**, **business visitors**, **students** and **tourists**.

The City of London is the main business and financial centre of London.

Practice Questions

Q1 What is counter-urbanisation?
Q2 What is a megacity?
Q3 Give two characteristics of world cities.

Exam Question

Q1 Outline how global patterns of urbanisation have changed since 1945. [3 marks]

Megacity — not quite an awesomecity, but better than a coolcity...

It all seems very confusing. First people move to the city for jobs, then into the suburbs for space, then back to the city once they realise that they're missing all the amenities of the city. I'm surprised they don't get dizzy and fall over more.

Topic Five — Contemporary Urban Environments

Urban Change

In the developed world in particular, cities have gone through rapid change since the 1970s.

There are **Many Processes** Associated with **Urbanisation**

Cities **develop** in lots of different ways as they **urbanise**:

Economic
- Cities attract people from **rural areas** because they offer more **job opportunities**, and jobs are often **better paid**.
- As the urban population increases, **businesses** such as factories and shops **grow** in size and become **more profitable**. This leads to more **jobs** and **wage rises**.
- As countries develop, **commercial farming** overtakes subsistence farming as the **primary method** of **food production**. The **decline** in agricultural jobs **drives** even more **people** into **towns** and **cities**.

Social
- Cities tend to have **higher living standards** than rural areas, e.g. better access to healthcare and education, which attracts people. As more people move to a city and the economy grows, it can become a **centre** for **cultural expression**, e.g. **museums** and **art galleries** open.
- The **migration** of people into urban areas **increases** the **mix of people** from different social backgrounds. This can make people **more tolerant** of others, creating a **welcoming environment** that attracts more migrants. However, **segregation** of people from different social backgrounds is also common (see pages 82-83).

Technological
- With the emergence of **factories** in cities, **urban areas** become **hotspots** for **technological advancement**. For example, in the 19th century, **Manchester** became the **first industrialised city** in the world and was branded '**Cottonopolis**' because of its **cotton-processing factories**.
- More recently, areas with a large number of **high-tech industries** have emerged, e.g. **Silicon Valley** in California. These areas attract people because they offer **specialised** and **highly paid jobs**.

Political
- Urban growth may lead to increased **inequalities** between rich and poor people. A new '**working class**' emerges, often made up of people who work in **manufacturing industries**.
- New **political movements** emerge to represent the '**working class**' population. **Political reform** focuses on **issues** that **affect urban life**, e.g. poor sanitation, quality of housing, working conditions in factories.

Demographic
- As **cities** become **larger** and **wealthier**, they **attract migrants** from all over the world. Urban areas become more **culturally** and **ethnically diverse** and **new areas** emerge, e.g. Chinatown in New York City.
- Many **young people** are **attracted** by **jobs** and **entertainment** (e.g. bars and clubs). They often choose to stay and **raise families** in the city, so cities tend to have a **younger population** than rural areas.

Developed Countries Have Experienced Deindustrialisation Since the 1970s

Cities in developed countries have undergone several **processes of change** in the last **fifty years**:

1) **DEINDUSTRIALISATION** — in the **1960s**, some **developing nations**, such as Singapore and Taiwan, became **industrialised**. These countries were able to **produce goods** at a **cheaper price** than Europe or North America, mainly due to **lower labour costs**. By the 1970s, the **developed world** was **struggling to compete** with the products being manufactured in the developing world. Entire **industries collapsed**, e.g. steel in Sheffield, which led to mass **unemployment** and **poverty**. In the UK, **deindustrialisation** caused **unemployment** to rise above **3 million** in 1983. This was the **highest rate** of unemployment since the **Second World War**.

2) **RISE OF THE SERVICE ECONOMY** — during the 1980s, many **service industries** (e.g. retail and banking) began to expand and **dominate western economies**. These industries have been **responsible** for the majority of **economic growth** in developed countries since deindustrialisation.

3) **DECENTRALISATION** — as **land prices** in city centres increase, businesses such as shops and offices may **relocate** to suburbs. This has led to the rise of out-of-town **retail parks**, e.g. Meadowhall near Sheffield. Decentralisation has caused city centre shops and offices to **close** — this has led to buildings being **abandoned**, **job losses** and urban **poverty**.

Urban Change

Since 1979 British Governments Have Tried to Regenerate Cities

There have been **lots of schemes** to improve cities in the UK since 1979:

Urban Development Corporations — 1979-1990s

- By 1979, many UK city centres were in **catastrophic decline**. The government created agencies called **Urban Development Corporations** (UDCs), which used private sector funding to restore derelict areas.
- The first UDCs were established in 1981 in the **London Docklands** and Liverpool. The main aims of the London Docklands UDC were to attract **new businesses**, improve the local **environment**, create **jobs** and build **new houses** for professionals. Between 1981 and 1998, the Corporation built **24 000** new homes and created **85 000** jobs. In addition, the Corporation built **new schools**, **parks** and **community facilities**, including a sailing and watersports centre and Surrey Quays shopping centre.
- By 1993, **twelve UDCs** had been established, helping to redevelop some of the most rundown areas of the country. However, the UDCs were criticised for **ignoring** the needs of **local residents**, e.g affordable homes and suitable jobs.

Enterprise Zones — 1981-Present

- In 1981, **Enterprise Zones** (EZs) were **established** in areas with **high unemployment**. Their aim was to attract **start-up companies** to the area to **create jobs** — they did this by **reducing tax**, e.g. on corporations and land.
- By 1990, the EZs housed over **5000 companies**, employing more than **125 000 people**. However, tax reductions encouraged many **existing companies** to **move** their premises and staff to the EZs, which **limited** the number of **new jobs** that were created.

City Challenge — 1991-1997

- In the **City Challenge** programme, local authorities **competed** for government funding to regenerate deprived urban areas. They worked with the local community and private companies to improve the **physical**, **economic** and **social environment** of the area.
- Funding was allocated to projects that **benefited** the **local community**, e.g. improving housing, providing vocational training and creating jobs for local people. By 1997, over **50 000 jobs** had been created and **40 000 houses** improved. However, many deprived areas didn't receive any **funding**.

Partnership Schemes — 2010-Present

- Since 2010, the government has worked with private companies to provide **financial support** and **expertise** for urban regeneration — these are called **partnership schemes**.
- These schemes are designed to improve **physical**, **economic** and **social** conditions in deprived areas, e.g. by building new **homes**, providing **parks** and **sports centres**, and **reducing unemployment**.
- For example, the **Liverpool City Region Local Enterprise Partnership** was established in 2012 — it aims to increase **business activity** in Liverpool and create new **jobs**.

Peter and Lara's partnership scheme was heading straight for divorce.

Practice Questions

Q1 Give one economic reason why people might move from the country to the city.

Q2 What is deindustrialisation?

Q3 Name three regeneration schemes used by the UK government since 1979.

Exam Question

Q1 Suggest how urban growth might affect the demographic characteristics of a city. [3 marks]

Wonder if I can get funding to redevelop my local area...

Ideally, I'd like to improve my environmental conditions (by replacing the floors of my house with trampolines) and my social conditions (by making life an endless party). You grab the party hats, and I'll start putting together a bid for funding...

Urban Forms

From the smallest city in the world (Vatican City, in case you're wondering) to megacities and world cities (see p.77), every city has its own unique form. Here's a reminder of exactly what that means — try not to get too excited.

Urban Form is Affected by Physical and Human Factors

1) Urban form is the **physical characteristics** that make up a city, including its **size** and **shape**, **population density** and how the city is **arranged** (e.g. **land-use patterns** in different areas).

2) Many cities were initially established in areas with good **water supplies**, **fertile soil** for growing food, plentiful natural **resources** (e.g. woodland for fuel) and good **defensive** positions (e.g. on top of a hill).

3) Over time, the urban form of cities **changes**. These changes are influenced by a number of factors, including:

Physical Factors

- **Topography** — **physical features** often influence the growth of cities. E.g. **steep slopes** are harder to build on and **less accessible**, so poorer housing (e.g. slums) may be built on them. Large **flat** areas encourage **low density** developments because there's lots of space to build.

- **Water** — the presence of **lakes** and seas **limits** urban growth in those areas, while cities may grow **along** the course of a **river**. City centre shops and businesses are usually located close to the **waterfront**, rather than at geographical centre of the city.

- **Natural resources** — rich resources (e.g. coal, metal) **encourage growth** in size and population of cities.

- **Land type** — some ground surfaces are more difficult or expensive to build on than others, e.g. **swamps** and **wetlands** can **limit** urban growth.

Human Factors

- **Planning** — urban expansion can be **planned** or **unplanned**. For example, a lot of urban growth in **developing countries** is caused by the unplanned expansion of **slums**. In contrast, **planned** developments often include open space, leisure facilities etc.

- **Infrastructure** — new developments are often built along **transport links** (e.g. motorways), leading to **linear growth**.

- **Land value** — the **highest** value land is often found in the **city centre**, so **profitable** businesses (e.g. chain stores) normally locate there, while **less profitable** businesses (e.g. independent shops) may be found **further** from the centre.

Cities in the Developed World Have Different Land-Use Patterns...

1) Cities in **developed** countries tend to have a **Central Business District** (CBD) — a central zone of shops and businesses.

2) The CBD is **surrounded by housing**. Although **land value** tends to be **highest** in the city centre, **houses** generally increase in value with distance **away** from the centre:

- **Inner city areas** have **high** land value, so housing is typically **high density**, e.g. **skyscrapers**. Wages are often low, and many residents live in relative **poverty**. The proportion of people from **ethnic minorities** tends to be high.

- Land value is **lower** in rural and semi-rural areas, so residential areas are **less dense** and have more **open space**. **Houses** are usually **larger** and **newer** than those in inner city areas. Residents are generally quite **wealthy** and earn relatively high wages. The proportion of people from **ethnic minorities** tends to be low.

3) Because of the availability of **cheap land** in **semi-rural areas** close to urban centres, many **science parks** and large **shopping centres** are constructed there, e.g. Bristol and Bath Science Park, the Trafford Centre in Manchester.

...To Those in the Developing World

1) Cities in the developing world also have **CBDs** — these zones contain shops, offices and entertainment services.

2) The CBD is surrounded by housing, which **decreases** in **value** with distance away from the centre:

- Land value is **highest** around the city centre, so **high-cost housing** (e.g. luxury apartments) is built there. Wages are generally **high**, and residents are **wealthy**. These areas are often home to **wealthy immigrants** from developed countries and emerging economies.

- Surrounding the high-cost housing there is often a zone of **medium-cost** housing. It may have started as an **informal settlement**, but gradually the housing has been **improved** and some **services** have been provided.

- Land value is very **low** on the **outskirts** of cities, so **low-cost** and **informal** housing is built there, often with **limited access** to services such as clean water and electricity. Most residents have **poorly paid** jobs and **poverty** levels are high. Immigrants from **elsewhere** in the country and from **other** developing countries may settle there.

3) **Industrial areas** are often located along **transport links**, e.g. major roads.

Topic Five — Contemporary Urban Environments

Urban Forms

Cities in Developed Countries Have Seen Recent Changes

Modern urban areas have a **range** of **recent features**:

Town Centre Mixed Developments

- These are areas where **land use** is **mixed** — luxury flats, offices, shops and entertainment facilities (e.g. bars, cinemas, gyms) are all located there, so **residential**, **commercial** and **leisure** uses are combined.
- Developments are **planned** by local councils, often with **private investment**. The aim is to **attract people** back to city centres by giving them opportunities to live, work and relax there.

Cultural and Heritage Quarters

- These areas focus on the **history** or **character** of a city, e.g. Southampton's Cultural Quarter includes SeaCity Museum, which has exhibits about the city's maritime history.
- Such areas are often home to **theatres**, **art galleries** and **historical buildings**.
- They are often developed by **local councils** to regenerate former industrial areas. They attract **visitors**, encouraging **economic development** and creating jobs.

Fortress Developments

- These are developments (e.g. for residential or retail use) with lots of **security**, such as CCTV, guards and high walls. They are often located in **suburban** areas of large cities, and only those with permission can enter them.
- They are designed to give a **safe environment** for families, but they are very **divisive** — only rich people can afford to live in or use them.

Gentrified Areas

- Gentrification is when **wealthier people** move into **rundown inner city areas** and regenerate them by improving **housing**.
- Gentrified areas often have a large range of **services**, e.g. shops and restaurants, and contain **high-quality housing**. However, **poorer residents** may be **displaced** as the cost of living increases, leading to social and ethnic segregation.

Edge Cities

- Edge cities are new areas of **offices**, **shops** and **leisure facilities** that develop close to major **transport links**, e.g. motorway intersections outside city centres, where land is **cheaper**. They often contain some housing, but most people **travel to them** for work or to use the services available.
- The majority of edge cities have developed since the **1950s** and **1960s** as **car ownership** has **increased**. They are most common in the USA, e.g. Las Colinas near Dallas, Texas.

Many Cities Are Evolving to Become Post-modern

Many cities, especially in developed countries, are gradually moving **away** from **uniformity** in **architecture** and from clear-cut patterns of **land use** — these are known as **post-modern western cities**. They have a number of characteristics:

1) **Multiple centres** with different purposes (e.g. high-tech industry, retail, heritage) rather than a single centre.
2) A focus on **tertiary** and **quaternary industry** (e.g. IT, media) instead of secondary industry.
3) Less uniform architecture — buildings have a wide range of styles.
4) Planning **prioritises** the **aesthetics** of the city (how it looks) over practical use.
5) Higher **social** and **economic inequality**.

Many cities have **elements** of post-modernism — e.g. in London, buildings such as the **Gherkin** and **Cheesegrater** are examples of **post-modern architecture**, and social and economic **inequalities** are **growing**.

Practice Questions

Q1 What is meant by the term 'urban form'?

Q2 Give two characteristics of post-modern western cities.

Exam Question

Q1 Assess how far traditional urban forms are being challenged by new urban forms in the developed world. [9 marks]

Move to Las Colinas — live life on the edge...

If you're stuck for something to do tonight, and there's nowt on telly, have a think about a town near you and all the things that give it a unique urban form. Or just watch some footage of cats falling off fences on the internet. Your call.

Urban Issues

With all those people crammed together, it's no wonder cities face social and economic problems...

All **Cities** Face **Economic Inequality**

1) **Economic inequality** is the **unequal distribution** of **money** amongst a **population**.

2) Economic **inequalities** are **higher** in the **developing world** than in developed countries. This is because many developing countries **lack the resources** to **support** their **poorest citizens**, whereas most developed nations have **welfare states** which **provide basic services** and **income** for people who are struggling financially.

3) Economic inequality can cause lots of **issues** in cities, for example:

   - **Political** and **social unrest**, e.g. rioting.
   - A **rise** in **crime**, **drug use** and **violence**.
   - **Health** problems, e.g. cities with **higher levels** of **income inequality** have more **malnourished children**.

"Looks, charm, dress sense... it's not just money that's unevenly distributed," brooded Hugo.

Cities Are **Culturally Diverse** but Often Experience **Social Segregation**

1) Cities tend to be **culturally diverse** — they have a wide mix of people from different **ethnic** and **cultural** backgrounds.

2) This can have lots of **benefits** — ethnic diversity can **enrich** a city's **character** and increase **tolerance**, while cultural events and ethnic quarters within a city can attract **tourists**, boosting the city's **economy**.

3) However, cultural diversity can also cause **problems** in cities, for example:

   - **Tensions** between different groups, sometimes leading to **violence**.
   - Increased pressure on **services**, e.g. schools may need extra staff for pupils who can't speak the native language.
   - Minority communities can feel **isolated** and **under-represented politically**.

4) Cities with high diversity, including people from different **ethnic**, **social** or **cultural backgrounds**, may also experience **social segregation**. This is when different groups are **separated** from each other, e.g. poorer people or people from a particular ethnic background are **concentrated** in a specific area of a city.

5) This can be **voluntary**, e.g. followers of a particular **religion** may choose to **settle** close to their **place of worship**. It can also be **forced**, e.g. many Roma people in Italy can't access social housing, so they end up in **camps** on city outskirts.

6) Social segregation can cause **issues** in urban areas, for example:

   - Lack of integration between different groups can cause **prejudice** and **discrimination**.
   - People in some areas may have less access to **education** and **jobs**, widening **inequalities**.
   - Segregation can lead to **anxiety** and have negative impacts on **health** and **life expectancy**.
   - In developing countries, poorer areas may lack access to **facilities**, e.g. electricity, clean water, public transport. They are also more likely to be close to industry and rubbish dumps, affecting **health** and **wellbeing**.

There Are **Strategies** to **Manage** Urban **Issues**

There are lots of strategies to **reduce poverty** and **economic inequalities** in urban areas:

   - Improving **transport systems** can make it easier for the urban poor to access jobs.
   - Subsidising the construction of **affordable housing** can help less wealthy people to buy property.
   - Introducing **minimum wages** can help to stabilise wage inequalities between the poor and rich.
   - Governments can offer **subsidies** for new companies, increasing local **employment** opportunities.
   - In developing countries, many cities have introduced **upgrading programmes** for slum settlements. Investments in **road-building**, **sanitation**, **drainage** and **water supply** increase the quality of informal housing.

There are also strategies to encourage **social and cultural integration**:

   - Governments can encourage **political participation** of minority groups, e.g. by sending postcards and text messages encouraging them to **vote**. This ensures minority groups have opportunities to influence **decision-making**.
   - Governments can pass **laws**, e.g. to prevent companies **discriminating** against employees on the basis of race.
   - **New developments** can include luxury homes and lower-cost housing, **reducing divisions** between rich and poor.
   - Communities can help ease **racial tensions**, e.g. by involving different groups in projects to clean off racist graffiti.

Urban Issues

London has Tried to Manage its Social and Economic Issues

London, a city in the **developed** world, has issues associated with **economic inequality**, **cultural diversity** and **social segregation**:

1) London is home to some of the **richest** and **poorest** people in the UK — this gap has **widened** since the 1980s.

2) The average annual **income** in Kensington and Chelsea is more than **£130 000**, but in Newham it's less than **£35 000**. Low wages and few job opportunities in some areas mean that more than **25%** of people in London live in **poverty**.

3) Many **inner city** areas, e.g. Notting Hill, have been **gentrified** — this has **forced poorer residents** out of the area.

4) London is culturally diverse — more than 50% of the population is **not white British**. Proportions of ethnic minorities **differ widely** between boroughs — e.g. in **Brent** over **60%** of people are not white British, whereas in **Havering** the proportion is only around **16%**, suggesting that ethnic segregation is an issue.

5) **Hate crime** based on race and religion is a problem in London, e.g. in the twelve months before July 2015, there were over 800 **anti-Muslim** incidents (including verbal abuse and violence) in the city.

6) Social segregation based on **age** and **class** is also an issue — London residents have less interaction with people of different age groups and classes than people elsewhere in the UK. This could lead some residents to feel **isolated**.

There are **strategies** in place to tackle these issues, e.g.:

1) From 2016, the **London Living Wage** increased to **£9.75** per hour (compared to £8.45 in the rest of the country). This should **increase income** and **social mobility** in deprived areas.

2) London mayor, Sadiq Khan, plans to build more **affordable homes** in London — this could allow less affluent people to remain in more expensive areas, **reducing** social segregation.

3) The police are working to tackle **hate crime**, e.g. by encouraging people to **report** it and offering **support** to victims.

4) Some charities are calling for better access to English **language classes** for immigrants, and **mentoring** schemes to help recent immigrants adjust to life in the UK, with the aim of **increasing integration** between groups.

São Paulo is Struggling to Tackle its Issues

São Paulo in Brazil, an **emerging** economy, also has issues of **economic inequality** and **social segregation:**

1) Economic inequality is **high** — the richest 10% of households earn nearly **forty times** more than the poorest 10%.

2) There is clear **segregation** between the richest and the poorest residents:

- The city's poorest residents live in slums (favelas), e.g. 80 000 people live in **Paraisópolis**, São Paulo's largest favela. It has **high crime** rates, **poor sanitation** and high incidence of illnesses such as **cholera**. The favelas **lack educational facilities** — this limits job options and social mobility.

- The wealthiest residents live in the **southwest** of São Paulo, in areas such as **Vila Nova Conceição**. These areas have more **green space**, better **healthcare** and access to amenities such as luxury **shops** and **restaurants**. These areas have large numbers of **white immigrants**, but the **lowest** proportion of **black people** in the city.

There are **strategies** in place to tackle these issues, e.g.:

1) In 2016, the **minimum wage** was raised by nearly **12%**, to increase **income** for the poorest workers.

2) In 2001, the government passed a law that allowed favelas to be recognised as **legitimate** residential areas. This led to investment in **sanitation**, **road building** and **housing improvement** in favelas, e.g. **10 000** new homes are currently being built to **replace** slum housing or housing in high-risk areas.

Practice Questions

Q1 Give two possible consequences of economic inequalities.

Q2 What is meant by 'social segregation'?

Exam Question

Q1 Analyse how social and economic issues can affect the character of cities. [9 marks]

Brown leather, small heel, slightly muddy — these are my urban-ish shoes...

Don't talk to me about managing social issues — I'm just try to arrange a nice birthday dinner, but Helen's fallen out with Raj, and Tom won't speak to Laura after she laughed at his hair. So yeah, I totally get the difficult issues that cities are facing.

Urban Climate

Urban climate characteristics — or 'what the weather's like in cities' to you and me. Geographers and their fancy names...

Urban Areas are Warmer than the Surrounding Rural Areas

1) The phenomenon of urban areas being warmer than rural areas is called the **urban heat island effect**.

2) Urban areas with higher air temperatures than the surrounding rural areas are called **urban heat islands** (UHIs). For example, **London** has a clearly defined UHI.

3) The **highest temperatures** are found in **industrial areas** and in the most **densely built up** areas, e.g. the **CBD** (Central Business District).

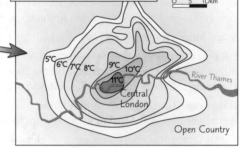

LONDON'S HEAT ISLAND

0 5 10km

5°C 6°C 7°C 8°C 9°C 10°C 11°C Central London

River Thames

Open Country

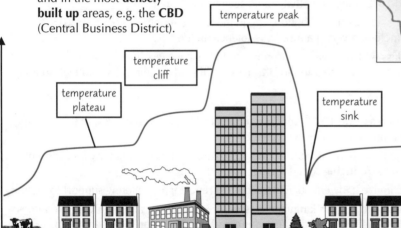

temperature peak

temperature cliff

temperature plateau

temperature sink

Temperature

4) There are **pockets** of **cool air** above **parks** and **bodies of water** (e.g. rivers or ponds). These are called temperature '**sinks**'.

5) Areas within the city with the **same land use** (e.g. industry) generally have the **same temperature**. These are called temperature '**plateaus**'.

6) Temperature can **change rapidly** when **land use changes** (e.g. from inner city housing to CBD high rise buildings). Rapid changes are referred to as temperature '**cliffs**'.

There are Four Main Causes of the UHI Effect

Urban surfaces have a low albedo — they absorb lots of energy instead of reflecting it.

1) **ABSORPTION OF HEAT BY URBAN SURFACES:**
Concrete, brick and tarmac surfaces **absorb** and **store heat from the sun** during the **day**.
They slowly **release** the heat as **long wave radiation** — this is most noticeable at **night**, when it warms the air.

2) **AIR POLLUTION:**
Air pollution from cars and factories **increases cloud cover** over the city. It also creates a '**pollution dome**' — a layer of pollution over the city. Both these things **trap outgoing heat radiation** and **reflect it back** to the surface.

3) **HEAT FROM HUMAN ACTIVITY:**
Cars, factories, offices, central heating, air conditioning units and people themselves all release heat.

4) **LESS EVAPOTRANSPIRATION:**
When it rains the water's quickly removed by **drainage systems**, so there's **little surface water** to **evaporate**. Also, there isn't much **vegetation**, so there's **little transpiration**.
Evapotranspiration uses heat energy, so less evapotranspiration means higher temperatures.

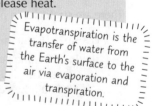

Evapotranspiration is the transfer of water from the Earth's surface to the air via evaporation and transpiration.

The Effect Varies Seasonally and Diurnally (Between Day and Night)

1) The UHI effect is stronger at **NIGHT**. Urban **daytime** temperatures are on average **0.6 °C warmer** than surrounding rural areas, but **night time** temperatures can be **3-4 °C warmer**. This is because rural areas cool down at night, but **urban areas don't cool as much** because **urban surfaces continue to release heat** that they've absorbed during the day.

2) It's stronger in **SUMMER** (in mid-latitude cities like London). Average **winter** temperatures can be **2 °C warmer**, but average summer temperatures can be up to **5 °C warmer**. This is because there's **more solar radiation in summer**, so urban areas absorb more heat.

3) It's stronger when there's an **ANTICYCLONE**. Anticyclones cause **clear skies** and **low winds**. If there are no clouds, **more solar radiation** reaches and heats the ground. **Low winds** mean **warm air isn't blown away**.

Urban Climate

Winds are Affected by Buildings in Urban Areas

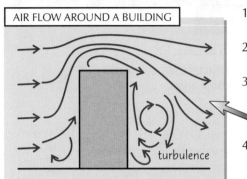

AIR FLOW AROUND A BUILDING

turbulence

1) **Average wind speed** is usually **lower** in cities than in rural areas. This is because **tall buildings create friction** that slows down the moving air.

2) There are areas where **wind speed** is **zero**, because some areas are **totally sheltered** from wind by **buildings**.

3) You get **turbulence around buildings**. This happens when **wind hits** the **face** of a **building** — some of it's **deflected down**, some **around the sides** and some **over the top**. When these winds hit other buildings or the ground they causes **vortices** (bodies of swirling air).

4) You get **powerful gusts** of wind when wind is **channelled down streets** — this is known as the **canyon effect**.

The canyon effect has implications for building design and town planning, e.g. positioning of buildings, and the location of doorways on larger buildings.

There's More Rain, Fog and Thunderstorms...

1) It **rains more often** in urban areas than in the surrounding countryside.

2) The rain is also **more intense** and there are **more thunderstorms**.

3) There are **two** main reasons for these things:

- The **UHI effect** means the air in urban areas is warm, and warm air can hold more water. The **warm, moist air rises** — this is called **convectional uplift**. As it rises it **cools**, the **water vapour condenses** and it **rains**. This type of rain is called **convectional rainfall**.

- Urban areas generate huge amounts of **dust** and **pollution**. Particles of dust and pollution floating about in the air act as **condensation nuclei** (they trigger water to condense around them). This **encourages clouds** to form, rather than allowing the warm, moist air to disperse.

4) The higher concentration of **condensation nuclei** in urban areas also **increases** the **frequency** of **fog**.

...but Less Snow and Frost

1) It **doesn't snow as often** in urban areas, and when it does, the **snow melts faster**. This is because it's **warmer** due to the **UHI effect**.

2) Urban areas have **fewer days of frost** for the same reason.

Darn that UHI effect — now I've gone and got my sleigh stuck.

Practice Questions

Q1 What is the urban heat island effect?

Q2 Briefly describe the four main causes of the urban heat island effect.

Q3 Explain why the urban heat island effect is stronger at night than during the day.

Q4 What effect do urban structures have on average wind speed?

Q5 Why is fog more frequent in urban areas than in rural areas?

	City A	City B
Annual average rainfall (mm)	1200	1300
Average July temperature (°C)	21	23
Average number of thunderstorms per year	18	25
Average number of days with fog	17	23
Average number of days without cloud cover	180	120

Exam Question

Q1 The table on the right shows climate data for two cities.
Analyse the possible reasons for the differences between the two urban climates. [6 marks]

UHI — I'm sure you can buy cream for that...

If you know what causes the UHI effect, you should be able to use your common sense to answer any exam question on it, e.g. if you're asked why parks are cooler than built up areas, talk about the fact that they have more vegetation and less tarmac. If you're asked why one city has a stronger UHI than another think about whether it might be more polluted, or more built up.

Urban Air Quality

Urban air pollution causes a range of pretty horrible health problems. Today, *cough* — sorry. Today, most pollution comes from road traffic. Cities all over the world have tried to solve the pollution problem simply by reducing traffic.

There's a lot of **Particulate Pollution** in Urban Areas

1) **Particulates** are **tiny pieces** of **solids** and **tiny droplets** of **liquids** floating in the air.

2) **More** particulates are found in **urban areas** than in rural areas. The concentration of particulates in urban areas is around 10-40 $\mu g/m^3$, compared to less than 10 $\mu g/m^3$ in rural areas.

3) **Sources** of particulates include:

   - **Vehicle exhausts** — they produce very **fine particulates** (0.01 μm-1.0 μm). About **80%** of fine particulates in urban areas are from vehicle exhausts.
   - **Burning** of refuse, cigarettes and fuel, e.g. coal — this produces both **fine** and **coarse particulates**, e.g. sulfates, nitrates, soot and ash.
   - **Construction**, **mining** and **quarrying** — these activities produce **coarse particulates** (10 μm-100 μm), e.g. tiny fragments of rock, brick and cement dust.
   - **Plants and moulds** — also generate **coarse particulates**, e.g. pollen and mould spores.

   A microgram (μg) is one millionth of a gram and a micrometre (μm) is one thousandth of a millimetre.

4) Particulates can cause **health problems**. **Coarser particulates** are usually **filtered out** by the nose and throat, but **finer particulates less than 10 μm** in diameter (often called PM10) can enter the **lungs**. PM10 could **cause** or **make worse** problems like asthma, bronchitis, lung cancer and heart disease.

Other Types of Pollution Lead to **Photochemical Smog**

1) Pollutants such as **nitrogen oxides**, **sulfur oxides** and **hydrocarbons** come from **burning fossil fuels** (e.g. in vehicles and factories).

2) When these **pollutants** come into contact with **sunlight**, the **UV light** causes them to **break down** into **harmful chemicals** (e.g. ozone) which form **photochemical smog**.

3) Photochemical smog is a **problem** in **many cities**, e.g. Los Angeles (USA), Beijing (China), Mexico City (Mexico) and Barcelona (Spain). It's more common in places with **hot** and **sunny climates** because there's **more sunlight**.

4) These locations often have a **temperature inversion** (a layer of warm air trapped below denser cooler air), which keeps the pollutants at **ground level**.

5) Photochemical smog is linked to **health problems** such as **breathing difficulties** (coughing, shortness of breath), **respiratory disorders** (e.g. asthma) and **headaches**.

Smog over Mexico City.

Ozone is useful in the upper atmosphere (protecting us from UV radiation), but when it's in the lower atmosphere it causes health problems.

There are Lots of Different Ways to **Reduce Air Pollution**

Lots of cities have tried to **reduce pollution** by **reducing traffic**. There are various ways that this can be done:

CONGESTION CHARGING

- **People** are charged if they **use their vehicles** in **certain places** at **certain times**.
- This reduces pollution by **reducing road traffic**. In **Central London** congestion charging reduced traffic and emissions in the congestion zone by around 15% in its first year of operation.
- However, some people **travel around** the edge of **zones** to avoid being charged, increasing traffic in these areas.
- It's hard to enforce the charge because the **volume of traffic** is so large that it's hard to process all the fines correctly.

PEDESTRIANISATION

- **Vehicles are restricted** from **entering certain places** at **certain times**. It reduces pollution by **reducing road traffic**.
- Many cities have pedestrianised zones — including London, Cardiff, Manchester and Liverpool.
- Pedestrianisation can lead to shops receiving **fewer customers** because people can only get to them on foot.

Urban Air Quality

PUBLIC TRANSPORT IMPROVEMENTS

- Encouraging people to **use public transport** instead of their cars reduces pollution. For example, many cities have:

  - **Improved bus services** to make bus journeys cheaper, faster and more efficient. E.g. many cities have introduced bus lanes so buses don't get caught in slow-moving traffic.
  - **Park and ride schemes** (car parks on public transport routes) to make it easier to **access public transport**.
  - **Trams** and **light railway services** which run on lines, so they don't get caught in **road congestion**. They also **pollute less** than **buses**. E.g. The Metrolink in Manchester opened in 1992. It links the city centre to the suburbs and has been very successful — the line to Bury and Altrincham has taken about **2.6 million** cars off the roads.

- Public transport improvements are often **expensive** — e.g. construction of the Metrolink cost over £1 billion.
- New developments can also cause problems — e.g. **park and ride schemes** can shift traffic problems to rural areas.

OTHER SCHEMES FOR REDUCING TRAFFIC

- In **Mexico City** drivers are **banned** from using their cars **one weekday** per week, based on the last digit of their number plate, e.g. number plates ending in 5 or 6 can't be used on Mondays. However, some richer households get around the system by **buying two cars**.
- **Birmingham**, **Bristol** and **London** have council-run **car sharing** schemes to encourage people making the same journey to share a car. However, some people find car sharing inconvenient, or worry about sharing a car with a stranger.

There are **larger scale** ways of tackling urban air pollution too. For example:

LEGISLATION (LAWS)

Laws aim to **reduce pollution** by **limiting emissions** and setting **air quality standards**. For example:
- The **UK Clean Air Acts** of 1956 and 1968 reduced domestic pollution by introducing **smoke control areas** where only smokeless fuels could be burned, and **reduced industrial pollution** by introducing the use of **tall chimneys** (which mean that pollutants are dispersed higher in the atmosphere, so they're less harmful to people in the city).
- The **Road Vehicles Regulations** reduce exhaust emissions by ensuring cars pass an **emissions test** in their MOT.
- In Scotland, legislation allows local authorities to do **roadside emission tests**, where they can **issue fines** if the vehicle fails. Throughout the UK, local authorities can issue fines to people who leave their engines running unnecessarily.

ALTERNATIVE FUELS

Petrol and diesel are replaced with **cleaner fuels** that **pollute less**. For example:
- **Biofuels** (e.g. **bioethanol** and **biodiesel**) are produced from **plants**. They can **directly replace** petrol and diesel, and have **lower particulate emissions**. However, growing the crops needed to make biofuels can **reduce biodiversity**, e.g. biofuels like corn-based ethanol need a lot of land to grow, which means clearing other vegetation.
- **Liquefied petroleum gas** (**LPG**) is a **gas** produced from **fossil fuels** that has **lower emissions** than petrol or diesel. However, cars have to be **converted** to use LPG, and **service stations** have to be **adapted** to distribute it.
- **Electric vehicles** have **lower emissions** because they run off **batteries**, rather than **conventional fuel**. Electric vehicles need **recharge points**, and **producing** and **disposing** of the **batteries** can cause environmental problems.

Practice Questions

Q1 What are particulates?
Q2 How is photochemical pollution produced?
Q3 Why is photochemical pollution more common in hot climates?

Exam Question

Q1 Outline how air pollution in urban areas can be reduced. [3 marks]

Country Mouse came to visit Town Mouse... and died due to poor air quality

Ah, the lesser known version of the classic tale. The health and environmental problems caused by urban air pollution really are serious — make sure you learn about the potential solutions and their drawbacks. If only we could all live in the country...

Urban Drainage

Attention all human geographers — these pages may look a bit too much like physical geography.
But don't worry, there's still plenty of human geography to get your teeth into.

Infiltration is Low and Surface Runoff is High in Urban Areas

1) Urban areas are covered in **impermeable materials**, e.g. concrete and tarmac. Many urban structures are designed to **shed water quickly**, e.g. camber on roads funnels water to drains.

2) This means that **infiltration** is **low** in urban areas, so replenishment of groundwater stores is slow. Groundwater feeds rivers, so during **drier periods**, river **discharge** in urban areas is **low**.

3) **Precipitation** is higher in urban areas than in rural areas, and storms are more intense (see p.85) — this increases surface runoff.

4) **Runoff** is channelled through man-made pipes, which transport water to rivers and streams.

5) **Low infiltration rates**, **high surface runoff** and channelling of water means that water enters rivers quickly. This gives a **short lag time** and **high peak discharge** (see page 8), with a **fast** return to **base flow**.

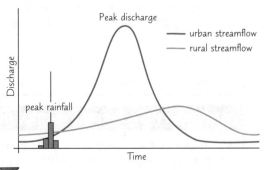

Catchment Management Aims to Reduce Urban Drainage Issues

1) **Catchment management** is a way of managing rivers and improving drainage systems by looking at the **whole** river catchment, and the **interactions** between water and land.

2) It aims to minimise issues such as **flooding**, **drought**, **water pollution** and **erosion** in sensitive areas, and to improve **river ecosystems**.

3) There are two main methods that can be used to **manage river catchments**:

- **Hard engineering** — this involves man-made structures such as **dams**, **floodwalls** and **reservoirs**, which are often used to prevent **flooding** and ensure a constant **water supply**. However, hard engineering schemes are often **expensive** and can **disrupt natural systems**, e.g. silt can be trapped behind dams, starving downstream areas of sediment and increasing erosion. They can also alter wildlife **habitats**, e.g. dams can prevent salmon migrating upstream to breed.

- **Soft engineering** — this uses knowledge of the river basin and its **processes** to try to **work with nature**. It involves **land use management**, e.g. planting trees to decrease flood risk and water pollution, and preventing building on the flood plain. It can also involve **river restoration and conservation** (see next page). It is generally **cheaper** than hard engineering, and it can **improve** the local environment. However, **planning restrictions** can limit the construction of new homes and businesses, and land use management is hard in areas that are already urbanised.

4) Decisions about what methods to use are made by **experts** in water management rather than **residents** — what is best for the catchment as a whole may not be best for all individuals, so some residents and communities may feel **ignored**.

5) Catchment management schemes can also be **disruptive** — e.g. construction of the **Three Gorges Dam** in China flooded 13 cities and 140 towns, forcing over **1.2 million** people to move.

Catch men?
Man-agement?
James didn't
like the sound
of this.

SUDS can Make Urban Drainage More Sustainable

1) **Sustainable Urban Drainage Systems** (SUDS) aim to imitate **natural** drainage systems, rather than channelling water through pipes and drains. They use several methods to decrease **flooding**, **water pollution** and **drought** in urban areas:

- **Vegetated trenches** increase interception of rainfall, and **retention basins** store water. They help to increase infiltration and water storage — this **decreases runoff** and **channel flow**, which lowers **flood risk**. Increased infiltration also decreases the amount of **pollutants** entering watercourses.

- **Vegetated roofs** intercept rainfall and increase **evapotranspiration**, which reduces **flood risk**.

- **Containers** on the roofs of buildings catch and **store rainwater** for reuse. This helps to reduce **drought risk**.

2) SUDS are **more sustainable** than traditional urban drainage methods because they **work with** the **natural environment** to improve drainage and water quality. Vegetated trenches and roofs also provide new **habitats** and increase **biodiversity**.

Topic Five — Contemporary Urban Environments

Urban Drainage

Enfield is Restoring its Water Systems

1) River **restoration** and **conservation** aims to restore river systems to a more **natural** state. It can help to reduce **flood risk**, decrease **water pollution**, create new **habitats** and increase **biodiversity**.

2) One area that is restoring its rivers is **Enfield**, north London. Enfield has had **regular floods**, e.g. in 2006, 2007 and 2008.

3) The area is heavily **urbanised** — this has caused **problems** for drainage and water quality, including:

- The spread of urban structures has **increased surface runoff** and channel flow, e.g. in the River Lea. This has increased the frequency and intensity of **floods** — over **9000** homes in Enfield are at risk of flooding.
- Surface runoff from roads has increased levels of **pollutants** such as oil and heavy metals in watercourses.
- Water pollution also comes from **domestic sources** — up to **10%** of houses in Enfield have wastewater pipes (from e.g. toilets, showers and dishwashers) that feed **directly** into rivers.

4) In 2012, a project began to **restore** rivers in the area, with the following **aims**:

- **Reduce flood risk** and limit the **impacts** of flooding on habitats and residential areas.
- **Reduce surface runoff** from roads and pollutants entering rivers in order to improve **water quality**.
- Provide more **habitats** for wildlife and new **recreational areas** for residents.

5) The project has used **SUDS** to help restore river systems and meet these aims, for example:

- **Vegetated trenches** have been created around roads to **absorb runoff** and decrease **flood risk**.
- **Rain planters** have been installed in schools — these collect rainwater and **manage** the **flow of water** into drains, lowering flood risk. This also provided opportunities to **educate** children about water management.
- **Wetlands** have been constructed to improve **water quality**. E.g. reed beds were created around Salmons Brook to decrease surface runoff from roads and **filter** water before it enters the river.

6) Lots of **groups** have been **involved** in the project, for example:

- **Defra** and **Thames Water** are providing **funding**. In 2012, Defra granted **£340 000** to the project to construct more SUDS.
- **Local residents** — reactions from the community have been **very positive**. Volunteers have been involved in **water quality monitoring** and **litter pickups**.
- **Local schools** — Thames21 offers education sessions for local schools to **increase engagement**. In 2015, **1000 students** were involved in litter picking and wildlife monitoring.

Defra is the Department for Environment, Food and Rural Affairs.

7) The project is ongoing, but it's had some **successes** already:

- **Flood risk** seems to be **reduced** — e.g. high rainfall in December 2013 and January 2014 did not cause significant flooding in Enfield.
- SUDS have reduced **ammonia** levels in Salmons Brook by 67% and **nitrogen** levels by 43%.
- Populations of **eels** and some species of **insects**, e.g. dragonflies, have increased.

8) However, **pollution** and **litter** are still an issue in many rivers.

Practice Questions

Q1 Give two reasons why surface runoff is higher in cities than in rural areas.
Q2 Give one issue that catchment management can cause in urban areas.

Exam Question

Q1 Assess the extent to which river restoration and conservation can reduce urban drainage issues. [9 marks]

When I hear the word 'revision', I always runoff...

So that's that — your one-shop, whistle-stop, tip-top guide to urban drainage. Read back over these pages until they're as familiar as your favourite pair of socks. It's more likely you'll get a question on this stuff than on your favourite socks, too.

Urban Waste

Urban waste may sound like a load of rubbish. But there's a lot of important stuff on this page, so keep focused...

There Are Three Primary Sources of Waste in Urban Areas

1) **Industrial waste** — any waste that has been produced in the **manufacturing** process or from **industrial** activity, e.g. in power plants or building sites. Industrial waste can include scrap metal, solvents and chemicals, which can be **toxic** or **corrosive**.

2) **Commercial waste** — any waste that is produced by **businesses**, e.g. shops, restaurants, offices. Commercial waste often includes food, paper, cardboard and plastics.

3) **Personal waste** — any waste produced by **private homes**. This can include plastic bottles, food packaging, newspapers, food waste, etc.

CGP Moral Guidance Tip #31 — your younger brother doesn't count as personal waste.

Types of Waste and Methods of Disposal Vary Between Countries

1) Globally, the largest components of waste are **organic material** (46%), **paper** (17%), **plastic** (10%) and **glass** (5%). The majority of waste is easy to manage, but some material is **hazardous**, e.g. medical waste.

2) A **waste stream** is the **flow** of waste from its **origin** through to its eventual **disposal**:
   - Some products (e.g. paper, glass) can be **recycled**.
   - Others need to be **broken down** into their component parts and each part disposed of **separately** (e.g. by recycling, sending to landfill, processing to extract useful chemicals or metals, or treating to reduce risk).

3) Waste streams and components of waste vary depending on **many factors**, including:

(1) Economic Characteristics

- As people get **richer**, they tend to consume more goods. This means that **developed** countries produce **more waste** (**2.1 kg** per person per day) than **developing** countries (**0.6 kg** per person per day).

- The **components** of waste also vary depending on the development level of the country. In developed countries, the main components are **paper** (31%), **organic material** (28%) and **plastic** (11%). In developing countries, the largest components are **organic material** (64%), **plastic** (8%) and **paper** (5%).

- **Waste streams** vary between countries, but there is **no clear-cut link** to wealth. For example, Austria recycles 63% of all waste, whereas Japan only recycles 21%. Most developing countries do not have **formal** recycling systems, but many people collect recyclable goods from landfill and sell them to **make a living**.

(2) Lifestyles

- **Amount** and **type** of waste produced varies depending on whether people live in the city or the country — **urban** dwellers produce **more waste** than **rural** residents. People in rural areas produce **more organic** waste (e.g. food), and people in cities produce more **manufactured waste** (e.g. plastic, glass).

- The **facilities** available to people affect the **waste streams** they use — for example, people are more likely to **recycle** waste if recycling facilities are easily **accessible**, and if authorities **encourage** them to.

- **Diet** is likely to affect waste **components** and **streams** — e.g. producing **processed food** creates waste, and finished products tend to come in a lot of **packaging**. In contrast, fruit and vegetables tend to produce more **compostable waste** (e.g. vegetable peelings) and **less packaging**.

(3) Attitudes

- Many developed countries have a **throw-away culture** — e.g. electronics are replaced regularly, and clothing may be bought, worn a few times then thrown away. This results in high levels of waste, much of which cannot be **recycled** or has a long and **complex waste stream**.

- Increasing concerns about **health** may cause people to throw away food that is near or just past its **sell-by date**, resulting in high levels of **food waste**.

- People have different attitudes towards the **environment** — people who are concerned about the environmental **impacts** of excess waste are more likely to **reuse** or **recycle** waste.

- In some groups, there has been a recent move towards a decrease in **consumption** and **waste**. For example, many **freegans** forage for food, including **salvaging** it from supermarket bins, **repair** broken goods and **give away** things they don't need, instead of throwing them away.

Urban Waste

There Are **Many Ways** to **Manage Urban Waste**

There are **lots** of **methods** of **waste disposal**, all of which have environmental impacts:

1) **UNREGULATED** — waste is **dumped** in places that aren't official disposal sites — e.g. solid waste is left on the street, or untreated liquid waste enters water courses. Waste that isn't properly disposed of can **damage ecosystems**, e.g. if chemicals from it enter the environment. **Animals** and **birds** can be harmed if they swallow or get tangled in plastic waste.

2) **RECYCLING** — waste is **reprocessed** into **new** products, e.g. plastic bottles can be turned into fleece jumpers. Recycling **reduces demand** for **raw materials**, which decreases the environmental impacts of resource extraction, e.g. deforestation. Producing recycled products generally uses **less energy** than making them from scratch, so less **greenhouse gases**, such as CO_2, are emitted. However, recycling requires **separate collections** and the construction of **new facilities** to process waste — these contribute to **greenhouse gas emissions** and **air pollution**.

3) **INCINERATION** — this is when waste is **burnt**. It **reduces** the amount of waste going to landfill, but it emits **greenhouse gases** and causes **air pollution**. Waste that is burnt can be used to generate **electricity** — this is called **energy recovery**. This reduces use of **fossil fuels**, but burning some waste can release **toxic chemicals** into the air or water.

4) **RECOVERY** — this involves using **waste** instead of **new products**, e.g. waste concrete can be crushed and used as a base for new roads and buildings. This **reduces** the amount of waste being sent to landfill and means that fewer **natural resources** are exploited because goods are reused.

5) **BURIAL (LANDFILL)** — waste is placed in disused **mines**, quarries or **landfill sites**. Many sites are **lined** with e.g. clay or plastic to prevent leaching of chemicals into the environment, but if sites are not properly regulated, hazardous chemicals can contaminate **groundwater**, while gases such as methane from decomposing waste cause air **pollution**. Some countries collect gases for **energy production**, reducing air pollution and fossil fuel use.

6) **SUBMERGENCE** — disposing of waste by dumping it in **oceans** is illegal, but it is still common in some areas, e.g. off the coast of Somalia. Submerged waste can release **toxic** or **radioactive** substances, damaging ocean **ecosystems**.

7) **TRADE** — waste can be **bought** and **sold** by countries. For example, developed countries may pay developing countries to take their **hazardous waste**. However, developing countries may not dispose of hazardous waste safely, meaning that it can **damage** local environments, e.g. heavy metals can **pollute groundwater** and local watercourses.

Singapore Has Moved From **Landfill** to **Incineration**

1) Singapore is an **island** off Malaysia. It is almost entirely **urban**. The amount of **waste** produced in Singapore increased from **1260 tonnes per day** in 1970 to **8400 tonnes** in 2015. **Land** is **scarce**, so waste management is important.

2) In the 1960s and 1970s, most waste was sent to **landfill sites** around the city. However, in the late 1970s the government changed their main waste disposal method to **incineration** with **energy recovery**.

3) The first incineration plant was constructed in **1979**. Today, there are four plants across the city, which provide about **3%** of Singapore's **energy needs**. Each incinerator is fitted with **pollution control systems** to limit greenhouse gas emissions.

4) Singapore now has only one landfill site, Semakau, which was built on reclaimed land between two small islands. It is lined with an **impermeable membrane** and a layer of **clay** to prevent leaching of chemicals. Once each area of the site is full, it is covered with topsoil to support vegetation. The landfill is now home to rare species, e.g. Malaysian plovers.

5) Singapore's waste disposal systems are effective. In 2015, only **2% of waste** was sent to **landfill** — **38%** was **incinerated** and **60%** was **recycled** (recycling facilities were built in 2001). Only waste that **can't** be recycled or burnt goes to landfill.

6) However, pollution control systems cannot remove **all** harmful emissions from **incinerators**, and incinerators only last around **ten years** before they need to be replaced. The current landfill site is expected to be **filled** by around **2040**.

Practice Questions

Q1   What are the three main sources of waste in urban areas?

Q2   Briefly describe how economic development affects urban waste.

Exam Question

Q1   Evaluate the environmental impacts of different approaches to urban waste disposal.   [9 marks]

Waist recovery — that's what the post-Christmas diet is for...

We can all do our bit towards environmentally friendly waste disposal — for example, you could write your revision notes on scrap paper and then recycle them once you've passed your exam. Just make sure you read them carefully in the meantime...

Urban Environmental Issues

As if problems with climate, drainage and waste aren't enough, cities also have issues with air pollution, water pollution and dereliction. But there's no need to panic just yet — there are loads of ways to fix these problems...

Urban Atmospheres Are Being Polluted by Human Activities...

1) Atmospheric pollution is often a **problem** in **urban areas** (see pages 86-87).

2) In many **developed** countries, reliance on **fossils fuels** is **decreasing**, and use of less-polluting energy sources (e.g. natural gas) is increasing. As a result, **air quality** in many cities has **improved since 1950**. However, **car ownership** is **increasing**, and congestion can cause significant atmospheric pollution.

3) Many **developing** countries and **emerging** economies still rely heavily on **fossil fuels** to meet their energy needs. **Increases** in **industrial activity** and **car ownership**, combined with a **lack of regulation** of emissions, mean that atmospheric pollution is often severe.

4) In many developed countries, there are **strategies** to **limit air pollution**, such as promoting **'green' modes of transport**, e.g. cycling, and expanding **green spaces** (e.g. parks) in urban centres. Other strategies are outlined on pages 86-87.

5) In the developing world, there has been **some progress** towards reducing urban air pollution. For example, most countries have phased out the use of **leaded petrol**. However, **progress** is **slow**.

Yep, I've got this green transport thing licked.

...and so are Urban Rivers and Streams

1) Water pollution is also common in cities (see pages 88-89). There are several reasons for this:

   - Cities have a **high population density**, so they produce a lot of waste. This includes **wastewater** and **sewage**, as well as **oil** and **metals** on road surfaces from cars. These pollutants can enter **watercourses**, e.g. if sewers are inadequate, or in runoff when it rains.
   - Many cities have a high concentration of **factories**, which may **discharge** industrial waste into watercourses.

2) Water pollution can cause **damage** to **ecosystems**, and **contaminated drinking water** can cause **health problems**, e.g. dysentery and cholera.

3) Water pollution can be managed through **laws** to stop discharge of untreated waste from industries and provision of plants to treat wastewater. Strategies such as **catchment management** and **SUDS** can also help (see page 88).

4) In **developed** countries, there are strict **regulations** about discharge of untreated water, and water quality is **monitored**. However, **litter** dropped in or around water and pollutants in **surface runoff** still cause pollution.

5) In many **developing** countries and **emerging** economies, there are **few regulations** and inadequate provision of **treatment facilities**. This means that untreated industrial waste and sewage often enter watercourses and water pollution is **common**.

Litter in the River Tees in Stockton.

Urban Dereliction can Impact on Local Environments

1) **Urban dereliction** happens when **economic activity** in urban areas **declines** and buildings become run down. It often follows a pattern:

   - The **movement** of **manufacturing overseas** and the **decentralisation** of industry leads to industrial decline. Many unemployed people **leave** urban areas in **search of work**.
   - If lots of people leave the area, shops may be forced to close and services go into decline. As industry, people and services move out, they leave **empty buildings** — e.g. factories, homes and shops.
   - Empty buildings and derelict areas often have problems with **vandalism**, **graffiti** and **crime**.

2) Urban dereliction is more **common** in **developed** countries where widespread deindustrialisation has occurred.

3) Strategies to manage urban dereliction include the **redevelopment** of former factories into **commercial** and **residential properties**, the construction of **new housing** in derelict areas and the creation of **green spaces**, e.g. parks.

4) However, some cities **lack investment** and large areas remain derelict, e.g. Detroit.

Topic Five — Contemporary Urban Environments

Urban Environmental Issues

Bangkok Has Lots of Environmental Issues

Bangkok is in Thailand, an **emerging** economy. Lack of regulation and poor planning has led to **environmental problems**:

Air Pollution
- A rapid rise in **car ownership**, coupled with poor vehicle maintenance, is causing high levels of air pollution. In 2011, some pollutants, e.g. benzene, were more than **three times** acceptable levels in some areas.
- In the early 21st century, air pollution caused around **5000 premature deaths** per year in Bangkok.
- The government has taken steps to reduce air pollution, including improvements to **public transport**, such as bus lanes and a new subway. Drivers can be **fined** if their cars are found to emit high levels of exhaust fumes.

Water Pollution
- Poor **sewage systems** and ineffective **waste management** mean that water pollution is severe. River water contains **unsafe** levels of ammonia and coliform bacteria, which come mostly from **human waste**.
- Since the 1960s, there have been various plans for **improving** sewage systems in the city in order to reduce pollution levels in the rivers. However, these plans have been too **expensive** to implement.

Dereliction
- A lot of buildings in Bangkok were left **half-finished** when Asia experienced a **financial crisis** in 1997. Some have since fallen into disrepair, and suffered from **vandalism** and **graffiti**.
- However, **economic growth** since 2010 has led to the **completion** of many unfinished buildings. The government offers incentives for **foreign investment** — this may help to decrease the number of empty buildings.

Manchester has Overcome Many Environmental Issues

1) Manchester is in the UK, a developed country. During the **19th** and **early 20th centuries**, Manchester was **very polluted**. Factories and mills produced huge amounts of greenhouse gases and industrial waste, which polluted **air** and **water**.

2) **Deindustrialisation** and **strategies** to improve the urban environment have had a big impact on the city:

Air Pollution
- **Closure** of factories and better **management** of air quality has **reduced** air pollution. This has reduced the frequency of **illnesses** associated with poor air quality, e.g. bronchitis.
- **Cars** are the largest contributor to air pollution in Manchester today. To reduce car use, the local government is improving **bus services**, constructing **cycle paths** and expanding **pedestrian walkways** across the city.

Water Pollution
- Until the late 20th century, the River Irwell and Manchester Ship Canal were badly polluted by **industry** and **sewage**. Since 1987, extensive work has been done to clean up these waterways, e.g. by increasing the **oxygen** content of the water, encouraging **aquatic plant growth** and collecting **litter**.
- To reduce water pollution caused by **surface runoff** from roads, the local government is installing **SUDS** (see p. 88), e.g. green areas and porous pavements have been installed in Salford Quays.

Dereliction
- In the late 1980s and early 1990s, **deindustrialisaton** and **job losses** had caused many people to leave the city. The city centre was **underpopulated** and many shops and residential areas were **abandoned**.
- Large-scale **redevelopment** of the city began in **1996**. Former mills and factories were **converted** to luxury flats, **open spaces** were improved and funding was provided for **new businesses**, such as the Lowry Gallery in Salford Quays. From 2001 to 2011, the population of the city centre nearly **tripled** to around **18 000**.

Practice Questions

Q1 Give one cause of urban air pollution.

Q2 Briefly describe one strategy to manage water pollution.

Exam Question

Q1 Outline how urban dereliction can be managed. [3 marks]

Noise pollution from snoring — a major environmental issue in exam halls...

It may seem like there's a lot to take in on these pages, but it's worth learning — Geography examiners love it when you can relate theoretical issues to the real world using facts and figures. Almost as much as they love tweed jackets with elbow patches.

Sustainable Urban Development

I know it seems like cities have a million and one problems. But there's still hope — with a bit of effort, cities can become clean, green, energy-efficient models of sustainability. Well, maybe...

Urban Areas Have **Environmental Impacts**

1) Cities **impact** on the **environment** at a **local scale**, for example by increasing **air pollution** (see pages 86-87), **water pollution** (see page 88), **flood risk** (see page 88) and by generating large amounts of **waste** (see page 90).

2) Urbanisation also causes **loss** of **open space** in and around cities, resulting in loss of habitats and biodiversity.

3) At a global scale, cities increase **demand** for **resources** such as **food**, **water** and **energy**. Cities are home to around half the world's population, but account for about **three-quarters** of **resource use**. This is putting **pressure** on **finite resources**, leading to food, water and energy insecurity.

4) Cities are also responsible for about **60%** of **greenhouse gas emissions**, which contribute to climate change.

Many Factors Influence a **City's Ecological Footprint**

1) An individual's **ecological footprint** is the amount of land that is needed to produce **everything** they consume, e.g. food, water and fuel, and to absorb their **waste**. The ecological footprint of an **area combines** the footprints of its **residents**.

2) The ecological footprint of a **city** depends on a range of factors, including:

   • **Wealth** — e.g. **consumption** and **waste production** is **higher** in cities in richer countries.

   • **Size of city** — e.g. **compact** cities are easier to travel around on foot or by bike, so they produce **less pollution**.

   • **Quality of public transport** — **efficient** public transport systems decrease car use, and therefore reduce **pollution**.

There Are **Many Ways** Urban Areas Can be **Sustainable**

Clive hoped his tightrope would prove physically sustainable.

1) To be sustainable, a city must meet the **needs** of people **today** without preventing **future generations** from meeting their **needs**.

2) There are different **dimensions** to sustainability — how sustainable a city is depends on its **natural**, **physical**, **social** and **economic** characteristics. Sustainable cities have a range of **features**:

1) Natural

• Natural sustainability is about how the **environment**, **resources** and **waste** are managed.

• Cities with a high level of natural sustainability rely on **renewable energy** sources (e.g. wind). They produce relatively little **waste**, and **reuse** or **recycle** the waste they produce.

• Cities where people **walk**, **cycle** and use **public transport** a lot produce **less pollution**, so they are more sustainable.

2) Physical

• Physical sustainability is about **how well** a city is able to **support** the people living there.

• To be sustainable, a city must provide enough **resources** to **support** the population and let them be **productive**, e.g. have jobs.

• Features of physically sustainable cities include plentiful **high quality housing** and **secure supplies** of nutritious **food**, safe **water** and **energy** for all residents.

3) Social

• Social sustainability is about how people **live together**, their **quality of life**, and the availability of basic **services**, e.g. healthcare.

• Cities offer good living conditions for all residents, with **access** to basic **services**, e.g. hospitals, schools etc. are within easy reach.

• Socially sustainable cities are **peaceful**, **tolerant**, **respect human rights** and are politically stable.

4) Economic

• Economic sustainability is about maintaining **economic growth** without causing long-term **negative effects**, e.g. environmental damage, social inequality.

• Cities with high levels of economic sustainability are **wealthy**, have low levels of **inequality** and **little debt**. They are home to **profitable**, **ethical** businesses that offer plenty of **well-paid jobs**.

3) Sustainability can affect the **liveability** of a city — this is a measure of how good **living conditions** in an area are.

4) Liveability depends on many factors, including **job opportunities**, **crime rates**, **open space** and access to **education**. Different factors matter more to **different people**, so everyone's **view** of what makes a city liveable will be different.

Sustainable Urban Development

There are Opportunities to Make Cities More Sustainable...

There are several **factors** that make **sustainable development** of urban areas easier than rural areas, including:

1) People are more **densely concentrated** in cities than in rural areas, so the **provision** of services such as clean water and public transport is **easier** and **cheaper**.

2) Understanding of the **importance** of **urban sustainability** has increased — this has encouraged **more research** and **investment** into how urban areas can be made more sustainable.

3) Governments may **invest** more in **urban** sustainability initiatives than **rural** ones, because they benefit **more people**.

... But There Are Also Challenges

Increasing urban sustainability can be **difficult** — there are many reasons for this, such as:

1) It requires significant **investment**, which many cities **cannot afford**.

2) Many cities are **growing**, so public services need to expand rapidly to meet the needs of a larger population.

3) Some people are **unwilling** to **change** their **habits**, e.g. driving less or using less water.

4) Some cities don't have appropriate **infrastructure**, e.g. roads may be **too narrow** to build **cycle lanes**.

In the **developing world**, **urbanisation** is **happening** at a **faster rate** than in the developed world, and growth is often **unplanned** — this makes it **harder** to **increase** urban **sustainability**.

There Are Lots of Strategies for Increasing Urban Sustainability

Different **strategies** for increasing sustainability are used in different cities:

1) **Reducing the number of cars on the road** — strategies can include constructing new **cycle lanes**, introducing **park and ride schemes** and improving **public transport provision** (see pages 86-87 for more strategies). E.g. in Freiburg, Germany, cycling routes, pedestrian-only zones and a light rail system have reduced car use.

2) **Increasing the amount of green space** — green spaces, e.g. parks, can reduce **pollution** and increase **biodiversity**. Programmes such as **river clean-ups**, **wetland restoration** and **tree planting** can provide **habitats** for wildlife.

3) **Improving urban waste disposal** — many cities have introduced measures to **reduce** the amount of **waste** being **sent to landfill**. These include expanding **recycling facilities**, converting to **incineration with energy recovery** (see p. 91) and encouraging people to **compost** green waste.

4) **Increasing renewable energy use** — using **renewable energy sources**, such as wind and solar power, **decreases** fossil fuel use and carbon emissions. For example, UK and Welsh governments are currently considering building a **tidal lagoon** in Swansea Bay to supply renewable energy to the UK.

5) **Reducing water use** — authorities can insist that new buildings are fitted with **water meters** and **water-efficient fittings**, and ensure that people use less water. E.g. in Cape Town, South Africa, water pressure was **reduced** so that showers, hosepipes etc. would use less water.

6) **Making buildings more energy efficient** — governments can offer **incentives** to encourage homeowners and businesses to improve the **insulation** in buildings, install **solar panels** and use **energy-efficient** light bulbs.

I'm a big fan of renewable energy.

Practice Questions

Q1 Give one way that cities impact on the environment on a global scale.

Q2 What is a person's ecological footprint?

Q3 Briefly describe two challenges to urban sustainability.

Exam Question

Q1 Assess the extent to which cities can be made sustainable. [9 marks]

Reusing toilet paper — when sustainability goes too far...

Sustainable living does seem like a chore — we'd have to change our lifestyles quite dramatically in order to be entirely sustainable. But even doing a little bit, e.g. recycling paper or using less electricity, can make a massive difference.

Mumbai — Case Study

Cities in the developing world are growing faster than in the developed world. This means that some — like Mumbai — have grown very rapidly and are facing significant social, economic and environmental issues.

Mumbai Has Many **Social** and **Economic Inequalities**

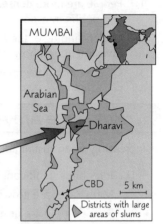

Dharavi is one of the largest slums in Mumbai and is home to more than 1 million people.

1) **Mumbai** (formerly Bombay) is a **megacity** (see p. 77) on the west coast of **India**.

2) Mumbai is **globally important** — it is a major **port** on the Indian Ocean, India's **financial centre** and a hub of **industry** and **services**. The city is also a **cultural centre** — it's home to the **Bollywood** movie industry.

3) Migrants from **rural** areas of India have moved to Mumbai in search of jobs. The population of Mumbai **increased** from **5.9 million** in 1971 to **20.7 million** in 2016.

4) This rapid urbanisation has created a number of social and economic **issues**:

- **More than half** of the population live in **poverty** in slums — these cover large areas of the city. **Living conditions** in the slums are poor — homes are **cramped** and **poorly built**, often without water supply or sanitation. The **lack of toilet and sewage** facilities is a risk to **health** (e.g. raw sewage spreads disease).

- In contrast, over a **quarter** of all India's **millionaires live in Mumbai**. The urban rich **live close** to Mumbai's **CBD**, usually in **high-rise apartments**. Some of the richest districts of Mumbai include **Bandra** and **Andheri**, both of which offer **amenities** such as shopping centres, restaurants and private hospitals.

- There are also **inequalities** in **education** — literacy rate is around **60%** in the slums, compared to about **90%** in the city as a whole. Literacy rates are **lower** for **women** than for men.

- There are **few opportunities** for **women** in **slum areas**. With **no qualifications**, some women resort to **prostitution** to earn a living. This leads to **higher rates** of **HIV** and other **STIs** among **poorer communities** than in wealthy areas.

- Only around **30%** of slum residents have access to **public healthcare**. Outbreaks of **disease** (e.g. malaria and dengue fever) are common, and the **infant mortality rate** is relatively high (26 deaths per 1000).

- Psychological problems such as **depression** are more common in **slum areas** than in richer districts.

- As Mumbai has developed economically, there has been an influx of **African migrants**. Many have experienced **racial discrimination** — e.g. they struggle to find formal jobs or rent apartments, and are forced to live in **slums**. They also face **racial prejudice**, including **verbal abuse** and greater risk of **arrest** by police.

Despite these inequalities, 42% of Mumbai's residents class themselves as very happy with life.

Mumbai is **Vulnerable** to **Natural Disasters**

1) Mumbai is at risk of **flooding**. There are several reasons for this:

- India has a monsoon climate — a long dry season is followed by a period of intense rainfall. Mumbai has one of the highest amounts of annual precipitation in India — average precipitation in July (monsoon season) is **960 mm**.

- Five rivers flow through Mumbai, including the Dahisar and Mithi. Mumbai has limited room to expand, so many new developments have been built on floodplains.

- Mumbai experiences tropical storms, which bring heavy rain and may cause storm surges.

In **July 2005**, monsoon rains caused the **Mithi River** to burst its banks — the flooding killed about **400** people and left thousands homeless. Flooding of drainage systems caused water contamination and an increase in **waterborne diseases**, e.g. cholera and leptospirosis, which killed more people.

2) Mumbai is also vulnerable to **tectonic hazards**:

- It is located in a seismically active area, so it is at risk from **earthquakes** (although they are quite rare).

- Earthquakes can cause tsunamis (see p.64) — Mumbai is low-lying, so a tsunami could cause extensive damage.

3) **Slum areas** are more **vulnerable** to natural disasters than richer areas. Slums have **poorly constructed houses** and are often built on **floodplains** — e.g. 70% of the Mithi River's embankments are occupied by informal settlements.

Mumbai — Case Study

Current Conditions in Mumbai are *Unsustainable*

1) Most slum areas in Mumbai **lack adequate sanitation** — this is causing **water pollution**. Contaminated water is contributing to the spread of **illnesses** such as hepatitis, and reducing local fish populations.

2) Mumbai's water supply is dependent on the **monsoon rains**, and in dry years water has to be strictly **rationed**. As population increases, **demand** for water grows — this is unsustainable in the long term.

3) The **road network** in Mumbai carries millions of cars each day. There are problems with **long journey times**, **congestion** and **air pollution**.

4) **Economic growth** is leading to the construction of factories and increased car ownership — there are around 450 more vehicles on Mumbai's roads **every day**. This is adding to air pollution, and Mumbai regularly suffers from **acid rain**.

5) The increasing population produces **more waste**. This can cause problems, e.g. in the neighbourhood of Chembur, waste on open rubbish dumps is burnt, adding to **air pollution**. This has **health impacts** on local residents, e.g. **25%** of deaths in Chembur between 2008 and 2010 were caused by **respiratory problems**.

6) **HIV** and **AIDS** rates are **increasing** in Mumbai, putting extra pressure on **healthcare** services. HIV/AIDS-positive people regularly face **discrimination** — e.g. some have been **refused treatment** in hospitals, **sacked** from their jobs or **prevented** from entering communal areas.

There are Efforts to Make Mumbai *More Sustainable*

The Indian government, local authorities and non-governmental organisations are working on **strategies** to make Mumbai a **cleaner**, **safer** and more **pleasant** place for residents. For example:

1) In 2004, the government first announced a **redevelopment project** to clear the Dharavi slum and create a new independent township. Plans include building new **apartments**, a **water** and **sewage** system, **hospitals** and **schools**. Some residents of Dharavi **object** to the redevelopment — it's an established community with successful industries, e.g. **recycling** rubbish from all over the city, and residents are worried that the redevelopment will destroy their **livelihoods** and the **community spirit** of the area.

2) To increase water security, the local authority has made **rainwater harvesting** systems (collecting rainwater from rooftops) compulsory on all **new residential buildings** in Mumbai on plots larger than 300 m². However, since 2007 only **half** of the eligible buildings have actually installed rainwater harvesting systems.

3) Mumbai's **public transport** system is being upgraded, with the aim of improving air quality. In 2011, the World Bank provided **$1 billion** of funding to **upgrade roads**, **rebuild** train tracks and purchase more **fuel-efficient buses**. However, many families have had to be **relocated** to make space for upgraded roads.

4) The **Clean-Up Mumbai Campaign** is cleaning up the streets by clearing litter and **educating** local residents and shopkeepers about **how to recycle** and **dispose of waste** to limit environmental damage.

5) The National AIDS Control Organisation runs **condom promotion campaigns** in Mumbai to reduce HIV rates. New government legislation plans to make it **illegal** to discriminate against HIV/AIDS-positive people.

Practice Questions

Q1 Give one reason why Mumbai is at risk of flooding.

Q2 Briefly describe one way that conditions in Mumbai are environmentally unsustainable.

Exam Question

Q1 "For every problem caused by urbanisation there is an effective solution."
To what extent do you agree with this view? [20 marks]

Poverty management strategy #12 — win the lottery...

Phew — the first case study of the section and it's a bit of a whopper. Mumbai is a big city with some big problems — make sure you learn the issues with urbanisation and sustainability thoroughly. Oh, and everything else on these pages as well...

Birmingham — Case Study

From the sun-drenched, monsoon-battered slums of Mumbai to the... well, slightly less exotic Birmingham.
On the plus side, there's a lower risk of contracting cholera if you end up doing fieldwork there.

Birmingham *is a* Post-Industrial City *in the* UK

1) **Birmingham** is a city in central England. It is a political, social and economic **hub**. In the 19th century, the growth of metalworking and heavy industry caused a **boom** in **population** and **economic growth**.

2) During the 1970s and 1980s, Birmingham suffered from **deindustrialisation**. The **decline** of the metalworking industries led to widespread **unemployment**, **poverty** and **dereliction**.

3) **Urban regeneration** programmes have helped to **redevelop** Birmingham's city centre (see next page). However, the city still suffers from **social** and **economic issues**:

- Birmingham is **divided** into **rich** and **poor** areas. The poorest areas tend to be close to the city centre, e.g. Sparkbrook and Aston, whereas richer areas tend to be further from the centre in more **rural areas**, e.g. Sutton Coldfield.

- The average **income** in Handsworth, the poorest area of Birmingham, is **£19 000** per year, compared to **£37 000** in Edgbaston, the richest area.

- More than **100 000 children** in Birmingham live in **poverty**, and many families rely on **food banks**.

- Average **life expectancy** is **8 years lower** for **men** and **6 years lower** for **women** in the **most deprived areas** of Birmingham than in the least deprived.

- Around **6%** of people in Birmingham are **unemployed** — unemployment is higher in **poorer areas** such as Hodge Hill (10.7%) than in richer areas, e.g. Sutton Coldfield (1.6%).

- **Crime rates** in Birmingham city centre are high. In 2016, an average of around **1100 crimes** were reported **every month** — the most common crimes were **anti-social behaviour** and **shoplifting**. In comparison, only about 270 crimes a month were reported on average in Edgbaston.

- Birmingham's **population** is **ethnically diverse** — in 2011, around 40% of the population were **non-white**. The **largest** minority **groups** were **Pakistanis** (13%), followed by **Black or Black British** (9%). There are **social** and **economic inequalities** between ethnic communities. For example:

  - **Life expectancy** is **higher** in **areas** with a majority white population than in minority communities.

  - **White families** are **more likely** than minority groups to **be homeowners** — 64% of white people own their home, compared to 48% of Bangladeshis and 29% of Black Africans.

  - Many ethnic minorities face **prejudice** and **discrimination**, e.g. verbal abuse and difficulty finding a job.

Birmingham's *Physical Environment Affects* Environmental Sustainability...

Birmingham's **environment** has **improved** since the industrial decline of the 1970s and 1980s, but there are still **issues**:

1) **Air pollution** — some areas of central Birmingham have very **poor** air quality, e.g. high levels of **nitrogen dioxide**, which is produced by burning fossil fuels (e.g. in **cars** and **factories**). Air pollution can cause acid rain — this may contribute to **acidification** of rivers and canals, which can **harm aquatic life**.

2) **Water pollution** — many rivers and streams in Birmingham are very polluted. Pollution comes from surface **runoff** from roads, wrongly connected **drains** and incorrect disposal of waste such as **engine oil**. High levels of pollution have reduced populations of some species of **insects**, with **knock-on effects** on other wildlife.

3) **Lack of green space** — central Birmingham has relatively little **green space**. This reduces the city's ability to absorb greenhouse gases and other pollutants, and to moderate its climate (see p.84).

4) **Flooding** — lack of green space also contributes to high **surface runoff** and **flash flooding**. Flooding can increase erosion and deposition of sediment, which can damage **ecosystems**, e.g. by silting of fish breeding habitats.

5) **Urban waste** — Birmingham produces **3.2 million tonnes** of **waste per year**. The majority of waste is sent to **landfill** or incinerated — only around **25%** is **reused** or **recycled**. This is adding to air and water **pollution** in the city (see p.92).

6) **Extreme weather events** — Birmingham has a **temperate** climate with relatively little extreme weather. However, extreme events seem to be increasing in **frequency** — recent events including storms, drought and tornadoes.

Birmingham — Case Study

... And Has Impacts on *Residents*

Birmingham's physical environmental conditions affect the **social sustainability** of the city and people's **experiences** of living there:

1) High levels of **air pollution** can cause **respiratory** problems, e.g. bronchitis, and worsen conditions such as asthma. Air pollution is linked to over **500 deaths** in Birmingham each year.

2) Lack of **green space** impacts on the **health** and **well-being** of residents — levels of **obesity** in Birmingham are high, and around **40%** of adults who don't do enough exercise claimed they would exercise **more** if they had better access to attractive open spaces.

3) **Flooding** causes **damage** to **properties** and businesses. For example, heavy rainfall in June 2016 flooded hundreds of **houses**, disrupted **train services** and forced several **schools** to close temporarily.

4) Extreme **weather events** can also cause damage to property, e.g. in 2005 a **tornado** damaged hundreds of houses — over 100 families were **evacuated** and there was about **£50 million** of damage. Heatwaves and icy conditions also cause **health problems**.

5) Some parts of Birmingham, e.g. Aston, have large numbers of **derelict buildings**. These can be targets for **vandalism**, and some residents feel **unsafe** in abandoned areas.

There Are Attempts to *Increase Sustainability*

Birmingham City Council is **redeveloping** the city to increase its sustainability. They have **four key objectives**:

1) **Improve transport links** — the council is expanding New Street **train station** and constructing **cycle lanes**. This will help to **limit** the number of **cars** in the city centre, reducing **air pollution**.

2) **Redevelop derelict areas** — there are ongoing projects to **regenerate** derelict areas, e.g. by demolishing abandoned buildings and building new ones. For example, the council is undertaking extensive **redevelopment projects** in Eastside, including **restoring** canal-side properties for residential use and creating new **museums** and **art galleries**.

3) **Increase green spaces** — the council is creating new **parks** and green areas to improve the local **environment**, limit **air pollution**, reduce the **risk of flooding** and provide habitats for **wildlife**.

4) **Improve waste management** — there are plans to decrease the amount of waste going to **landfill**, e.g. by encouraging **composting** and expanding facilities for **recycling** and **energy recovery**.

The redevelopment of Birmingham's city centre has changed its **character** and people's **perceptions**:

1) **Regeneration** of derelict areas and creating a more **pleasant** urban environment is attracting people back to the city. Since 2004, the city's population has **increased** by about **10%**.

2) **Redevelopment** of city centre shopping areas, e.g. the Bullring, has increased the number of people **visiting** — Birmingham is now the second most popular **shopping** destination in the UK, after London.

3) Birmingham has become a major **tourist destination** — about **37 million people** visited the city in 2014. Visitors are drawn to the city by its **industrial heritage**, e.g. canals and historic buildings. Campaigns by **Visit Birmingham** have also raised national and international **awareness** of the city, e.g. by marketing the city's German Christmas markets.

Practice Questions

Q1 Briefly describe some of the social and economic issues in Birmingham.

Q2 Give three ways in which environmental sustainability in Birmingham is being improved.

Exam Question

Q1 To what extent do you agree with the view that urban issues affect poorer communities more than richer ones?   [20 marks]

Get the defibrillator — we need to revive the city centre...

If you've studied different cities and want to use them in the exam instead, that's fine. I mean, just because I've gone to all this effort tracking down everything you need to know and putting it in pretty boxes, don't feel you need to use it. No, no, it's fine.

The Concept of Place

Geographers are interested in the location of places, and also all the things that contribute to the characteristics and perceptions (what people think and feel) of those places — this is the study of the concept of 'place'.

Place is More Than Just Location

1) A place can be thought of as a **location** which could be plotted on a **map** or defined by a **grid reference**, e.g. latitude 51.5074°N, longitude 0.1278°W (London).

2) But this doesn't tell us anything **about** that place, i.e. what it's like, who lives there or how it has changed.

3) So to help them study places, many **geographers** use a **broader definition** of the term '**place**'. The idea is that 'place' is made up of **all** the things that **come together** to make a place **what it is**:

> - Its **location**.
> - The **physical characteristics** of the landscape, e.g. the topography or physical features.
> - The **human characteristics** (who lives there and what they're like) plus the human features of the landscape, e.g. the land use or the built environment.
> - All the things that **flow** in and out of that place, e.g. people, money, ideas, resources.
> - The **sense of place**, i.e. the **emotional meanings** the place has, either to individuals or groups of people. For example, an individual may think of a place as 'home', and they may share that sense of place with the other members of their family.

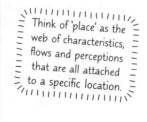
Think of 'place' as the web of characteristics, flows and perceptions that are all attached to a specific location.

4) Apart from location, all aspects of places and the meanings they have are **constantly changing**:

> - The **physical characteristics** of a place can change over **long time scales**, e.g. as rivers migrate, or **short time scales**, e.g. when a volcano erupts and alters the landscape.
> - The **human characteristics** of a place can change over **whole lifetimes**, e.g. as new people are born in a place and others die, or **shorter time scales**, e.g. as people migrate in and out of a place.
> - The **flows** in and out of a place change, e.g. flows of money could change when a multinational corporation (MNC) invests in a new factory or decides to close an existing factory.
> - The **sense of place** individuals or groups have may change, e.g. the places a person played in as a child will not have the same meanings to that person when they return there as an adult.

5) Different groups or individuals may also have a **different sense** of the **same place**. For example, one person may think of a city centre as a place of excitement and opportunity, whilst another person may think of it as a place of stress.

Place can Create Insiders and Outsiders

1) The idea of place is important because many people create their **identity** (the sense of who they are) based on the places that they feel **connected** to, e.g. a person may consider coming from Manchester to be a part of who they are.

2) This is because individuals **share characteristics** that they feel bind them together as a group, creating a **shared identity** for all the people from that place. This can be seen at a variety of scales:

> - **Local** — e.g. the individuals from a village sharing a positive sense of that village.
> - **Regional** — e.g. the individuals from a region sharing an accent.
> - **National** — e.g. the individuals of a nation sharing a language, religion or a love for that nation.

3) Relating identity to **particular places** means that people can be perceived as **belonging** to those places or not. This is the idea that people are '**insiders**' or '**outsiders**' in particular places:

> - An **insider** is someone who is **familiar** with a place and who feels **welcome** in that place, i.e. they feel that they **belong** there. E.g. residents of a country, who all share the same cultural values, may feel like insiders in that country.
> - An **outsider** is someone who feels **unwelcome** or **excluded** from a place, i.e. they **don't** feel that they **belong** there. E.g. international immigrants, who don't share the same cultural values as the residents of a country, may feel like outsiders in the country they move to.

4) There are many **factors** that can make a person feel like an insider or an outsider, e.g. **age**, **sexuality** or **gender**. For example, a young person may feel like an outsider in a retirement village, and an elderly person may feel like an outsider in a nightclub.

The Concept of Place

People *Can Have a* Sense *of Place for* Experienced *or Media Places*

People can have a **sense of place** for places they've **been to**, and places they **haven't been to**.

- **Experienced places** are places that people have spent time in. When a person visits or lives in a place their **experiences**, such as the things they see and the people they meet, shape their **sense** of that place.
- **Media places** are places that people have **not been to**, but have created a **sense of place** for through their depiction in **media** (e.g. books, art and films).

A person's **sense** of a media place can be very **different** to the **lived experience** of the same place — this is because the media may present a place in a **particular way** and for a **particular purpose**. E.g. tourist websites may present holiday destinations such as the Caribbean as a place of relaxation and opulence, but the reality for people who live there may be that it is a place of poverty and hardship.

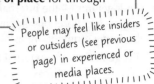
People may feel like insiders or outsiders (see previous page) in experienced or media places.

Places *can be* Categorised *as Near or Far*

1) **Near places** can be thought of as **geographically near** to where a person lives, and **far places** as **distant** from where a person lives.

2) People are more likely to feel like **insiders** (see previous page) in near places, as they are more likely to have **experienced** them and feel **comfortable** in them.

3) Not **all** people will feel like insiders in **all** geographically near places though — people may feel **excluded** from near places for **many reasons**, e.g. their age, gender, sexuality etc.

4) People are more likely to feel like **outsiders** in far places, as they are less likely to have **experienced** them and feel **comfortable** in them.

5) In more recent decades, **globalisation** (the process of the world's economies, political systems and cultures becoming more closely integrated) has affected people's **experience** of geographical distance:

- Improvements in **travel technology** mean that far places are **quicker** to get to, and can therefore be experienced more **easily** and **frequently**.
- Improvements in **ICT** mean that people can be very familiar with **media places** — places they have no lived experience of.
- People can also remain **closely connected** with **people** and **activities** in far places via the **Internet**.

6) So it's **increasingly likely** today that people may feel closely **connected to**, and even like **insiders**, in places that are geographically far away.

7) **Global companies** and **products** also mean that far places can feel **very similar** to near places, e.g. city centres in different parts of the world may have all the same chain stores, selling the same products.

8) Geographers use the term '**placelessness**' to describe how globalisation is making distant places look and feel the **same**.

Practice Questions

Q1 Define the term 'insider'.

Q2 What is a media place?

Q3 Briefly outline the effect of globalisation on people's experience of far places.

Exam Question

Q1 Explain what geographers mean by the concept of 'place'. [3 marks]

This is no plaice for a bad fish joke...

I know there are a lot of definitions on these two pages, and some of them might be a bit tricky, but you will be expected to know all of them for the exam. Examiners are mean like that. So put your reading eyeballs back in and get cracking...

The Character of Places

Here's a bit more about the main factors that give places their character — the physical and human characteristics, plus the flows in and out of them. Take a look back at page 100 to remind yourself of the definition of 'place' if you need to.

Places are **Shaped** by **Endogenous** and **Exogenous Factors**

All places have a unique **character** which is formed by their many different **characteristics**. These factors can be classified as **endogenous** or **exogenous**:

1) **Endogenous** — the **internal** factors which shape a place's character. These could be **physical**, e.g. its location, topography and physical geography, or they could be **human**, e.g. the land use, built environment, infrastructure and demographic and economic characteristics.

2) **Exogenous** — the **external** factors which shape a place's character, including the **relationship** to other places and the **flows** in and out of a place, e.g. the flows of people, resources, money and ideas.

Many **Endogenous Factors Influence** the Character of **Places**

Endogenous factors can include the **physical characteristics** of the landscape. For example:

Location

1) Location refers to **where** a place is, e.g. on the coast or inland, in a rural or urban area, at a bridge point or a confluence of roads.

2) Places can be characterised by the **features** that are present **because** of their location, e.g. a coastal place may be characterised as a port due to its direct proximity to the sea. An inland place may not be a port, but could be a local centre of trade if it was located at a confluence of road routes.

Jack didn't think his character had been influenced by his location at all.

Topography

1) Topography refers to the **shape** of the landscape.

2) Places can be characterised **directly** by their topography, e.g. in a valley, places would be characterised as flat, whereas in a mountainous region, places would be characterised by steep slopes.

3) Topography also affects **other factors** that give places their character. E.g. land use — flat places may be suitable for large-scale arable farming (crops), whilst mountainous regions may be suitable for certain types of pastoral farming (grazing animals).

Physical geography

1) Physical geography refers to the **environmental features** of a place, e.g. altitude, aspect, soil and rock type.

2) Places can be characterised **directly** by their physical geography, e.g. a place could have igneous, sedimentary or metamorphic rocks, which form different landscapes.

3) Physical geography also affects **other factors** that give places their character. E.g. economic characteristics — a place that is rich in natural resources such as iron or coal may be characterised by the industries that can exist there, such as mining or smelting.

Endogenous factors can also include the **human characteristics** of a place and the **activities** that occur there. For example:

Land use

1) Land use refers to the **human activities** that occur on the land, e.g. farming, industry, leisure, residential use etc.

2) Land use is one of the most important human factors in **directly defining** the character of places, e.g. a place could be thought of as rural if the land use is farming, or urban if the land is used for commercial businesses.

3) Land use also affects **other factors** that give places their character. E.g. the built environment — high-rise, high-density buildings are often required for businesses in city centres, whereas residential and leisure land uses often require a lower density built environment.

4) Land use **changes over time**. For example, processes such as deindustrialisation can lead to industrial land use being replaced by other land uses, such as housing or recreation.

Deindustrialisation is the process of manufacturing industries declining in wealthier countries.

The Character of Places

Built environment and infrastructure

1) The built environment refers to aspects of places that are **built by humans**.

2) Infrastructure specifically refers to the **structures** built for **transport**, **communications** and **services**, e.g. roads, phone and broadband networks and sewer systems.

3) Places can be characterised **directly** by their built environment and infrastructure, for example:

- Town and city centres will have **higher density** buildings, may have **tower blocks** and are likely to have **complex** and **dense** networks of roads and railtracks, as well as **communications** networks and sewers. They may have other built features such as **sports stadia** or **cathedrals**.

- Villages will have **fewer**, **smaller** buildings at a **lower density** and **less complex** infrastructure networks. They may have built features such as **market squares** or **village halls**.

Demographic and economic characteristics

- Demographic characteristics are about **who** lives in a place and what they're **like**. Demographic factors include things like age, gender, education level, religion, birth rates, ethnicity and population size.

- Demographic factors can **directly contribute** to the character of places, e.g. many people retire to seaside locations, which means they can have higher proportions of older people. Seaside places may then be characterised as 'old' places (i.e. places where older people feel like insiders, and younger people feel like outsiders).

- Economic characteristics are factors to do with **work** and **money**, e.g. income, employment rates and the types of job available.

- Economic factors can **directly contribute** to the character of places, e.g. places such as Kensington in London have a high proportion of above average earners and low unemployment and as such are characterised as wealthy.

Processes such as gentrification — where wealthy people move into run-down areas and improve the housing — change the built environment, demographics and economics of places over time.

Exogenous Factors are External to Places

Exogenous factors are about how places are **related** to other places, and how these relationships can **affect** their **character**. Places can be **connected** by things like **relative location** and by flows of **people**, **resources**, **money** and **ideas**:

1) The character of places can be **influenced** by their relative location to **other places**. For example, villages and towns outside major cities can be characterised as commuter settlements — people live in the villages for the nice environment, but work in the city where there are greater employment opportunities.

2) Tourism **influences** the **character** of many places. For example, the land use and economic characteristics of Las Vegas are affected by tourism — the casinos and hotels are there for the tourists, and these create employment opportunities for local people.

3) Flows of investment **affect** the **character** of places. For example, Japanese car manufacturer Nissan has a factory in Sunderland. The flow of investment from Japan has influenced some of the characteristics of Sunderland, including the land use around the factory, the built environment of the factory and the type of employment available.

4) Migration can **influence** the **character** of places. For example, parts of the UK have an ethnically diverse population due to migration from other parts of the world. This gives some places their unique demographic characteristics, e.g. 27% of the population of Birmingham are of Asian descent.

Practice Questions

Q1 What are exogenous factors?

Q2 Name three endogenous factors that influence the character of places.

Exam Question

Q1 Outline how physical geography can influence the character of places. [3 marks]

Exogenous Factor — for geographers who dream of making it big one day...

It's a lot to take in, but here's a tip. Think about the place where you live, and what it's like — work out how these endogenous and exogenous factors have contributed to creating that character. You'll be crystal clear on the subject before you know it.

Changing Places — Shifting Flows

As you may have guessed from the topic title, places are always changing. On these pages we'll take a closer look at how flows in and out of places can affect their characteristics, causing the places to change over time.

External Flows cause Places to Change

1) Places are **constantly changing** because all the factors that create their character are constantly changing (see p.100).

2) Historically, the character of a place was heavily affected by the **local (endogenous)** factors of that place, e.g. mining towns developed in places with natural resources, or towns were built at naturally defensive points, such as on bends in rivers.

3) The original character of many places has **changed** because of the **external (exogenous)** influences that have occurred **over time**, e.g. flows to and from places of things like people, resources, money and ideas.

4) In recent history, flows of **people**, **money**, **resources** and **ideas** between places have **increased** — this is because of improvements to **transport**, which have made it easier for people and goods to be transported, and **communications** (e.g. the Internet), which allow people to communicate with anyone else on the planet **instantly**. These flows have caused more places to become more **strongly connected** to each other, and over increasing distances — this is **globalisation**.

5) You need to focus on how the flows of people, resources, money and ideas have affected <u>either</u> the **demographic** and **cultural** characteristics <u>or</u> the **economic** and **social** characteristics of places.

Demographic Change is Caused by Shifting Flows

1) Demographic characteristics are to do with **who** lives in a place and what they're **like** — they include factors such as age, gender, education level, religion, birth rates, ethnicity and population size (see p.103).

2) The demographic characteristics of places can **change** due to the effects of **changing external flows**:

- **Flows of people** can change **any** of the demographic characteristics of a place, e.g. the age or gender balance. For example, on a **local** scale, younger people have been **leaving** the town of Uckfield in East Sussex as they are **unable to afford** to buy a house in the area, leaving an increasingly high proportion of **older** people. On an **international** scale, there are concerns that the **large-scale** migration from North Africa to Europe that started in 2015 altered the **gender balance** of some host towns, as a high proportion of the migrants are **male**.

- **Flows of money and investment**, either by **governments** or **businesses**, can change the demographic characteristics of places. For example, governments can invest money in specific places in order to **attract people** to **live** there. In the UK, the **London Docklands Development Corporation** was a group set up by the government in 1981 to **redevelop** the Docklands area of London. The schemes undertaken by the LDDC improved the **economy** and the **built environment**, which resulted in an **increase** in population in the area — between 1981 and the early 21st century the population more than **doubled**.

- **Flows of ideas and resources** — ideas such as the use of **birth control** can flow to new places and affect their demographic characteristics, e.g. by **reducing** the birth rate and affecting the **population size**. For example, many of the poorest countries in the world have the **lowest** usage of birth control and **rapid population growth**. International organisations such as the UNFPA (United Nations Population Fund) have been set up to spread **knowledge** and **ideas** about birth control, as well as **supplying** resources to aid birth control, such as **condoms**.

These Flows Also Affect the Cultural Characteristics of a Place

1) The cultural characteristics of places are to do with **how** people **live their lives**, e.g. the foods, customs, clothing, traditions, language, art, attitudes, beliefs and values people have.

2) The cultural characteristics of places can **change** due to the effects of **changing external flows**:

The Commonwealth is a group mostly made up of former British Empire territories.

- **Flows of people** — new people **moving** to a place, or even **visiting** it, bring their **culture** with them, which can **change** the characteristics of the place. E.g. in the 20th century the UK experienced mass international **migrations** from India, Pakistan and other Commonwealth countries. This has created **multi-ethnic** communities in many places, where there is a **greater mix** of languages spoken, religions practised and foods eaten.

- **Flows of money, investment and ideas** — new **cultural ideas** introduced to places can **change** the characteristics of those places, e.g. **fast food** companies from the USA such as KFC®, McDonald's and Pizza Hut® opened restaurants in **China** in the 1980s and 1990s and have **grown rapidly** since. It is thought that **eating habits** have changed in China as a result, with **increasing numbers** of people favouring western-style fast food over traditional Chinese food.

Changing Places — Shifting Flows

Economic Characteristics are Affected by Many Different Flows

1) The economic characteristics of places are to do with **work** and **money**, e.g. income, employment rates and the types of job available (see p.103).

2) The economic characteristics of places can **change** due to the effects of **changing external flows**:

- **Flows of people** — people visiting places can **change** the economic characteristics of those places, e.g. St Ives in Cornwall used to be a **fishing** settlement, but is now a popular **tourist destination**. The flows of tourism (combined with a decline in the fishing industry) have altered the **types of jobs** available in the area to **service-based** jobs in hospitality, shops and restaurants.

- **Flows of resources** — the outward flow of **local products** or **natural resources** from a place can have a large impact on local economies. Products that may once have been consumed **locally** or **regionally** can now be sold to **global markets**, e.g. the Scottish whisky industry has grown to be one of the **largest industries** in Scotland due to international **exports**. This has brought **employment** and **money** to a wide range of places across Scotland, including **remote** island communities where many distilleries are located.

- **Flows of money and investment** can have **positive** and **negative** impacts on the economic characteristics of places. E.g. **reduced** investment and competition from global markets has led to the **decline** of some primary industries in the UK (**deindustrialisation**), which has **damaged** the economies of many places. For example, thousands of jobs were lost in South Wales when many coal mines were **closed** between the 1950s and 1980s. **Inward** flows of investment can have **positive** effects though, e.g. investment in the **finance** industries in the City of London has created many **high value** service sector jobs and made it a **wealthy** place.

These Flows also Affect Social Inequality

1) The social characteristics of places are to do with what people's **lives** are **like**, e.g. their overall quality of life, their access to adequate food supplies, healthcare, education, sanitation, leisure facilities etc.

2) **Social inequalities** are the **differences** in these factors between different **groups of people**.

3) Social characteristics and inequalities in places can **change** due to the effects of **changing external flows**:

- **Flows of people** — regional **migration** from **rural** areas to **urban** areas in poorer countries has changed social characteristics and levels of social inequality. E.g. in India, large-scale rural to urban migration has resulted in **slums** (illegal, overcrowded settlements that often lack basic services) developing in cities such as Mumbai. The migrants often have a **very low** quality of life, without access to electricity, sanitation or clean water — this **contrasts** with the **high** quality of life that **wealthier** residents in these cities have, and this gap is **widening**.

- **Flows of resources** — the **outward** flow of **natural resources** from poorer countries can change levels of social inequality. E.g. large amounts of **oil** are extracted around Warri in Nigeria then **exported** round the world, but most of the **wealth** that is generated goes to a **few individuals** who have a **high** quality of life, while **large numbers** of people remain in **poverty** with a **very low** quality of life.

- **Flows of money and investment** — the process of **gentrification** (where wealthier people buy property in run-down areas and improve the housing) has **improved** the social characteristics of some places, but it can also **increase inequality**. E.g. Notting Hill was once one of the **most deprived** areas in London, but now has much **lower** levels of deprivation. As the area has changed though, social inequality between the wealthy newcomers and existing poorer residents has **increased**.

Practice Questions

Q1 Give one example of how shifting flows of ideas have affected the cultural characteristics of a place.

Q2 Give one example of how shifting flows of money have affected the economic characteristics of a place.

Exam Question

Q1 Analyse how shifting flows have affected **EITHER** the demographic and cultural characteristics **OR** the economic characteristics and social inequality of a place you have studied. [9 marks]

External flows — nothing to do with going to the loo...

The trouble with this lot is that there's so much of it. Flows of this and that affect these characteristics... and maybe these too... and don't forget about these. Nothing for it but to get your brain box in gear and set a course for Revisetown, USA.

Changing Places

Use the external force... this page is about the external forces that cause change and affect the character of places. The next page is about how places have been shaped by their connections to other places and the way they developed in the past.

External Forces are Driving Changes in Many Places

You need to know about **at least one** of the **external forces** below, and how they can affect the **demographic**, **cultural**, **economic** and **social** characteristics of places.

Government policies

- Governments can directly affect the **demographic** characteristics of places, e.g. by introducing policies to **control population**. In China, the **one-child policy** was introduced as a method of **reducing** rapid population growth, but in France the government introduced policies (such as lower taxes and better maternity leave conditions) to **increase** the birth rate. Both were **successful** at altering the demographic characteristics of their countries.

- Other government policies can affect the **cultural** characteristics of places, e.g. by **controlling immigration**. For example, in the 1960s the German government **invited** Turkish people to **live** and **work** in Germany — many people migrated and stayed **long term**. As a result, aspects of Turkish culture have become a **part** of German culture, e.g. Turkish fast food outlets are common across Germany, Turkish is the second most widely spoken language and Islam is widely practised.

- Some government policies can affect the **demographic**, **economic** and **social** characteristics of places. For example, governments can fund schemes aimed at **regenerating** run-down urban areas. In 1992 in Manchester, the **Hulme City Challenge Partnership** rebuilt houses, created a new park, refurbished shopping areas, built an arts venue and a business park. This scheme led to an **increase** in the population in the area, created jobs, reduced unemployment and increased quality of life for some residents.

Decisions of multinational corporations

- The decisions of MNCs can have **major impacts** on the demographic, social and economic characteristics of places. For example, **Detroit** in the USA was a major global centre of **car manufacturing** in the early and mid 20th century, with MNCs such as Ford, General Motors and Chrysler all located there.

- The investment from the MNCs gave the city a **massive economic boost** — large numbers of **jobs** were created, many of which offered comparatively **high wages**.

- This altered the **demographic** characteristics of the city by attracting large numbers of **migrants**, both from the USA and other parts of the world — the population **grew** to a peak of around **1.8 million** in the 1950s.

- After the 1950s, many of the manufacturing MNCs **closed** or **relocated factories** to places with **cheaper labour**, such as Mexico. These decisions had a number of effects:

  - Massive **population decline** — the population of Detroit at the 2010 census had reduced to around 700 000.

  - Huge **reductions** in **employment** — at the 2010 census, 24.8% of the workforce in Detroit was unemployed.

  - **Social deprivation** — Detroit has some of the highest crime rates in the USA.

D. Trout, at your service — car manufacturer extraordinaire.

Impacts of international or global institutions

- The **World Food Programme** (WFP) is an international organisation that provides **food assistance**, often as emergency **aid**, wherever it is needed. The WFP affects the social and demographic characteristics of places by ensuring that people have **enough food**, and preventing **deaths** from famine and starvation. For example, there has been intense conflict in **Yemen** since 2015, which has meant that millions of people don't have **regular access** to food. The WFP has distributed **food aid** to millions of malnourished people.

- The **World Bank** is an international organisation that **invests in**, and helps to **set up**, thousands of **projects** round the world that are aimed at **reducing poverty**. Many of these projects affect the demographic, cultural, economic and social characteristics of the places where they are set up. For example, between 2010 and 2016 the World Bank provided funding for the **Ningbo New Countryside Development Project** in Ningbo, China. This project improved the **social conditions** in the area by providing wastewater disposal services to 144 rural villages that previously had no wastewater collection or treatment services.

Changing Places

Past and Present Connections and Developments Shape Places

1) **Connections** between places in the **past** shape their **character** in the **present**, e.g. for centuries London and New York have been connected to each other and other major cities by **sea trade routes**. These connections helped them to become more **wealthy**, attract more people, and be more **closely linked** to other cultures. They gradually became **world cities** — global centres of trade, politics, finance and culture often with huge, diverse populations.

2) **New connections** are made between places in the present which can affect their character. E.g. London and New York have made new connections which **strengthen** their character as world cities — they are now more closely connected through industries such as **finance** and **banking** because of the **internet** and **faster air travel**.

Take a look back at pages 76-79 to remind yourself about urbanisation and urban change.

3) The way in which places **developed** in the **past** also strongly affects their **character** in the **present**. For example, the past development of cities shows how their present-day character was created:

- Many settlements in the UK **initially developed** because of factors to do with their **location** (endogenous factors, see page 102). E.g. Sheffield originally located at the confluence of two rivers, near to coal and iron ore reserves — these would have been important factors for the early development of industry.

- During the **Industrial Revolution**, large industrial cities developed that were **globally connected** through the trade of the goods produced. This resulted in large-scale rural to urban **migration** as people moved to the cities in search of work in the factories. Today, these old industrial centres **remain** as large cities, e.g. Sheffield became a major centre of the steel industry, trading items such as cutlery all round the globe. The work available in the steel industry attracted workers and made Sheffield a major population centre.

- In the later part of the 20th century, many UK cities were heavily affected by **deindustrialisation** — the closure of factories due to increased automation, competition from abroad and the removal of manufacturing to developing countries where labour is cheaper. These cities **remained** as large population centres, but were **less well connected** globally due to the loss of trade, and suffered **economic** and **social decline**. E.g. the steel and mining industries collapsed in Sheffield in the 1970s and 1980s, which resulted in factories being abandoned, mass unemployment and a reduction in population.

4) The **character** of places is shaped by a **mix** of all the **connections** and **developments** they have undergone throughout their **history**, and the **present-day** connections and developments that are occurring. For example, the character of Sheffield is now a mixture of its **industrial past** and the **redevelopment** work that is being done today:

- Sheffield is still characterised as an **industrial city** — steel works such as Sheffield Forgemasters still supply steel to **international markets**, and the heritage of the city has been retained by creating a **conservation area** (the Cultural Industries Quarter) to preserve historically significant roads and buildings. New **art installations** around the city, such as the Cutting Edge sculpture, also reflect the industrial character of the city.

- **New connections** have been made that add to the character of Sheffield — today it is also characterised as a **student city**, with over 50 000 students in two universities, and a place of **academic** and **research excellence** (both universities have strong international academic reputations).

- The city has developed and made new connections in **high-tech industries**, e.g. the Advanced Manufacturing Research Centre (AMRC) carries out research into cutting-edge manufacturing techniques. In 2017, the car maker McLaren Automotive announced that it will build a plant near to the AMRC to build carbon fibre chassis for its new vehicles.

- Sheffield City Council has been **re-branding** the city as '**The Outdoor City**'. The aim is to encourage **tourism** and **boost events** surrounding activities such as running, cycling, climbing and walking.

Practice Questions

Q1 Give one example where the decision of an MNC has affected the character of a place.

Q2 Briefly outline how the past development of a place can influence its character.

Exam Question

Q1 Analyse the impact of **EITHER** government policies **OR** the decisions of multinational corporations **OR** the impacts of international or global institutions on the characteristics of a place you have studied. [9 marks]

Changing places — when the seating plan just isn't right...

The story of Sheffield above is a great example of how you could approach your own place studies — look back through the history of your places to understand all the things that have made them what they are today, and how they've changed.

Meanings and Representations of Place

Yep, it's more detail about sense of place right here. Take a look back at page 100 if you're already feeling confused...

People Perceive and Present Places Differently

1) Places have **meaning** to the people that **know** them — this is their **sense** of those places, i.e. how they **feel** about them.

2) Different people, or groups of people, can attach **different meanings** to the **same places**, e.g. different people may think of the same place as beautiful or unattractive, exciting or boring, stressful or peaceful.

3) How people **feel** about a place is often dependent on their **experience** of that place, e.g. people may feel like **insiders** or **outsiders** (see p.100) in a place depending on whether their experience of that place has been **positive** or **negative**.

4) How people feel about places can also be affected by how places have been **represented** to them.

> The **representation of place** is how individuals, or organisations such as businesses or councils, **portray** places they **know about** to **others**.

See below and the next page for more about how places are represented.

5) People or organisations can represent places in **different ways** depending on what their **perspective** is. For example:

- Individuals who are **proud** to come from a place may present it to others in a **positive** way, whilst individuals who have had a **bad experience** of a place may present it **negatively** to others.

- Organisations, such as **tourism companies** or **local councils**, may present places **positively** as they stand to **gain** from how the places are perceived. **Newspapers** may choose to focus on the **negative** aspects of a place in circumstances where it may help them to **sell more copies**.

6) Meanings and representations of places are important as they can change how people **behave** towards those places, e.g. **positive** feelings about a place may make a person decide to go on **holiday** or **invest** in a business there, whilst **negative** feelings may make them **avoid** that place.

7) Meanings and representations of places are also important as many people generate their **identity** (their sense of who they are) based on the places they feel **connected to**.

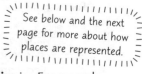

Come to Porkpiesville — the perfect place for your family holiday.

Many Groups Influence Our Perceptions of Place

1) Some groups try to **influence** people's sense of place, or even create **new meanings** for particular places, so that they can **change** people's **behaviour** towards those places:

- **Governments**, both nationally and locally, might do this to **attract people** or **investment** to particular places.
- **Corporate bodies** (e.g. businesses, government-funded agencies) might do this to **generate profit**, or because they have been set up for a **specific purpose**, e.g. VisitBritain is an agency set up to **promote tourism** to the UK.
- **Community** or **local groups** might try to change the **perception** of their place to improve the **local economy** or the lives of **local people**, e.g. local people and business owners in Ludlow promote the town through organising a **food festival** every year — this associates Ludlow with **good food** and **attracts visitors** to the area.

2) Here are three of the main **strategies** used to alter perceptions of place:

- **Place marketing** is how places are 'sold' like products to consumers — the people who will potentially **visit**, **move** to the area or **invest money** there. **Marketing companies** may be employed to produce websites, design logos, run advertising campaigns and social media pages — all of which are designed to **promote** a particular place. E.g. the Lake District is being promoted as the 'Adventure Capital' of the UK through a website and related social media pages which have details of all the available activities in the area.

- **Reimaging** is about **changing** existing **negative perceptions** of places. E.g. in the 1980s and 1990s some people's image of Birmingham was that it was a place of high unemployment, abandoned factories and poor architecture. Many places in Birmingham have been reimaged by turning old industrial areas into new developments, e.g. Brindleyplace is a former industrial site that has been repurposed into a town centre mixed development that include shops, offices, residential areas, restaurants, bars, a gallery and a theatre.

- **Rebranding** is about giving a place a **new identity** that is **appealing** to people and investors. It is achieved through reimaging, place marketing and regeneration schemes. As part of rebranding, many places create **logos** and **slogans** that are designed to be **instantly recognisable** and create **positive associations** with the place they're representing. For example, Glasgow's rebranding included the slogan 'People Make Glasgow' to highlight what makes Glasgow a great place — the people that live and work there.

Meanings and Representations of Place

Places Can be Represented Using a Variety of Different Forms

1) Some forms of representing places are **quantitative** — they can be quantified **numerically** and **statistical analyses** can be performed on them. E.g. representations based on data, such as tables of statistics, graphs and charts are quantitative.

2) Other forms are **qualitative** — they can't be quantified numerically and may be more **descriptive** or **creative**. E.g. representations such as art, poetry and photography.

3) Different forms can create **contrasting** representations of places. When investigating places, it's important to look at a **variety** of different sources to build up a **complete picture** of what a place is like.

Objective means based on facts, subjective means based on feelings or opinions.

Statistics

- Statistics, such as **census data**, can give you lots of **quantitative information** about what places are **like**, e.g. population, population structure, average income, crime figures etc. They can be in the form of raw data, or visually represented through things like charts or graphs.
- Statistics themselves are **objective**, but they can be used **subjectively**, e.g. people can **select** which data they use to show what they want to show. Statistics also don't usually tell you anything about **sense of place**.

Maps

- Maps can be used to show any sort of **data** that has a **location**, e.g. they can show where physical features are. They can also show **quantitative** demographic and economic data, e.g. different levels of income by location.
- Some maps can also show **qualitative** information, such as maps of indexes that show levels of **happiness** — these may be more helpful than quantitative maps for information about **sense of place**.
- Maps can show you **reliable** data, but they can also be **misleading**, e.g. historical maps may be inaccurate.

Films, photography and art

- Visual representations show what places **look like**, and can give some sense of the **character** of places. However, they only represent what the artist **wants** to show you, and can therefore be **misleading**.
- Photographs only show what a place looks like in a **given moment** — photographs taken at different times of day can make a place **look** and **feel different**. Photographs can also be **altered** so places look different to the reality.
- Films and television evoke a **sense of place** that is dependent on the **nature** of the story being told, e.g. a crime drama set in a city might give a different sense of place to a romantic drama set in the same city.
- Paintings or sculptures can be **less reliable** than films and photography at showing what a place **looks like** as they are the artist's **interpretation**. They can be more effective at conveying **sense of place** and character though.

Stories, articles, music and poetry

- Written representations can be used to **describe** places, and can also evoke a sense of how it **feels** to be in that place. They usually only offer the perspective of the **author** though, so they don't show a **complete picture**.
- Newspaper articles can give lots of **detail** about places but they may be **biased**, e.g. newspapers may focus on the topics and ideas that are likely to sell more copies, rather than give a balanced perspective on a place.
- Stories, music and poetry can give an **emotional impression** of places, but only from the **writer's perspective**.

Practice Questions

Q1 What is the meant by the term 'representation of place'?
Q2 Give three strategies that could be used to alter people's perception of place.

Exam Question

Q1 Distinguish between quantitative and qualitative representations of place. [3 marks]

Exam halls — places of stress or places of relaxation...

Once you start looking for it, you'll see place marketing everywhere — logos, slogans, events, festivals. All these things and more are done to create positive meanings for places. In fact, I think I feel a song about my home town coming on...

Place Studies

And so we come to it at last... the place studies. You need to bring together everything you've learnt about this topic to do the place studies properly — so these pages may well be the most important in the section so far... gulp.

You need to do Studies of Two Places

1) One of your place studies needs to be about a place that is **local** to you, i.e. where you **live** or where your **school** is. The other needs to be about a place that **contrasts** with your local place, and is likely to be **distant** from it.

2) Your distant place should contrast with your local place in terms of its **economy**, **demographics**, **social inequality** or **cultural characteristics** — ideally a **combination** of these factors so there are lots of ways to **compare** them.

3) The distant place could be in the **UK** or **abroad**, but think carefully about how easy it will be to **find information** about the place. Sources on UK places may be easier to find and more **comparable** to the sources on your local place.

4) Your places shouldn't be **too big** — think about places that are the size of a **village**, **small town** or **part** of a larger city.

5) Your research should focus on the **material** that's been covered throughout **this topic**, i.e. the characteristics of the places and how they've changed, the external forces that have caused change, past and present connections and developments, the meanings of those places to different people and how the places have been represented.

6) You also need to make sure that you've got a **mix** of **quantitative** and **qualitative** sources from both the **past** and the **present**.

7) Over the next four pages, we'll go over some **tips** for putting together your place studies, and give examples using two places we've chosen — central **Liverpool** and **Lerwick** on the Shetland Islands.

Research the Characteristics and History of Your Places

Take a look back at pages 102-103 for more about the character of places.

1) **Maps** are a good source for the **basic characteristics** of places — they can show you the **physical characteristics**, e.g. the location and topography, and some **human characteristics**, e.g. the built environment and infrastructure.

2) The **Ordnance Survey**® is the UK's mapping agency, providing a variety of types of map. OS® maps are available to view **online** or as paper maps that can be found in **libraries**.

3) **Google Maps™** can be viewed **online** and can provide both **maps** and **satellite images**. **Google Street View™** gives images at street level of many places round the world (this could be particularly helpful for your distant place).

4) **Historic maps** are also available, which can be **compared** to modern maps to show **change over time**. You could find these via **Internet searches** for organisations such as **local history societies**.

5) You should research the **history** of your places too — to see how they've **changed over time** and the **forces** that have affected their **development**. Your school or local library will have books, such as atlases and encyclopedias, that may provide more information on the history of your places.

6) Internet searches will allow you to find a **wide variety** of other sources about your places. For example, **local tourism websites** and **local government websites** may provide a lot of local information, and **news articles** can give you detailed information about **past** and **present** issues affecting your places.

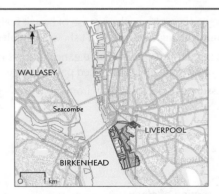

Central Liverpool, located on the River Mersey estuary, is the centre of one of the UK's largest cities. Liverpool was a major port for global trade and a centre of manufacturing between the 18th and mid-20th centuries, during which time the city grew and attracted immigrants from around the world. The docks and factories declined in the 1960s, leading to large scale deprivation. Recently though, Liverpool has attracted a lot of investment for regeneration and was chosen as the European Capital of Culture in 2008.

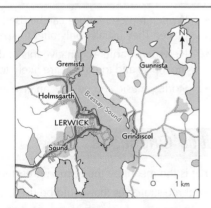

Lerwick, the capital of the Shetland Islands, is a small town and port located on the east of the main island. In its earlier history, the island was populated by Vikings but has been part of Scotland since the 15th century. Its major industry has traditionally been fishing, but North Sea oil was discovered in the 1970s which, along with increases in tourism, has led to improvements in the economy.

Place Studies

Demographic Characteristics are About People

1) The demographic characteristics of your places are about **who** the people are and what they're **like**. E.g. you might research the population size, density and structure (e.g. age and gender), birth rate or ethnicity of your places.

2) You need to look at how demographic characteristics have **changed over time**, and the **reasons why** they've changed — think about the external **flows** and **forces** and the changes they've caused (see pages 104-107).

3) A great source of demographic data is the **census** — the survey of the UK population conducted every ten years. This data, along with other statistics, can be accessed through the website of the **Office for National Statistics** (ONS).

4) It's possible to generate statistics and summaries about **specific places** through the ONS website ('neighbourhood' statistics).

5) The website **DataShine.org.uk** and the **Consumer Data Research Centre** also show demographic data, using interactive tools for displaying the data on maps.

Take a look back at page 104 for more about changing demographic and cultural characteristics.

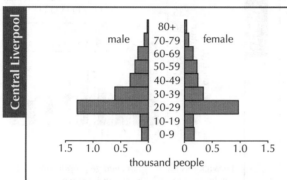

The central Liverpool census area (see previous page) had a population of 5436 in 2011. A large proportion of the population were young and working age (20-39) due to the high availability of work in the area (see p.112), and there was a high proportion of males.

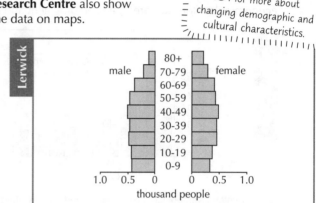

Lerwick had a total population of 6958 in 2011. There was a lower proportion of people of working age, and a higher proportion of older people compared to central Liverpool. As a result of the population structure, there are concerns that the Shetlands have an increasingly ageing population.

Cultural Characteristics Could be Shown Using Qualitative Sources

1) The cultural characteristics of your places are about **how** people live their lives. E.g. you might research the languages spoken, foods eaten, clothes worn, literature read, music listened to or the attitudes and beliefs people have.

2) Think about how these have **changed over time** and what **caused** those changes.

3) Sources for cultural characteristics may be **quantitative**, e.g. census data may be available on the religions practised or languages spoken in your places.

4) They could also be qualitative, e.g. **literature** or **music**. There may be **travel writing** or **biographies** of people who have experienced the **culture** of your places, and local people may also have written **poems** or songs that reflect their culture.

Central Liverpool

Many people consider poetry and music to be a key part of Liverpool's culture, and there are famous musicians and poets that are closely associated with Liverpool. For example, The Beatles were one of the most successful bands of all time. They wrote songs about places in Liverpool and gave the city global connections — with fans when they were playing in the 1960s, and by continuing to attract tourists from around the world.

Famous poets, such as Roger McGough, are also closely associated with Liverpool. In 2007, Roger McGough was involved in a project to celebrate the 800th birthday of the city. He wrote the opening and closing lines of an 800-line poem (The Liverpool Saga), with all the other lines written by the people of Liverpool — the idea was that the poem would reflect the varied history, people and culture of Liverpool. Lines such as, "Eight hundred different cultures, eight hundred different tongues" give an insight into the mixed cultures found in the city, which are the result of immigration throughout Liverpool's history.

Lerwick

Shetland has a distinct dialect (variety of a language) that is still in use today. The dialect is similar to other Scottish dialects but contains many features, words and sounds from an old form of Norwegian. This reflects the cultural history of the island, which has been populated by a mix of Vikings and Scottish people. Many of the place names on the islands reflect this, e.g. Lerwick is a similar name to Leirvik, a place in Norway, which means 'bay of clay'.

The dialect has been represented through poetry, and some poets are particularly associated with the Shetland Islands. For example, T.A. Robertson was a poet who wrote in Shetland dialect, and about Shetland, in the mid 20th century. The poem 'Kwarna Farna?' is about depopulation on the islands and contains lines such as, "Bit noo da laand is bare", to evoke the sense of emptiness on the island caused by emigration.

Place Studies

Yet more place study stuff on here. Well, we wouldn't forget the economic and social characteristics now, would we...

Economic Characteristics are About **Work** and **Money**

1) The economic characteristics of your places are to do with **work** and **money**. E.g. you might research employment and unemployment statistics, income, the types of job available or house prices for your places.

2) You need to look at how they've **changed over** time, and the reasons **why** they've changed — think about the external **flows** and **forces** and the changes they've caused (see pages 104-107).

3) You'll find data on economic characteristics in a lot of the **same places** as for demographic characteristics — data from the **census** and **Office for National Statistics** covers things like **employment** and **income**.

4) Other websites, such as **CheckMyStreet.co.uk** and **uklocalarea.com**, give reports of **economic** data for local areas, e.g. employment and house prices.

These websites also have data on social characteristics, e.g. crime and education.

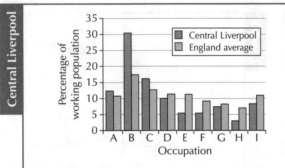

Central Liverpool has a very high proportion of workers in managerial and professional occupations, and a low proportion of the workforce in skilled trades and elementary occupations. This reflects the decline of the docks and manufacturing employment, and the rise of employment in the service sector — much redevelopment work on the city centre has focused on the creation of office space.

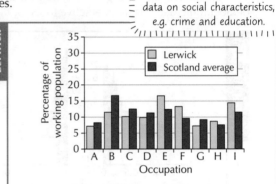

Lerwick has higher than average proportions of its workforce in skilled trades and elementary occupations, and lower than average proportions of its workforce in managerial and professional occupations. This reflects the continued importance of the seafood industry to Lerwick — the catching, processing and sale of fish around the harbour employs many people.

Key
A Managers, Directors and Senior Officials
B Professional Occupations
C Associate Professional and Technical
D Administrative and Secretarial
E Skilled Trades
F Caring, Leisure and Other Services
G Sales and Customer Service
H Process, Plant and Machine Operatives
I Elementary Occupations (e.g. labourers)

Social Characteristics can **Highlight Social Inequality**

1) The social characteristics of your places are to do with what people's **lives** are **like**. E.g. you might research things like quality of life, level of deprivation, crime, access to healthcare, education and leisure facilities for your places.

2) Think about how these have **changed over time** and what **caused** those changes.

3) **Compound indicators** of social and economic characteristics are a good overall indicator — these are indexes that take into account lots of different social and economic factors, e.g. the **Index of Multiple Deprivation** (IMD).

4) Data on **health** can be found at the website for the **Public Health Outcomes Framework**, and mapped **crime data** for local areas can be sourced at **police.uk**.

5) Social characteristics may be represented through **qualitative** sources as well, e.g. television programmes or films may highlight social issues in your places.

Take a look back at page 105 for more about changing economic and social characteristics.

Central Liverpool has a high crime rate. In January 2017 alone, there were 2076 crimes reported, including 362 violent and sexual offences.

Gang crime has historically been a problem across Liverpool, and media reports in the early part of 2017 have continued to highlight this, particularly in relation to gun crime. E.g. between April 2016 and February 2017 there were 79 shootings across the city, including 4 fatalities.

Central Liverpool continues to be associated with historic incidents of civil unrest, e.g. the Toxteth riots in 1981. Social and economic problems in the area led to a period of 9 days of rioting, in which many people were injured and 70 buildings were destroyed.

The Shetland Islands have a very low crime rate — in the year 2012-2013, a total of 1057 crimes were reported for the whole of the Shetland Islands.

Some media reports highlight this, e.g. the Shetland News reported in 2014 that "one of the safest communities in Scotland is becoming safer still". Other media reports highlight the rise of particular crimes. For example, in 2008 The Guardian highlighted a rise in drug crime on the islands.

Crime on Shetland has also been presented through a BBC crime drama, 'Shetland', which started in 2013. Fictional TV shows such as this may affect people's perception of the types of crime that occur in Shetland.

Place Studies

Meaning and Representation of Place are Important too

1) You need to cover the **lived experience** of people in your places, both in the **past** and in the **present**.

2) To do this you'll need sources that tell you, or show you, how people feel about the places you're studying (their sense of place).

3) You also need to look at sources that show how your place has been **represented** — this can affect and create people's **perceptions** and therefore their **sense** of those places.

Have a look at pages 108-109 for more about meaning and representation of place.

4) Sources that reflect the meaning and representation of places are likely to be **qualitative**, e.g. works of art, photographs, news articles, interviews with local people, stories or poems.

5) Art and photographs could be sourced from **image searches** on the **Internet**, or **image bank websites**. Older photographs may be available through **local history societies**.

6) News articles are available **online** via newspaper or news outlet websites. You should also consider **local newspapers** — they may offer **different perspectives** to national newspapers.

7) For your local place, you could conduct **interviews** or **surveys** of people's sense of place through **fieldwork**.

8) Stories and poems can be sourced through **libraries**, and many older poems are freely available online. Many authors and poets are **strongly associated** with particular places, and may have written a lot about the place and the **issues** that have affected it over time.

Central Liverpool

Stanley Dock tobacco warehouse

Albert Dock

Some major buildings in central Liverpool, such as the Stanley Dock tobacco warehouse, have been disused following the industrial decline of the mid to late 20th century (though there are current plans to redevelop them). Albert Dock was also abandoned but has been redeveloped as a multi-use attraction, including a major art gallery (Tate Liverpool).

Photographs such as these represent central Liverpool differently — the disused warehouse image shows decline and abandonment, whilst Albert Dock is presented as modern, exciting and attractive.

Lerwick

Burning longship at Up Helly Aa

The Viking heritage of the Shetlands is represented by an annual festival held in Lerwick. During Up Helly Aa (which means 'the end of the holiday') local people dress as Vikings and have a torchlit procession, which culminates in the burning of a Viking longship. Though the festival celebrates the Viking heritage of the Shetlands, its origin is relatively recent — it has been going in its present form since the late 19th Century. Local people are involved in the preparations throughout the year, including creating the costumes and building the longship.

Images such as this convey a sense of drama around the festival, which helps to communicate the lived experience of the people and create a sense of the place.

The festival also connects Lerwick to the world through tourists who come to experience it.

> Whatever sources you find (quantitative or qualitative), it's important to be **critical** about them — for each source think about what its **strengths** and **weaknesses** are. It might be that some sources are **biased**, or it might be that some are **inaccurate**. Other sources may be more **reliable**, but only offer the viewpoint of **one particular individual**.

Practice Questions

Q1 Briefly describe Lerwick's population structure.

Q2 Briefly describe the cultural characteristics of Liverpool.

Q1 Assess the extent to which the experiences of people living in a place that you have studied have been affected by the past development of that place. [20 marks]

Liverpool and Lerwick — like peas in a pod...

Having a good mix of qualitative and quantitative sources for your places studies, to show what they were like in the past and what they're like today, is vital. So take the time to do the research properly and it'll pay off big time come exam day.

Exam Structure

And now onto the unpleasant topic of exams (sorry, I had to mention them sooner or later).
It's a pretty good idea to know what's in store for you so there are no nasty surprises on the day.

You Have to Sit **Two Exam Papers**

Component 1 Exam — Physical Geography and People And The Environment

1) It's **1 hr 30 mins** long and there are **80 marks** up for grabs (worth 50% of your AS grade).
2) It tests five topics, but you only have to answer questions on **TWO** of them.
3) There are **two sections** in the paper — **A** and **B**:

SECTION A — PHYSICAL GEOGRAPHY	SECTION B — PEOPLE AND THE ENVIRONMENT
You have to **answer ONE multiple-part question** from a choice of three: • Water and Carbon Cycles **OR** • Coastal Systems and Landscapes **OR** • Glacial Systems and Landscapes. Each question is worth **40 marks**.	You have to **answer ONE multiple-part question** from a choice of two: • Hazards **OR** • Contemporary Urban Environments. Each question is worth **40 marks**.

Component 2 Exam — Human Geography and Geography Fieldwork Investigation

1) It's **1 hr 30 mins** long and there are **80 marks** up for grabs (worth 50% of your AS grade).
2) It tests your knowledge of two topics — **Changing Places** and your **Geography Fieldwork Investigation**.
3) There are **two sections** in the paper — **A** and **B**:

For both of the exams you have roughly 1 minute per mark — so if a question's worth 3 marks you should spend about 3 minutes answering it.

SECTION A — CHANGING PLACES
You **have** to answer the question on **Changing Places**. Section A is worth **40 marks**.

SECTION B — FIELDWORK AND GEOGRAPHICAL SKILLS
You **have** to answer **Question 2** — it's about **fieldwork** generally, and the **fieldwork investigation** that you've done. You also have to answer **EITHER** Question 3 **OR** Question 4 — each one will give you some **background information** about a fieldwork investigation and some **results**, and you'll have to answer questions about them. Section B is also worth **40 marks**.

Exams — who needs them, don't you know who my father is?

There are Different **Question Types** That May Come Up in the Exam

Each question is made up of **several parts**, each with a slightly **different format** and worth a different number of **marks**:

1) There will be some **multiple-choice** questions where you'll need to shade your chosen option.
2) Some questions come with **figures** (e.g. maps and tables) that you'll need to **refer to** when you write your answers. You may need to use your **understanding** of a topic to **interpret** these **figures**.
3) There'll also be questions that **test your knowledge** of the topics.
4) Some questions are worth **9** or **20 marks** — you'll need to write a longer, **'essay-style' answer** for these.
5) Sometimes you'll need to use **case study content** in your answers — see page 116 for more.

Answering Questions

No matter how much you revise, you aren't going to do well in your exams if you don't answer the questions properly. This can be trickier than it sounds, but fear not, I've included a whole page on it, because I'm nice like that...

1) Make Sure You Read the Question Properly

> There are loads of hints about how to answer the questions in this book in the Answers section at the back.

It's dead easy to **misread** the question and spend 10 minutes writing about the **wrong thing**. **Five** simple tips can help you avoid this:

1) Figure out if it's a **case study question** — if the question wording includes 'using **named examples**' or 'with reference to **a place that you have studied**' you **need** to include a case study.

2) <u>Underline</u> the **command words** in the question (the ones that tell you **what to do**):

'Assess', 'Evaluate' and 'Discuss' all mean pretty much the **same thing**. They're all about **weighing something up**, e.g. the **success** of a coastal management scheme. You need to give a **balanced** answer — talk about all the **different viewpoints** on the subject.

Answers to questions with 'explain' in them often include the word '**because**' (or '**due to**'). E.g. for the question 'Explain where earthquakes occur', your answer would include 'Earthquakes occur at plate boundaries because of a build up of pressure...'.

Command word	Means write about...
Analyse	what the information **means**
Assess	
Evaluate	the **advantages** and **disadvantages OR** the **arguments for** and **against**
Discuss	
Compare	the **similarities AND differences**
Contrast	
Distinguish	the **differences**
Explain	
Suggest reasons...	**why** it's like that (i.e. give reasons)
Outline	the **main points**
To what extent	**both** sides of the argument **AND your opinion**

When writing about differences, '**whereas**' is a good word to use in your answers, e.g. 'Unemployment in north-east England in 2007 was 6.1%, whereas it was 4.1% in the south-west'.

In 'to what extent...' questions, you need to give a balanced discussion and a **well-reasoned** opinion, which is supported by evidence.

3) <u>Underline</u> the **key words** (the ones that tell you **what it's about**), e.g. wildfires, urban waste, social impacts etc.

4) For **essay** questions, **re-read the question** a couple of times **whilst you're answering it**, just to make sure you're still **sticking** to what the question is asking you to do.

5) For **all** questions, **re-read** the question and your answer **when you've finished**, just to check that your answer really does address **all parts** of the question being asked. A **common mistake** is to **miss a bit out** — like when questions say 'use data from the graph in your answer' or 'use evidence from the map'.

2) Figure Out Your Structure Before You Start

For any **longer answers**, you need to think carefully about how to **structure** your answer. Jot down the **order** you're going to cover things in. **Label** your **plan** and **answer** clearly so the examiner knows which is which.

Q1 Assess whether <u>short-term</u> or <u>long-term</u> <u>responses</u> are more effective in reducing the impacts of <u>seismic hazards</u>.

PLAN
1. Intro — define the types of response
2. Short-term — e.g. rescuing people — reduces immediate danger but doesn't reduce future danger
3. Long-term — prevention, preparedness, adaptation — reduce impacts of future hazards, but can be expensive
4. Conclusion — long-term more effective

ANSWER
Responses to seismic hazards can be either short or long-term...

3) Include Relevant Geographical Terms

Use the **proper geography words** for things, e.g. say 'tributary' rather than 'little river', and 'migration' instead of 'movement of people'.

Don't Forget all the Usual Rules

1) Your answer should be **legible** (you won't get many marks if the examiner can't read it), use **correct grammar**, and **everything** should be **spelt correctly** (double-check jazzy geography words).

2) **Use diagrams** where they're appropriate — drawing a diagram can be way **quicker** than describing the same thing in words.

3) If you're **running out of time** at the end of the exam, **don't panic** — just write what you can as **bullet points**. You'll still get some marks for doing this.

Answering Case Study Questions

Geography examiners are even keener on case study questions than they are on tweed jackets with fetching elbow patches...

Don't Forget the **Three Tips** When Answering **Case Study Questions**

1) For **every question** you need to do the following three things:

> ① **Read** the question properly.
> ② **Figure out** your **structure before** you start.
> ③ **Include** relevant **geographical terms**.

2) But for case study questions you also **need to**:

Include PLENTY of RELEVANT DETAILS

3) This includes things like **place names**, **dates**, **statistics**, **names** of **organisations** or **companies**.

4) Don't forget that they need to be **relevant** though — it's no good including the exact number of people killed in a tropical storm when the question is about the causes of a storm.

5) For many case study questions, a great way to show your specific knowledge is to learn an **annotated map** and re-draw it in the exam (e.g. the Kashmir earthquake map on page 67) — but take care to only include labels relevant to the specific question being asked.

Jeremy's case study revealed very few relevant details... black, handle, smells a bit funny...

Here's an **Example Answer** to a Case Study Question

'For a coastal area beyond the UK' means you have to include a case study, and it must not be from the UK.

> **Q1** For a coastal area beyond the UK, <u>evaluate</u> human <u>responses</u> to the <u>challenges</u> the region presents. **[9 marks]**
>
> PLAN
> 1. Introduce the Sundarbans region and some of the challenges (flooding, tropical cyclones, salinisation, difficult access).
> 2. Describe the responses to these challenges (storm shelters, early warning systems, salt-resistant crops, better roads), and how successful they have been.
> 3. Conclude — some success, but also some problems.
>
> ANSWER
> The Sundarbans is a flat, low-lying coastal area in southwest Bangladesh and east India. Much of it is covered by mangrove forests, but it is home to 4 million people.
>   There are several challenges to living in and developing the Sundarbans. The area is low-lying and vulnerable to coastal flooding and damage from tropical cyclones. As well as endangering people and destroying buildings and infrastructure, these hazards can cause salinisation of soil, making it difficult to grow crops. In addition, access to the Sundarbans is difficult because there are few roads, and those that do exist are of poor quality.
>   Human responses to these challenges include increasing resilience, mitigating the challenges or their impacts and adapting behaviour to work around the challenges. One way of increasing resilience is by building new roads and bridges to improve access. However, this can lead to increased deforestation of mangroves, which may cause further challenges, e.g. increased flooding.
>   To mitigate the impacts of tropical cyclones, the government and NGOs are funding storm shelters and early warning systems. Early warning systems give people a chance to evacuate the area or prepare for cyclones, reducing the death toll and damage to property. However, not everyone receives early warnings, and some people may not be able to evacuate because they do not have transport available.
>   Adaptation responses include planting salt-resistant varieties of rice to minimise the impact of soil salinisation. This allows people to grow crops for food and income, which can help to increase food security and reduce the impacts of hazards. However, relying on a smaller range of crops can reduce biodiversity and may increase vulnerability to pests and diseases.
>   In conclusion, there are many human responses to the challenges in the Sundarbans, including increased resilience, mitigation and adaptation. These bring benefits, but they may also cause problems or have drawbacks.

Don't think 'Ah, this is about the bit of coast I've studied' and then write everything you know about a particular coastline. The key words are '**responses**' and '**challenges**' and the command word is '**evaluate**', so you need to write about the challenges, responses to them and how well the responses have worked.

Use relevant **geographical terms**, e.g. **salinisation**, **resilience**, **mitigation** and **adaptation**.

End with a **conclusion**. You'll often want to mention **both** sides of an argument — things are rarely **totally brilliant** or **absolutely awful**.

Include **relevant details**, e.g. if different crops are being planted, say exactly what sort of crops are being grown.

Answering Resource Interpretation Questions

In the exam, you're going to get some questions where you have to interpret a resource.
The next few pages show you the kind of thing that might crop up. Knock yourself out...

You Might Get a Question Based on a *Map*...

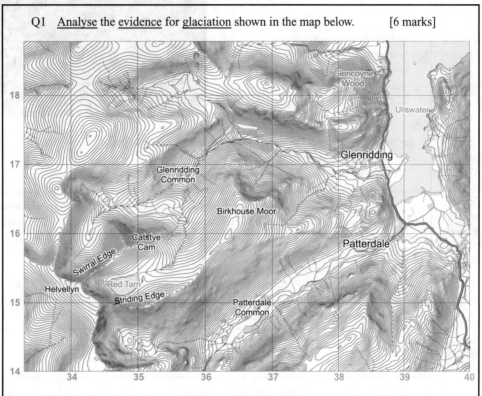

Q1   <u>Analyse</u> the <u>evidence</u> for <u>glaciation</u> shown in the map below.   [6 marks]

The question asks for **evidence of glaciation**, so you shouldn't mention any non-glacial features.

PLAN
1. Describe area shown and mention evidence for past glaciation.
2. Give evidence from map — glacial trough, corrie, tarn, arête, truncated spur.

ANSWER

The map shows an upland, mountainous area. It appears not to be glaciated at present (there is no ice shown), but there are several landforms that indicate that the area has been glaciated in the past.

Patterdale Common is a glacial trough. It was probably formed when a glacier flowed northeast along the valley, eroding a V-shaped river valley. This glacial trough is a clear sign that the area in the map was glaciated in the past.

There is a corrie and a tarn (Red Tarn) at grid reference 347153. The corrie is a bowl-shaped hollow that formed at the head of a glacier through plucking and abrasion. Red Tarn formed in this corrie after the glacier retreated.

Give the **grid reference** when you're talking about somewhere specific.

To the northwest and southeast of Red Tarn there are two arêtes, which are ridges that form when two glaciers flow in parallel valleys. One of these is Striding Edge, which formed as the corries at grid references 347153 and 347145 eroded the valley sides, forming a steep-sided ridge between.

Include specific place names.

The ridge to the north of Glenridding, at grid reference 383176, ends abruptly, so it may be a truncated spur. It could have formed by a glacier flowing in the valley in which Ullswater is now located; this glacier could have truncated ridges of land sticking into the main valley.

In conclusion, the map shows landforms that can only form through glacial processes, such as glacial troughs, corries and arêtes. This shows that the area was glaciated in the past.

Answering Resource Interpretation Questions

...or a Photo...

Q1   Suggest how human activities might affect flood risk in the area shown in the photograph.   [6 marks]

PLAN

1. Deforestation — reduced interception, evapotranspiration and infiltration — increased runoff
2. Cattle — trampling decreases infiltration — increased runoff

It's a good idea to put key **geographical terms** in your plan, to remind you to use them in your answer.

The command word in the question is 'suggest' so you need to use **evidence** from the photo to come up with **possible ways** in which flood risk might be affected.

Scour the photo to make sure you've got everything — it'd be really easy to miss the **tree stumps** if you hadn't looked properly.

ANSWER

There is evidence of two human activities likely to be affecting flood risk in the area shown in the photo: deforestation and agriculture.

Trees have been felled to create the clearing shown in the photo. This reduces the amount of precipitation that is intercepted and the amount that is taken up by tree roots and returned to the atmosphere by evapotranspiration. This means that more rainwater reaches the ground surface. Deforestation also reduces the amount of leaf litter on the ground; leaf litter can help to hold water, giving it time to infiltrate, so removing it decreases infiltration. These factors are likely to increase surface runoff, which will increase the likelihood of flooding.

The other human activity shown in the photo is the use of the land for livestock grazing. This will increase flood risk further, because trampling by cattle compacts the soil, which decreases infiltration and therefore increases surface runoff.

...or a Graph...

Q1   Study the graph, which shows changes in the percentage of people living in urban areas in Ireland (a developed country) and Botswana (a developing country) from 1960 to 2015.

The command word is 'explain' so you need to **describe** the trends on the graph **and give reasons** for them.

Explain the differences in rate of urban population change between the two countries.   [6 marks]

PLAN

1. Describe trends in Ireland.
2. Suggest reasons for the trends.
3. Describe trends in Botswana.
4. Suggest reasons for the trends.

Use **evidence from the graph** to back up your points. To get **accurate figures** from a graph it often helps to **draw lines** on with a ruler.

ANSWER

In 1960, a fairly high proportion (45%) of the population of Ireland lived in urban areas. It grew to 54% in 1975, after which the rate of increase slowed. Since 1995, the rate of increase has been slightly faster, and by 2015 63% of people in Ireland lived in urban areas.

Ireland is a developed country, so urbanisation happened before 1960 (the earliest date on the graph). Counter-urbanisation may have been responsible for the slowing down of urban population growth in the 1980s, and there may have been some urban resurgence since 1995, explaining the slight increase in rate of growth since this time.

As well as **describing general trends**, describe **specific details**, e.g. the percentage of people living in urban areas in Botswana increased in the period shown, but you also need to say it **increased rapidly between 1965 and 1990**.

In 1960, the percentage of the population living in urban areas in Botswana was very low (<5%). This increased rapidly from 1965 until 1990, when the rate of increase slowed down. By 2015 about 58% if people in Botswana lived in urban areas, nearly the same percentage as Ireland.

Botswana is a developing country; as a country develops, there is usually a big migration of people from rural areas to towns and cities. This could explain the very rapid increase in urban population from 1965 until 1990. In addition, a lot of the people moving to cities are young adults, so they often start families, which increases the number of people in the city even more. The rate of increase slowed down in 1990, and by 2015 it was increasing at roughly the same rate as Ireland. This may be due to Botswana becoming more developed so having slower rate of urbanisation.

Answering Resource Interpretation Questions

...or Some **Data**

This question is asking about how far the **information** in the table shows social and economic inequalities, **not** about the causes or effects of these inequalities.

Q1   The table below shows information about two areas of Bristol.

Using the data in the table, <u>assess the extent</u> to which there are <u>economic and social inequalities</u> between Hartcliffe and Clifton.   [6 marks]

Measure	Area of Bristol	
	Fulford Rd North, Hartcliffe	**Clifton Village, Clifton**
Total population (2011)	1515	1449
Average weekly household income (2008)	£480	£800
% Unemployed (2011)	8.1	1.8
% 'not good' general health (2011)	23.6	7.8
% not born in the UK (2011)	5.7	15.7
Police recorded burglaries (2016)	21	16
% people aged 16 or over with no qualifications (2011)	41.7	2.7
% households with >1 person per bedroom (2011)	35.0	19.0

The question asks you to 'assess the extent' so you need to describe the information in the table and explain how far the information does or doesn't show economic and social differences.

PLAN

1. Define economic and social inequalities.

2. Describe and explain data that shows economic and social inequalities.

3. Describe and explain data that doesn't show economic and social inequalities.

Quote data from the table to back up your points.

ANSWER

Economic inequalities are related to the uneven distribution of money. Social inequalities are related to differences in people's quality of life, for example their access to good education, healthcare and open space.

There is some evidence for economic and social inequalities in the areas shown. For example, the average weekly household income in 2008 was £320 higher in Clifton than in Hartcliffe, meaning that households in Hartcliffe earned less than two-thirds of the amount earned by households in Clifton. This is a significant economic inequality, and may be related to the much higher unemployment figures — in Hartcliffe in 2011, unemployment was 8.1% but in Clifton it was only 1.8%. Together, these data show that Clifton is wealthier than Hartcliffe.

There are also significant social inequalities shown in the table. The percentage of people aged 16 or over with no qualifications is much higher (41.7%) in Hartcliffe than in Clifton (2.7%) and the proportion of the population with 'not good' general health is around three times as high. Hartcliffe also has nearly twice the proportion of households with more than one person per bedroom, indicating that overcrowding may be an issue in this area. These data suggest that Hartcliffe has more social issues than Clifton.

Not all rows of the table show inequalities. There were more burglaries in Hartcliffe than Clifton in 2016, but the difference is only five, so it's difficult to know if this is significant or not. The areas have similar populations, so the number of burglaries per person is broadly similar.

Overall, the table shows that there are large economic and social inequalities between Hartcliffe and Clifton.

Manipulate data from the table where appropriate, e.g. instead of giving the average weekly income for each place, give the difference between them.

Investigative Skills

Whether you consider yourself a modern-day Poirot or not, you need to know this basic stuff about investigating things through fieldwork and research.

You Need to Have a **Research Question** and a **Hypothesis**

1) When you're doing fieldwork and research you won't get very far without a **research question** or an **issue** to investigate, and a **hypothesis** to **test**.

2) A research question is **what you want to find out**, e.g. 'Do coastal defences at Holderness affect the rate of erosion of the coastline?'. It has to be closely related to the content you have studied for AS level.

3) A hypothesis is a **specific testable statement**, e.g. 'Coastal defences at Holderness increase the rate of erosion downdrift of the defences'.

4) Your hypothesis should be '**developed**' — this just means that it has to be **really specific**. E.g. the hypothesis above is better than 'Coastal defences do affect erosion'.

Herman's hypothesis that large grey rabbits could play miniature pianos was very specific (and seemed to be correct).

You Need to **Collect Data**

1) You'll **collect data** when you're doing your **fieldwork** and when **researching** your fieldwork investigation.

2) There are two types of data — **qualitative** and **quantitative**:

- **Qualitative** data is **descriptive** — it might be in words or images, so you can't easily use it in calculations, e.g. interviews with residents.

- **Quantitative** data is **numerical** — it can be measured and used in calculations, e.g. pedestrian/traffic counts.

3) The data you use will be either **primary** or **secondary**:

- **Primary** data is data you **collect yourself** (i.e. the data you get from your **fieldwork**).

- **Secondary** data is data **someone else** has **collected** (i.e. the data you get from your **research**).

4) There are lots of **secondary data sources** that you could use, including:

- **Images** — e.g. historical and present-day images can help to show how an area has changed over time.

- **Factual text** — e.g. articles about a place or processes that you are investigating.

- **Creative material** — e.g. stories or songs about real places can provide information about how a place is perceived or what it was like in the past.

- **Spatial data** — information with a location, e.g. maps (see pages 123-124) and GIS.

- **Crowd-sourced data** — information that has been contributed by members of a community, e.g. online. One way it can be used is after a natural disaster, when people on the ground contribute information about who needs help, the extent of damage to infrastructure and so on.

- **Big data** — very large datasets that require powerful computers to analyse. They are often created from logs of digital actions, e.g. social media posts, transactions completed, journeys made.

5) In the exam, you might have to **describe** how you collected your data. This includes things like what type of **equipment** you used (e.g. a velocity meter), **how you did it** (e.g. you conducted a questionnaire containing 10 questions) or **what source** it came from (e.g. 2011 census data).

6) You might also have to **critically examine** any data you use — this means pointing out any **limitations** of the **data**, e.g. whether it could be **biased** due to the collection method, or if it might not be **representative** of the whole population.

You Need to **Select** Your **Sites Carefully**

1) When you're investigating an urban area, river or coast you **can't study** the **whole thing**, so you have to **select sites** to investigate instead.

2) Selecting sites can be **tricky** though — you need places that are **easy to get to** (e.g. places with **footpath access**) and **not too far** from a **parking place** (if you've got **heavy equipment** to carry you don't want to be walking for miles). But you also need sites that are a **good representation** of all the things you want to study, e.g. if you're studying how **characteristics** of a city change in different areas, it's no good selecting three sites in the **city centre** — this would be a **biased sample**. You need to select sites in **different** locations, from the **city centre** to the **rural-urban fringe**.

Don't forget to do a risk assessment — it might affect which sites you can use.

Investigative Skills

There are **Three Sampling Techniques** You Could Use to Select Sites

To make sure your sites are representative, you might want to use **random** sampling, **systematic** sampling or **stratified** sampling:

1 Random Sampling

1) You could use **random sampling** — e.g. using a **random number table** to find the distance of a site from the city centre.

2) As long as you're using a big enough sample this should **remove** any **bias** because each possible sample site has the same **probability** of being chosen.

3) However, there is a **risk** that **large areas** of the survey area might not be chosen if the random samples **happen** to fall in such a way that a large area is not sampled.

> To ensure any variation observed in the sample isn't just due to chance, it's important to analyse the results statistically (see pages 125-126). This allows you to be more confident that the results reflect what's going on in the whole population.

2 Systematic Sampling

1) **Systematic sampling** is often used to select sites in geography fieldwork — this involves selecting sites in a **regular**, **structured** way, e.g. **every 2 km** along a coastline, or **every third shop** on the high street.

2) Doing it this way means you should be able to **cover** the **whole area** in an unbiased way.

3 Stratified Sampling

1) This is when **different parts** of the study area are **identified** and **sampled separately** in **proportion** to their size or importance in the study area as a **whole**.

2) For example, in an urban fieldwork investigation you might identify **different neighbourhoods** and interview a **different number of people** in each in proportion to their population size.

3) This **reduces** the likelihood that some areas could be **under-represented** in your investigation.

You Also Need to **Process** and **Analyse** Your Data...

1) Once you've collected your results, you'll need **process** the data into a form that you can **use**, e.g. **collating** responses to questionnaires and adding them to a **spreadsheet**.

2) You'll need to **present** your data, e.g. in a **graph** (see page 122) or on a **map** (see pages 123-124).

3) You'll also need to **analyse** your data, e.g. by using **statistics** (see pages 125-126), to find any **patterns**.

4) You can then **interpret** your results to work out what they **show** in relation to your **original research question**.

...and Use it to Draw **Conclusions**

Draw Conclusions About Your Data

A conclusion is a **summary** of what you found out in relation to the **original research question**. It should include:

- A **summary** of what your results show.

- An **answer** to the question you are investigating (does your data agree with your **hypothesis**?), and an **explanation** of why that is the answer.

- An explanation of how your conclusion fits into **wider geographical knowledge**.

Evaluate Your Data and Methods

Evaluation is about **assessing** what went **well** and what could have been **improved** in your investigation.

- Identify any **problems** with any part of the investigation, e.g. problems with sampling or inability to access big data sources.

- Describe how **accurate** the results are and whether there are any problems with the **methods** used that might have affected the results.

- Comment on the **validity** of your conclusion — could any problems you encountered have **affected** your conclusion?

- Think about how your results could be used by **other people** or in **further investigations**.

Graph and Map Skills

As sure as death and taxes, there'll be graphs and maps in your exam. So make sure you know all the different types...

There are Loads of **Different Types** of Graphs and **Maps**

1) There are some types of graphs and maps that you'll have come across lots of times before.
   These include **line graphs**, **bar charts**, **pie charts**, **scatter graphs**, **atlas maps** and **sketch maps**.

2) Some graphs and maps are trickier than others — the next three pages will help you interpret the tougher ones.

3) When you're **interpreting** graphs and maps you need to remember to **read** the **scale** or **key really carefully**.

4) If you have to read from a graph, **draw working lines on** to help you get an accurate figure.

Triangular Graphs Show **Percentages** Split into **Three Categories**

1) To read a triangular graph, start by **finding the point** you want on the graph.

2) **Follow** the **line** that goes **down** from the **point** to the **lowest end** of the **scale** and record the percentage.

3) Then **turn the graph around** so that the next axis is at **the bottom**, **follow** the **line** down to the lower end of the scale and record that percentage.

4) Do the same for the **third axis**.

5) The three readings should **add up to 100%**.

6) The graph on the right shows the age distribution of three populations. There are **three age groups** so a triangular graph can be used. **Each point** represents **one population**.

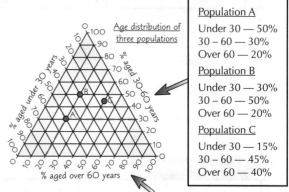

Population A
Under 30 — 50%
30 – 60 — 30%
Over 60 — 20%
Population B
Under 30 — 30%
30 – 60 — 50%
Over 60 — 20%
Population C
Under 30 — 15%
30 – 60 — 45%
Over 60 — 40%

On this scale the lowest end is on the **left**, so to find the percentage you follow the line down and towards the left of the scale.

Dispersion Diagrams Show the **Frequency of Data**

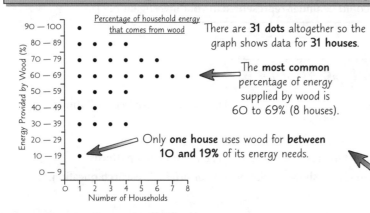

There are **31 dots** altogether so the graph shows data for **31 houses**.

The **most common** percentage of energy supplied by wood is 60 to 69% (8 houses).

Only **one house** uses wood for **between 10 and 19%** of its energy needs.

1) Dispersion diagrams are a bit like a cross between a **tally chart** and a **bar chart**.

2) The **range of data that's measured** goes on one axis. **Frequency** goes on the other axis.

3) **Each dot** represents **one piece of information** — the **more dots** there are in a particular category, the **more frequently** that event has happened.

4) The dispersion diagram on the left shows the **percentage of household energy** that comes from **wood** for **houses** in a **particular village**.

Logarithmic Scales are Used When the **Data Range is Large**

1) The **intervals** on logarithmic scales are **not fixed amounts** (e.g. they don't go up by 5 every time).

2) Instead, the **intervals get increasingly larger** at the top end of the scale (e.g. 10, 20, 40, 80).

3) This lets you fit a **very wide range of data** onto one **axis** without having to draw an enormous graph.

4) The graph on the right uses a **logarithmic scale** on the **vertical axis** to show how the world's population changed between 1950 and 2000.

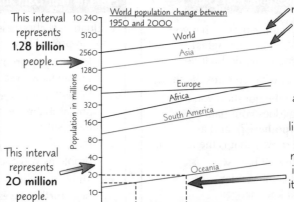

This interval represents **1.28 billion people.**

This interval represents **20 million people.**

Be careful, it looks like the world's population isn't much bigger than Asia's but that's only because there are **big jumps** at this end of the scale.

Graphs with log scales are **really tricky** to **read**. It's OK if your working line hits a label on the log axis (e.g. there were 20 million people in Oceania in 1975), but if it doesn't it's easiest to **give a range** (e.g. it was between 10 and 20 million in 1960).

Graph and Map Skills

Choropleth Maps Show Information Using Colours and Patterns

1) Choropleth maps show how something **varies** between **different areas** using **colours** or **patterns**.

2) The maps in exams often use **cross-hatched lines** and **dots**.

3) They're straightforward to read but it's **easy to make mistakes** with them as the patterns can be very similar.

4) If you're asked to talk about all the parts of the map with a **certain type of hatching**, look at the map carefully and put a **big tick** on each part with that hatching, to make them all **stand out**.

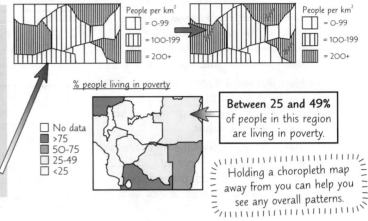

Between 25 and 49% of people in this region are living in poverty.

Holding a choropleth map away from you can help you see any overall patterns.

Dot Maps Show Distribution and Quantity Using Identical Symbols...

1) Dot maps use **identical dots** to show how something is **distributed** across an area.

2) Use the **key** to find out what **quantity** each dot represents

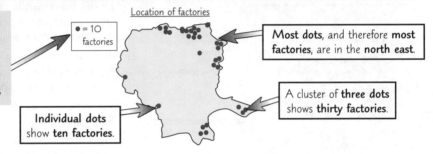

● = 10 factories

Most dots, and therefore **most factories**, are in the **north east**.

A cluster of **three dots** shows **thirty factories**.

Individual dots show **ten factories**.

...Proportional Symbol Maps Use Symbols of Different Sizes

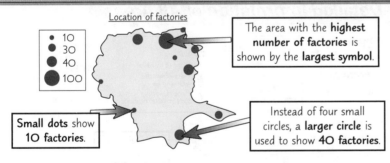

Location of factories

● 10
● 30
● 40
● 100

The area with the **highest number of factories** is shown by the **largest symbol**.

Small dots show **10 factories**.

Instead of four small circles, a **larger circle** is used to show **40 factories**.

1) **Proportional symbol maps** use symbols of **different sizes** to represent **different quantities**.

2) A **key** shows the quantity each symbol represents. The **bigger** the **symbol**, the **larger** the **amount**.

3) The symbols might be **circles**, **squares**, **semi-circles** or **bars**, but they're always read the **same way**.

Isoline Maps Show Where Conditions are the Same

1) **Isolines** are lines on a map **linking** up all the **places** where something's the **same**, e.g. on **weather maps** isolines show places that have the **same air pressure**.

2) If the place you're being asked about lies **on** an isoline you can just **read** the value off the line.

3) If the place is **between** isolines you have to **estimate** the value.

Helsinki and Lecce both lie **on** this line so both have a pressure of **996 mb**.

Madrid lies **between** the lines for **988** and **992**. It's pretty much in the middle of the lines, so has a pressure of roughly **990 mb**.

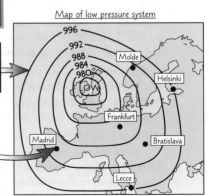

Map of low pressure system

Exam Skills

Graph and Map Skills

Flow Lines and *Trip Lines* Show *Movement*...

1) **Trip line maps** have straight lines showing the **origin**, **destination** and **direction** of movements, but they **don't** show the **volume** of movement.

2) **Flow line maps** have **arrows** on, which can be **different sizes** to show how many things **move** (or are moved) from **one place to another**.

3) The flow line map on the right shows the movement of people **into** and **out of** a **region**. The sizes of the arrows show **how many** people are moving.

The **largest flows** of people are **to Region A**, as these are the **largest arrows**.

Roughly the same number of people are **immigrating to Region A from Regions B and C**. This is shown by the arrows, which are the **same size**.

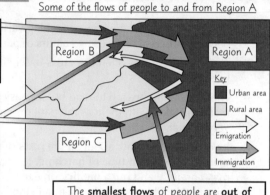
Some of the flows of people to and from Region A

The **smallest flows** of people are **out of** Region A, as these are the **smallest arrows**.

...and so do *Desire Lines*

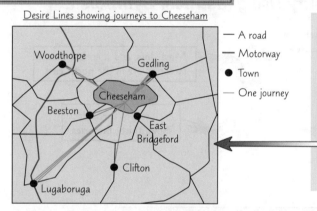
Desire Lines showing journeys to Cheeseham

— A road
— Motorway
● Town
— One journey

1) **Desire line maps** have **straight lines** that show **journeys** between two locations, but they **don't follow roads** or **railway lines**.

2) They're used to show **how far** a population has **travelled** to get to a **place**, e.g. a shop or a town centre, and **where it's come from**.

3) In the map on the left, the **number of lines** represents the number of **journeys**.

4) The **width** of the lines can also be changed to show the **volume** of the movements.

Ordnance Survey Maps Show *Detailed Information* of *All Areas*

1) Ordnance Survey® (OS®) maps use lots of **symbols**. It's a good idea to **learn** the most common ones.

2) You can find places on OS maps using **grid references**.

3) **Four-figure grid references** direct you to a 1 km × 1 km **square** on the map, e.g. for **1534** go **across** to the number **15** (the **eastings** value) and then **up** to the number **34** (the **northings** value). This grid reference refers to the **square above** and to the **right** of the point 1534.

4) **Six-figure grid references** are more precise and can direct you to a more **exact spot** (a 100 m × 100 m square). E.g. for 155341 the eastings value is 155, so go across to 15 again and then a further **5 "tenths"** across the square. For the northings value of 341 go up to 34 and a further **1 "tenth"** of that square. The spot you're looking for is where the easting and northing values **cross**.

5) Every map has a **scale** so that you can work out the **distance between points**. If the scale is **1:25 000**, it means that every **1 cm** on the map represents **25 000 cm** (250 m) in real life.

6) **Altitude** (height above sea level) is shown on OS maps using a type of isoline called **contour lines**. The **closer together** the contour lines are, the **steeper the gradient** is. Sometimes, the altitude of specific **spot heights** is also given.

Common OS Map Symbols

— Railway
▢ Building
+ Place of worship
⚲ Place of worship, with a tower
♦ Place of worship with a spire, minaret or dome

═══ Motorway
═══ Main (A) road
═══ Secondary (B) road

⬤ Bus station
PO Post office
PH Pub
-·-·- County boundary
═══ National Park boundaries
═══ Footpaths

Grid reference: 1534

Grid reference: 155341

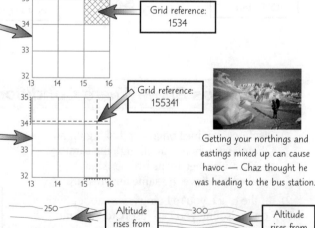

Getting your northings and eastings mixed up can cause havoc — Chaz thought he was heading to the bus station.

Altitude rises from **200 m** to **250 m**.

Altitude rises from **200 m** to **300 m**.

The contour lines on the right are closer together and show a **steeper slope** (there's a **greater increase in height** over the same distance).

Statistical Skills

As if knowing about loads of weird graphs and maps wasn't enough, you also need to be pretty familiar with statistics.
These next two pages cover the ones you need to know.

There are **Different Ways** of Finding the **Average** Value of a Set of Data

1) The **mean**, **median** and **mode** are different ways of finding the **average** value of a set of data.

2) You find the **mean** by **adding up** all the numbers in a set of data, then **dividing** by the number of **sample points**, n.

Take a look at the data in this table:

Location	1	2	3	4	5	6	7	8	9	10	11
Temperature in °C	3	7	4	3	7	9	9	5	5	7	6

n = 11, so the mean temperature is: $\dfrac{3+7+4+3+7+9+9+5+5+7+6}{11} = $ **5.9°C**.

3) The **median** is the **middle value** in an ordered set of data. So you need to **sort the numbers into order**, then work out which one is in the middle. So for the data above the median is **6 °C**.

3 3 4 5 5 ⑥ 7 7 7 9 9

If there are an even number of sample points the median is the mean of the middle two numbers.

4) The **mode** is the **most common value** in a set of data. So for the data above the mode is **7 °C**. ⟹ 3 3 4 5 5 6 ⑦ ⑦ ⑦ 9 9

Sometimes there isn't a mode, and sometimes there's more than one.

The **Interquartile Range** is a **Measure of Dispersion**...

1) The **range** of a dataset is the **difference** between the **highest** and the **lowest** values.

2) The **Interquartile range** (**IQR**) is the range of values covered by the **middle 50%** of a set of data.

3) To find the interquartile range you first need to find the median of the values **to the left** of the median. This is called the **lower quartile** (**LQ**). Next find the median of the values **to the right** of the median. This is the **upper quartile** (**UQ**). Then you just **subtract** the **LQ from the UQ** to give you the **IQR**.

4) So, for the data above, the **LQ** is **4** and the **UQ** is **7**, and the interquartile range is UQ – LQ = 7 – 4 = **3°C**.

5) The interquartile range tells you about the **spread** of data **around** the **median**. If it's a **big** number, it shows that the numbers are pretty **spread out**. And yep, you've guessed it — a **small** number means that a lot of the data is pretty **close** to the **median**.

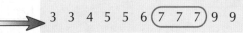

LQ   Median   UQ
3 3 ④ 5 5 ⑥ 7 7 ⑦ 9 9
IQR

...and so is **Standard Deviation**

1) The **standard deviation** is a bit trickier to calculate than the IQR, but it's often a **more reliable** measure of dispersion (spread). The symbol for it is σ.

The formula is $\sigma = \sqrt{\dfrac{\sum(x - \bar{x})^2}{n}}$

Σ just means 'sum of', and x̄ is just a way of writing 'mean'.

2) To calculate it, it's easiest to **work out** the **individual bits** in the formula **first**, e.g. the mean. It's a good idea to **draw** a **table** to help you. Below is a simple example for the set: 5, 9, 10, 11, 14.

- For these numbers, the **mean** is (5 + 9 + 10 + 11 + 14) ÷ 5 = **9.8**. This is shown in the 2nd column in the table.
- For each number, **calculate x – x̄** (3rd column in the table).
- Then **square** each of those values (4th column) — remember that the square of a **negative number** is always **positive**.
- Then **add up** all the squared numbers you've just worked out — this will give you $\sum(x - \bar{x})^2$.
- Now just **divide** your total by **n**, then take the **square root**.
- In this example, n = 5, so $\sigma = \sqrt{\dfrac{42.8}{5}} = $ **2.93** (2 d.p.)

x	x̄	x – x̄	(x – x̄)²
5	9.8	−4.8	23.04
9	9.8	−0.8	0.64
10	9.8	0.2	0.04
11	9.8	1.2	1.44
14	9.8	4.2	17.64
		Σ	42.8

3) If the standard deviation is **large**, the numbers in the set of data are **spread out** around the **mean**. If it's **small**, the numbers are **bunched** closely around the mean.

Standard deviation can be represented by σ or s.

Exam Skills

Statistical Skills

Make Sure You Know How to Find *Spearman's Rank Correlation Coefficient*

The Spearman's Rank correlation coefficient is a test to find out whether two sets of numbers are **correlated** (there's a **relationship** between them). The example below uses the test to see if **GDP per capita** ($) and **life expectancy** (in years) are correlated.

1) The bad news is that it's a bit of a pain to calculate. The first step is to give a **rank** to each number in both sets of data. The **highest** number is given rank **1**, the second highest is given rank 2... you get the idea.

2) Then you **calculate 'd'**, the **difference** between the ranks for each item, e.g. if the ranks for Country F are 4 and 6, the difference is 2.

3) Next you **square 'd'** and **add up** the **d^2 values** to give $\sum d^2$, which you use in the formula below.

4) Finally you need to work out the **Spearman's Rank Correlation Coefficient** (known as **r_s**).

The formula is: $r_s = 1 - \dfrac{6\sum d^2}{n^3 - n}$

Country	GDP per capita ($)	GDP rank	Life expectancy	Life expec. rank	d	d^2
A	14 000	5	72	5	0	0
B	19 000	4	71	6	2	4
C	9000	9	67	8	1	1
D	6000	11	61	11	0	0
E	21 000	3	75	3	0	0
F	13 000	6	74	4	2	4
G	22 000	2	76	2	0	0
H	35 000	1	78	1	0	0
I	5000	12	60	12	0	0
J	7000	10	65	9	1	1
K	11 000	8	64	10	2	4
L	12 000	7	69	7	0	0

$\sum d^2$ = 14

5) So for the example above, $\sum d^2 = 14$ and n = 12. So $r_s = 1 - \dfrac{6 \times 14}{12^3 - 12} = 1 - \dfrac{84}{1716} = 1 - 0.05 = \mathbf{0.95}$

6) The number you get is always **between –1 and +1**.

7) A **positive number** means the variables are **positively correlated** — as one variable **increases** so does the **other**. The **closer** the number is to 1 the **stronger** the correlation.

8) A **negative number** means that the two sets of variables are **negatively correlated** — as one variable **increases** the other **decreases**. The **closer** the number is to –1 the **stronger** the correlation.

9) If the coefficient is **0**, or near 0, there probably isn't much of a relationship between the figures.

10) The value of r_s in the example above was **0.95**, which is **close to 1**, so there's a **strong positive correlation** between the **data** for GDP per capita and life expectancy.

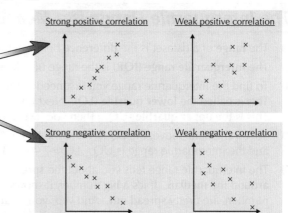

You *Have To Check* the *Correlation Is Significant* Though

1) A **Spearman's Rank correlation coefficient** might tell you that **two sets of numbers** are **correlated**. But you need to check whether this is evidence for a **genuine link** between the two quantities you're looking at. (You sometimes get correlations between sets of data **by chance**, even if there's no underlying relationship. For example, there **is** a correlation between GDP per capita and life expectancy **for the data shown above**, but this might have been a fluke and there might be **no real relationship** between the two things.)

2) You can check whether it's evidence for a genuine link by looking at the **probability** that a correlation would happen by chance. If there's a 5% (or higher) probability that a correlation is because of chance then it's **not significant** evidence for a link. If there's a **0.1% or less** chance, then it's **very significant** evidence for a link. (This is what's meant by the **significance level** of a statistical test — it's a kind of 'cut-off' probability.)

3) To test whether the value of r_s is evidence for a relationship between GDP per capita and life expectancy, you'll need a **graph** like the one on the right, or a **table** of critical values. You'll also need to know the **degrees of freedom** (in the example above this is just n – 2, so 12 – 2 = **10**). Since $r_s = \mathbf{0.95}$, you can use the graph to find that this correlation has a **less than 0.1%** probability of being due to chance. This means you have **very significant** evidence for a **relationship** between GDP per capita and life expectancy.

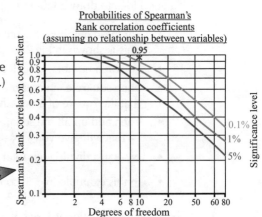

Probabilities of Spearman's Rank correlation coefficients (assuming no relationship between variables)

Answers

Topic One — Water and Carbon Cycles

Page 3 — Natural Systems

1 One mark for each valid point, up to a maximum of 3 marks. E.g.:
Both energy and matter can enter and leave an open system *[1 mark]*. In closed systems, matter can't enter or leave and can only cycle between stores *[1 mark]*. Energy can enter and leave a closed system *[1 mark]*.

2 One mark for each valid point, up to a maximum of 3 marks. E.g.:
Positive feedbacks are mechanisms which amplify a change in inputs or outputs *[1 mark]*. This means that the system responds by increasing the effects of the change *[1 mark]*. The system moves even further from its previous state *[1 mark]*.
You could use an example to help explain positive feedback, e.g. higher temperatures cause more ice to melt, so less solar energy is reflected and more is absorbed, leading to even higher temperatures.

Page 5 — The Water Cycle

1 One mark for each valid point, up to a maximum of 3 marks. E.g.:
Condensation is when water vapour changes state to become a liquid *[1 mark]*. It is an essential part of the water cycle, as without it, clouds would not form and precipitation would not occur *[1 mark]*. Precipitation is needed for water to flow from the atmosphere to stores on the Earth's surface *[1 mark]*.

Page 7 — Drainage Basins

1 One mark for each valid point, up to a maximum of 3 marks. E.g.:
In wet seasons (e.g. winter in the UK), precipitation is higher than evapotranspiration *[1 mark]*. This creates a water surplus *[1 mark]*. In dry seasons (e.g. summer in the UK), precipitation is lower than evapotranspiration *[1 mark]* and water in the ground store is depleted *[1 mark]*. This leads to a water deficit *[1 mark]*.

Page 9 — Variations in Runoff and the Water Cycle

1 Maximum of 6 marks available. This question is level marked.
HINTS:
- You need to describe the differences between the lines on the hydrograph for the two rivers and suggest reasons for them.
- Take your time to study the hydrograph and pick out the differences. Think about what might have caused each one — you could consider the effect of differences in drainage basin characteristics, land use and farming practices.

- Once you've done that, write about each difference individually — say what the difference is and give possible explanations for each one. E.g. 'River A has a higher peak discharge than River B. This could be because River A has a larger drainage basin than River B, which can catch more precipitation, so more water ends up in the river'.

2 Maximum of 9 marks available. This question is level marked. HINTS:
- Begin by briefly introducing the idea that both physical and human activities can cause variations in the drainage basin-scale water cycle.
- Then describe some of the physical causes of variation. For example, 'Seasonal variations in plant growth can affect the drainage basin-scale water cycle. Vegetation intercepts precipitation, which increases the amount of water being returned to the atmosphere through transpiration and evaporation from the vegetation rather than making it to the river channel. Interception is highest when there's lots of vegetation and deciduous trees have their leaves.'
- Make sure you cover some of the human causes of variation too. For example, 'Deforestation reduces the amount of water that is intercepted by vegetation, increasing the amount of water reaching the surface. It also means that there is less dead plant material on the ground — dead plant material helps to hold the water, allowing it to infiltrate the soil rather than leave the area as runoff, so removing it reduces infiltration.'
- Finish with a conclusion — it should briefly sum up how the factors you have covered affect the drainage basin-scale water cycle.

Page 11 — The Carbon Cycle

1 One mark for each valid point, up to a maximum of 3 marks. E.g.:
Photosynthesis transfers carbon stored in the atmosphere to the biomass store *[1 mark]*. Plants and phytoplankton use energy from the Sun to change carbon dioxide and water into glucose and oxygen, enabling plants to grow *[1 mark]*. Carbon is then passed from these plants through the food chain and is released back into the atmosphere through respiration and decomposition *[1 mark]*.

Page 13 — The Carbon Cycle

1 One mark for each valid point, up to a maximum of 3 marks. E.g.:
Increased levels of CO_2 in the atmosphere can increase the acidity of the oceans, which can affect marine life *[1 mark]*. Increased levels of carbon in the atmosphere can also cause global warming, which may increase the temperature of the oceans *[1 mark]*. This may mean that organisms that are sensitive to temperature change may decrease in number *[1 mark]*. Warmer water is less able to absorb CO_2, decreasing the amount of CO_2 that could potentially be dissolved in the oceans *[1 mark]*.

Answers

Page 15 — Water, Carbon and Climate

1 Maximum of 9 marks available. This question is level marked. <u>HINTS</u>:
   - Begin by briefly outlining the carbon cycle and water cycle and explaining what positive and negative feedbacks are.
   - Describe some of the feedbacks in the carbon cycle and how they can affect life on Earth. For example, 'If temperatures rise, the respiration rate of plants will increase. This means they will release more carbon dioxide, so the amount of carbon dioxide in the atmosphere will increase. This increases the greenhouse effect, which causes temperatures to increase more. This will cause plants to grow faster because their respiration rate is higher. This is a positive feedback.'
   - Then do the same for some of the feedbacks in the water cycle and their effect on life on Earth.
   - Finish with a conclusion — it should briefly sum up the feedbacks and their effects on life on Earth, as well as coming to a clear conclusion about the extent to which these feedbacks may affect life on Earth.

Page 17 — The Amazon Rainforest — Case Study

1 Maximum of 9 marks available. This question is level marked. <u>HINTS</u>:
   - Start by briefly outlining the natural water cycle, with reference to tropical rainforests.
   - Give some examples of human activities that take place in rainforests and examine the effect of each on the water cycle in the rainforest. For example, 'Many human activities cause deforestation of the rainforest. This can affect the water cycle in several ways, for example the lack of a canopy means that less rainfall is intercepted by vegetation, so more water reaches the surface. This causes runoff to increase...'.
   - The questions asks 'To what extent...', so you could also describe some ways in which people are trying to limit their impact on the water cycle. For example, you could talk about limiting deforestation and replanting trees that have been cut down.
   - You could use examples from your case study in your answer.
   - Finish with a conclusion that sums up the points you have made and comes to an overall conclusion about the extent to which human activity is affecting the water cycle in tropical rainforests.

Page 19 — The Eden Basin — Case Study

1 Maximum of 9 marks available. This question is level marked. <u>HINTS</u>:
   - Begin by briefly describing the location you have studied — where it is, what the landscape is like etc. You could use the Eden Basin case study to answer this question.
   - Then describe some changes in the water cycle in the drainage basin and how they have affected sustainable water supply or the risk of flooding. For example, 'Parts of the Eden Basin have been deforested. This means that there is less interception and infiltration during heavy rainfall than there would be if the area was still forested, so water reaches the Eden more quickly, meaning there is a greater risk of flooding.'

Answers

   - The question asks you to 'Assess the extent...', so you could also consider ways in which changes haven't affected flood risk or sustainable water supply, or have had a positive effect on it. For example, you could talk about the building of flood defences.
   - Finish up with a conclusion that sums up the ways in which changes in the water cycle have affected the risk of flooding or sustainable water supply, and come to an overall conclusion that answers the question.

Topic Two — Coastal Systems and Landscapes

Page 21 — The Coastal System

1 One mark for each valid point, up to a maximum of 3 marks. E.g.:
Constructive waves are flat and gentle *[1 mark]*. They have a low frequency *[1 mark]* of about 6-8 waves per minute *[1 mark]*. Their swash is greater than their backwash *[1 mark]* which carries material up the beach and deposits it *[1 mark]*.

2 One mark for each valid point, up to a maximum of 3 marks. E.g.:
Wind can bring energy into the coastal system as air moves from areas of high pressure to areas of low pressure *[1 mark]*. Energy can also be brought into the system by water, in the form of waves, tides and currents *[1 mark]*. The amount of energy brought into the system by movement of water is affected by fetch *[1 mark]*.

Page 23 — Coastal Processes

1 One mark for each valid point, up to a maximum of 3 marks. E.g.:
Freeze-thaw weathering and salt weathering occur when seawater enters cracks and pores in coastal rocks *[1 mark]*. Crystals of ice or salt form and expand when water freezes or evaporates *[1 mark]*. This exerts pressure on the rock, causing small pieces to fall off *[1 mark]*.
You could also have written about other types of weathering, such as wetting and drying or chemical weathering.

Page 26 — Coastal Landforms

1 One mark for each valid point, up to a maximum of 3 marks. E.g.:
Weathering and wave erosion forms a notch in a cliff which, over time, develops into a cave *[1 mark]*.
Rock above the cave is unsupported and so collapses *[1 mark]*. As this process is repeated the cliff retreats, leaving behind a flat wave-cut platform *[1 mark]*.

Answers

2   One mark for each valid point, up to a maximum of
    3 marks. E.g.:
    Spits form when longshore drift deposits material across
    a break in the coastline (e.g. at a river mouth) *[1 mark]*.
    This leaves a ridge of sand and shingle sticking out
    into the sea *[1 mark]*. If the dominant wind and wave
    direction changes, the spit may change direction and
    develop a recurved end *[1 mark]*.

Page 29 — Sea Level Changes

1   One mark for each valid point, up to a maximum of
    3 marks. E.g.:
    Coastal submergence happens when the sea level rises
    relative to the land *[1 mark]*. This creates a range of
    landforms, e.g. rias are formed when the sea drowns
    river valleys *[1 mark]*. Similarly, fjords are formed
    when sea level rise floods glacial valleys *[1 mark]*. In
    areas where valleys lie parallel to the coast, an increase
    in sea level can form Dalmatian coastlines *[1 mark]*.
    These occur when valleys are flooded, leaving islands
    parallel to the coast *[1 mark]*.
2   Maximum of 9 marks available. This question is
    level marked. <u>HINTS</u>:
    • Start off by briefly describing how climate is likely to change
      in the future, e.g. 'Climate change is likely to cause global
      temperatures to rise in the future, and may cause increased
      storminess in some areas.'
    • Describe some of the physical impacts that this could have on
      coastal areas, e.g. 'Increased global temperatures are likely to
      result in sea level rise. This would cause more frequent and
      more severe flooding of coastal areas, and the submergence
      of some low-lying areas. For example, sea level rise of 0.5 m
      would submerge most of the Maldives.'
    • You could also mention the possible impacts on people,
      e.g. 'Increased storminess could cause damage to coastal
      settlements, destroying people's homes and livelihoods.'
    • You could also mention factors that might mitigate the
      impacts of climate change, e.g. 'As sea level rises, governments
      might spend more on coastal defences to protect vulnerable
      areas from flooding and storm damage.'

Page 31 — Coastal Management

1   One mark for each valid point, up to a maximum of
    3 marks. E.g.:
    Hard engineering schemes involve built structures, e.g.
    sea walls and gabions *[1 mark]*. They are normally
    designed to hinder natural processes, e.g. erosion
    [1 mark]. Soft engineering schemes try to work with
    natural processes *[1 mark]*, e.g. beach nourishment
    involves adding sand and shingle to beaches to reduce
    erosion of the cliffs behind *[1 mark]*.

Page 33 — Coastal Environment — Case Study

1   Maximum of 20 marks available. This question is
    level marked. <u>HINTS</u>:
    • Start by outlining the reasons for coastal management, and
      some of the different options (e.g. hold the line, managed
      retreat).
    • Next, explain how coastal management can be made
      sustainable — you could outline different strategies (e.g.
      Integrated Coastal Zone Management) and soft engineering
      techniques (e.g. beach stabilisation and dune regeneration).
    • You should also consider some of the challenges to
      sustainability, e.g. 'It is socially unsustainable to allow homes
      and businesses to flood, but it may be economically and
      environmentally unsustainable to build and maintain defences
      for the area.'
    • The question doesn't specifically ask for a case study, but
      you can still use one, e.g. you could bring in details about
      management strategies on the Holderness coast.
    • Finish with a conclusion — it should summarise your
      discussion and come to a clear decision about the extent to
      which sustainable management of coastal areas is achievable.

Page 35 — Humans at the Coast — Case Study

1   Maximum of 9 marks available. This question is
    level marked. <u>HINTS</u>:
    • You could start by outlining the region you have studied and
      explaining some of the challenges to occupation.
    • You need to outline some of the ways that humans have
      responded to the challenges of the area, e.g. 'In some areas,
      people are growing salt-resistant varieties of rice, to prevent
      loss of crops during floods.'
    • For each response you talk about, you need to evaluate how
      successful it has been or is likely to be, e.g. 'Salt-resistant
      crops could help to increase food security for people in the
      region, which would have positive effects on health and quality
      of life. However, growing a smaller range of crops could
      reduce biodiversity in the region and increase vulnerability to
      pests and diseases that affect those particular crops.'
    • Finish off with a conclusion — it should briefly summarise the
      human responses to challenges in the region you've studied,
      and come to an overall conclusion about how successful those
      responses have been.

Answers

Topic Three — Glacial Systems and Landscapes

Page 37 — Cold Environments

1 Maximum of 6 marks available. This question is level marked. HINTS:
- Begin by outlining briefly where polar, alpine and periglacial environments are found today.
- Then outline briefly where polar, alpine and periglacial environments were found 21 000 years before present.
- Finally, describe the differences in the distribution of these areas. You could describe the overall trend, e.g. 'The extent of cold environments has reduced and they have moved polewards between 21 000 years before present and today.' Then give some specific examples, e.g. 'Most of Europe was polar or periglacial 21 000 years before present, whereas today there are only small patches of alpine areas.'

Page 39 — Glacial Systems

1 One mark for each valid point, up to a maximum of 3 marks. E.g.:
A glacial budget is the balance between accumulation (the input of snow and ice into a glacier) and ablation (the output of water from a glacier) over a year *[1 mark]*. If the glacial budget is positive, accumulation is exceeding ablation, and the glacier is advancing *[1 mark]*. If the glacial budget is negative, ablation is exceeding accumulation, and the glacier is retreating *[1 mark]*.

Page 41 — Glacial Processes

1 One mark for each valid point, up to a maximum of 3 marks. E.g.:
At the head of a glacier the valley is steep, so there's a strong gravitational force pulling the ice downwards *[1 mark]*. This makes the ice move quickly *[1 mark]*. The tension created causes the ice to crack into layers, which slip downwards over each other *[1 mark]*.

Page 43 — Glacial Landforms

1 Maximum of 6 marks available. This question is level marked. HINTS:
- There are three main landforms present in the photograph. You should name each one and describe how it formed.
- You could start with the arête, e.g. 'There is an arête in the centre-right of the photograph. An arête is formed when two glaciers flow in parallel valleys. The glaciers erode the sides of the valleys, which sharpens the mountain ridge between.'
- Then move on to the corrie on the left of the photo and the tarn in the corrie. You could also mention the glacial trough in the background of the photo.

2 One mark for each valid point, up to a maximum of 3 marks. E.g.:
Moraine is unsorted till left behind by glaciers *[1 mark]*. Lateral moraine forms where the sides of a glacier were as it retreats *[1 mark]*. Medial moraine is deposited in the centre of the valley where two glaciers converge (the two lateral moraines join together) *[1 mark]*. Terminal moraine builds up at the end of the glacier, and is deposited as semicircular hillocks of till *[1 mark]*.

Page 45 — Fluvioglacial Processes and Landforms

1 One mark for each valid point, up to a maximum of 3 marks. E.g.:
Kames are mounds of sand and gravel found on the valley floor *[1 mark]*. Meltwater streams on top of glaciers collect in depressions and deposit layers of debris *[1 mark]*. When the ice melts, the debris in the depressions is dumped onto the valley floor *[1 mark]*.

2 One mark for each valid point, up to a maximum of 3 marks. E.g.:
An outwash plain with layers of gravel, sand and clay forms as meltwater flows out of a glacier, depositing sediment *[1 mark]*. Gravel gets dropped first because it's heavier than sand and clay, so it forms the bottom layer of the outwash plain *[1 mark]*. Clay is dropped last and gets carried furthest away from the snout because it's the lightest sediment — it forms the top layer of the outwash plain *[1 mark]*.

Page 47 — Periglacial Processes and Landforms

1 One mark for each valid point, up to a maximum of 3 marks. E.g.:
Very low temperatures in winter cause the ground to contract and cracks to form in the permafrost *[1 mark]*. In spring, the active layer thaws and meltwater seeps into the cracks *[1 mark]*. The permafrost layer is still frozen, so the water freezes in the cracks, forming ice wedges *[1 mark]*. Ice wedges can grow each year as frost contraction re-opens existing cracks, which fill with water and freeze again, causing further expansion of the ice wedge *[1 mark]*.

Page 49 — Glacial Landscape — Case Study

1 Maximum of 9 marks available. This question is level marked. HINTS:
- Start by introducing the glaciated landscape that you have studied — outline where it is, when it was last glaciated and some of the features of the landscape.
- Then explain some of the glacial landforms found in the area — you should name them, say where each one is found and give an overview of how it formed. E.g. 'There is a blockfield at the summit of Glyder Fach in Snowdonia — this formed under periglacial conditions, principally by frost action.'

Answers

- You could also mention non-glacial processes that have influenced the development of the landscape, such as fluvial action and human activities.
- Finish off with a conclusion, briefly summarising how the landscape of the place you have studied has been affected by glacial processes.

Page 51 — Human Impacts on Cold Environments

1 Maximum of 9 marks available. This question is level marked. HINTS:
- Start by briefly outlining why cold environments are fragile, some of the human activities that may damage cold environments and why this means that management is necessary to limit damage.
- Next give some examples of management techniques that can be used to prevent damage. You might comment on how successful they have been and discuss whether they have prevented damage. E.g. 'Visitors can damage the Antarctic environment. There are strategies to manage tourism, e.g. the number of tourists who may visit is limited, and visitors must clean and disinfect footwear when they land. Strategies like these will help to prevent damage to the environment, e.g. by preventing non-native species from entering the ecosystem. However, demand for tourism is increasing, so it may become increasingly difficult to manage its impacts.'
- Finish off with a conclusion that clearly explains the extent to which you think management can prevent damage to fragile cold environments.

Page 53 — Humans in Glacial Landscapes — Case Study

1 One mark for each valid point, up to a maximum of 3 marks. Your answer will vary according to which case study you have learnt. E.g.:
There are very large oil and gas reserves in the north of Alaska, which could be extracted *[1 mark]*. Large amounts of mineral resources in the Tintina belt towards the centre of the state also offer opportunities for mining *[1 mark]*. There are rich stocks of salmon, crab and pollock in the waters around Alaska, which offer opportunities for fishing *[1 mark]*.

2 Maximum of 20 marks available. This question is level marked. HINTS:
- You could begin by briefly outlining some of the opportunities for development in cold environments.
- Next, outline some of the challenges to development in cold environments, e.g. 'It's difficult to construct buildings to support development in cold environments as such areas are often difficult to access. In addition, buildings may melt the permafrost, which would cause them to collapse.'
- Then suggest ways in which the challenges you outlined can be overcome, including responses of resilience, mitigation and adaptation, e.g. 'Humans can respond to challenges by mitigating risks. For example, buildings can be constructed on stilts to prevent them from melting the permafrost, so that they don't collapse.'

- For each challenge you write about, you should mention the pros and cons of overcoming it, e.g. 'Limiting permafrost melting helps to minimise damage to the environment. However, it also adds to the cost of construction and may not be possible for all buildings and infrastructure.'
- You might refer to examples from a cold environment you have studied, e.g. Alaska.
- Finish off with a conclusion that summarises the points you made and comes to a clear, balanced conclusion about the extent to which you agree that challenges to development can and should be overcome.

Topic Four — Hazards

Page 55 — Natural Hazards

1 One mark for each valid point, up to a maximum of 3 marks. E.g.:
Mitigation aims to minimise the impacts of future hazards, e.g. by making buildings fire-resistant *[1 mark]*. Preparedness is about planning how to respond to a hazard, e.g. installing warning systems *[1 mark]*. Response is how people react when a disaster occurs, e.g. evacuating the affected area *[1 mark]*. Recovery is about returning the affected area to normal, e.g. rebuilding houses *[1 mark]*.

2 Maximum of 6 marks available. This question is level marked. HINTS:
- Start by outlining some of the different perceptions of hazards, such as acceptance and dismissal of risk.
- Next, outline some of the factors that might affect perception — think about economic and cultural factors, e.g. wealth, education, religion.
- For each factor you give, explain how it might affect people's perception of the hazard. E.g. 'Richer people may be able to afford to move to areas that are less prone to hazards, or to build their houses to withstand hazards, so they may perceive the risk as smaller.'
- Finish with a conclusion that sums up your main points.

Page 57 — Plate Tectonics

1 One mark for each valid point, up to a maximum of 3 marks. E.g.:
Slab pull happens at destructive plate margins *[1 mark]*. Denser crust is forced under less dense crust *[1 mark]*. The sinking of the plate edge pulls the rest of the plate towards the boundary *[1 mark]*. This makes the whole plate move *[1 mark]*.

Answers

2   One mark for each valid point, up to a maximum of 3 marks. E.g.:
Sea-floor spreading happens at constructive plate margins *[1 mark]*. As tectonic plates diverge, magma rises up to fill the gap *[1 mark]*. It then cools, forming new crust *[1 mark]*. Over time, the new crust is dragged apart and more new crust forms between the two sides *[1 mark]*.

Page 59 — Types of Plate Margin

1   Maximum of 6 marks available. This question is level marked. <u>HINTS</u>:
- Start your answer by briefly describing what a magma plume is and what causes it, e.g. 'A magma plume is a vertical column of magma that rises up from the mantle, causing an area of volcanic activity away from a plate margin (a hot spot).'
- Describe the distribution of the Hawaiian islands, making sure that you include plenty of relevant details from the map. E.g. 'The oldest island is Kauai, at 6 million years old, and the islands become younger in age as you move towards the south-east'.
- Next, give reasons why the islands are distributed in this way. State that the chain of volcanic islands has formed due to the magma plume staying still, whereas the plate has moved over it in a north-westerly direction.

2   One mark for each valid point, up to a maximum of 3 marks. E.g.:
At a conservative plate margin, the two plates are moving past each other *[1 mark]*. The two plates get locked together in places and pressure builds up *[1 mark]*. This causes the plates to jerk past each other, releasing the energy as an earthquake *[1 mark]*.

Page 61 — Volcanic Hazards

1   One mark for each valid point, up to a maximum of 3 marks. E.g.:
Basaltic lava is very hot and has a low viscosity, so it flows easily *[1 mark]*. This means that eruptions of basaltic lava are long-lived but not very violent *[1 mark]*. Andesitic and rhyolitic lava are cooler and more viscous, so they don't flow easily *[1 mark]*. Eruptions of these lava types are briefer but more violent *[1 mark]*.

Page 63 — Volcanic Hazards — Impacts and Responses

1   Maximum of 20 marks available. This question is level marked. <u>HINTS</u>:
- Start by briefly outlining some of the impacts of volcanic eruptions — you could mention social, environmental, economic and political impacts.
- Next, outline some of the ways that these impacts can be managed, including responses of mitigation, preparedness and adaptation.

- For each response to mention, you could suggest how successful it is likely to be at managing the impacts of the eruption, e.g. 'Evacuating people before an eruption could help to save lives. However, it won't help to protect buildings and infrastructure, so the economic impacts of the eruption would remain high.'
- You should also discuss whether or not the impacts of an eruption can be prevented, e.g. 'It is not possible to prevent volcanic eruptions, but some of their impacts could be prevented. For example, authorities could prevent the land around a volcano from being developed, so that an eruption would pose less threat to people. However, this would not reduce the environmental impacts of an eruption, or the impacts of widespread hazards such as ash clouds.'
- You could bring in the impacts of and responses to a specific eruption, such as the Soufrière Hills eruption in 1997.
- Finish with a conclusion that sums up your points and clearly states how far you agree with the statement in the question.

Page 65 — Seismic Hazards

1   One mark for each valid point, up to a maximum of 3 marks. E.g.:
Type of plate margin is a major control on earthquake magnitude *[1 mark]* — the biggest earthquakes occur at destructive margins and the smallest at constructive margins *[1 mark]*. The depth of the earthquake focus also influences magnitude *[1 mark]*. Deep focus earthquakes tend to have a higher magnitude than shallow focus earthquakes *[1 mark]*.

Page 67 — Seismic Hazards — Impacts and Responses

1   Maximum of 9 marks available. This question is level marked. <u>HINTS</u>:
- Start by outlining the different forms of seismic hazard and distinguishing between primary and secondary impacts.
- Next, outline some of the primary impacts of seismic hazards, e.g. 'People can be drowned if a coast is hit by a tsunami, and may be buried by landslides or avalanches.'
- Then, outline some of the secondary impacts of seismic hazards, e.g. 'Earthquakes can damage gas pipes — if gas is ignited, the resulting fire can kill many people. Damage to water supplies and sanitation could lead to the spread of disease, potentially affecting many people.'
- You could bring in impacts from a specific case study, e.g. the Kashmir earthquake in 2005.
- Finally, sum up your points and come to a clear conclusion about whether you think the primary or secondary impacts of seismic hazards are more dangerous.

Answers

Page 69 — Storm Hazards

1 One mark for each valid point, up to a maximum of 3 marks. E.g.:
Tropical storms need water that is above 27 °C to at least 50 m below the surface to form *[1 mark]*. They also need a disturbance near the sea surface, such as an area of low pressure *[1 mark]*. The air in the lower atmosphere must be converging *[1 mark]*. Tropical storms can only form more than 5° from the Equator *[1 mark]*.

Page 71 — Storm Hazards — Case Studies

1 Maximum of 20 marks available. This question is level marked. <u>HINTS</u>:
- Start by outlining some of the forms of storm hazards, such as high winds, heavy rain and storm surges. Describe some of the impacts that these hazards can have.
- Next, you could outline some of the ways in which storm hazards are likely to have a greater impact in less developed countries, e.g. 'Less developed countries may not have the warning and communication systems needed to predict tropical storms and urge people to evacuate vulnerable areas. This means that the death toll of a tropical storm in a less developed country is likely to be higher than in a more developed country.'
- Back up your points using examples from the case studies you have learned. E.g. 'Hurricane Katrina, which hit the south-east USA in 2005, killed around 1800 people. In contrast, Cyclone Nargis, which hit Myanmar in 2008, killed more than 140 000 people. This supports the view that the social impacts of tropical storms are greater in less developed countries.'
- Make any points that contradict the view that tropical storms always have greater impacts in less developed countries. For example, you could discuss the economic impacts of tropical storms, which are likely to be higher in more developed countries.
- Finish by summing up your points and coming to a clear conclusion about how far you agree with the statement in the question.

Page 73 — Wildfires

1 Maximum of 9 marks available. This question is level marked. <u>HINTS</u>:
- Start by introducing the area you are going to write about — give a brief overview of where it is, when the wildfires occurred and what caused them. You could use the wildfires in south-east Australia in 2009.
- Next, describe the impacts of the wildfires — you could include the number of people killed, injured or made homeless, the total cost and the impacts on habitats and animals.
- Go on to outline the responses to the wildfires — this could include short-term responses, such as evacuation and fire-fighting, and long-term responses, such as rebuilding houses to be more fire-resistant.

- The question asks you to evaluate the impacts and responses, so you need to discuss how successful the responses were at reducing the impacts — think about ways in which they were successful and ways in which they were not.
- Finish with a brief conclusion that sums up the impacts of and responses to the wildfires, and outlines how successful the responses were.

Page 74 — Multi-Hazard Environment — Case Study

1 Maximum of 9 marks available. This question is level marked. <u>HINTS</u>:
- Start by briefly outlining some of the hazards that people in multi-hazard environments have to cope with. You could mention the hazards of a specific geographical area.
- Next, outline how humans have responded to these hazards — this could include changes in people's perception of hazards, e.g. accepting them as a natural and unavoidable part of life. It could also include attempts to manage hazards and mitigate their impacts.
- You should also discuss how successful these responses are — think about ways in which they work, and ways in which they don't work.
- You could refer to the Philippines, which experiences volcanic and seismic hazards and tropical storms. Individuals have responded by trying to increase their own resilience to disasters, e.g. by stockpiling food. Authorities have responded by attempting to increase large-scale resilience, e.g. adapting buildings to cope with earthquakes. Such responses can help people to manage the impacts of hazards, but cannot prevent hazards or eliminate their impacts.
- Finish with a conclusion that sums up your points and outlines how successful human responses to multi-hazard environments are.

Page 75 — Hazardous Setting — Case Study

1 Maximum of 9 marks available. This question is level marked. <u>HINTS</u>:
- Start by outlining the area you are going to write about — give a brief overview of where it is and the hazard(s) it experiences.
- Describe how the character of the location has been affected by its hazardous setting. You could write about social, economic and political character.
- You could use L'Aquila in central Italy as an example, e.g. 'The social character of L'Aquila has changed as a result of past earthquakes and the threat of future earthquakes. For example, much of the city centre was destroyed by the 2009 earthquake, and people were rehoused in suburban areas and new towns. As a result, the city centre is much less populated and much quieter.'
- Finish with a conclusion that sums up how the character of the study area has changed as a result of its setting.

Answers

Topic Five — Contemporary Urban Environments

Page 77 — Urbanisation

1 One mark for each valid point, up to a maximum of 3 marks. E.g.:
Between 1950 and 2014, the percentage of people living in urban areas increased from 30% to over 50% *[1 mark]*. In developed countries, the proportion of people living in urban centres has been high and has increased slowly since 1945 *[1 mark]*. In developing countries, the proportion of people living in cities is lower, but it is increasing very rapidly *[1 mark]*. Rapid growth has created megacities in emerging economies, for example in Asia *[1 mark]*.

Page 79 — Urban Change

1 One mark for each valid point, up to a maximum of 3 marks. E.g.:
As cities increase in size and wealth, they attract migrants from all over the world, so cultural diversity increases *[1 mark]*. Migrants may form their own communities, leading to concentrations of people from the same ethnic background in particular areas, e.g. Chinatown in New York City *[1 mark]*. Migrants tend to be of working age, which may decrease the average age of the population *[1 mark]*. Young migrants may also start families, further decreasing the average age *[1 mark]*.

Page 81 — Urban Forms

1 Maximum of 9 marks available. This question is level marked.
HINTS:
• Start by briefly describing traditional land-use patterns of cities in the developed world, including patterns of residential and commercial use.
• Next, give some examples of new urban forms, such as town centre mixed developments, cultural and heritage quarters and fortress developments.
• For each one, explain how it may replace or alter traditional urban forms, e.g. 'Town centre mixed developments are areas where land use is mixed, so residential, commercial and leisure uses are combined. This challenges traditional urban forms, where different land uses are generally kept more separate.'
• You could also explain some of the ways in which the urban form of cities has not changed, e.g. 'Although many cities have some elements of these new forms, they are generally restricted to certain areas, for example there may be only a few fortress developments on the outskirts of a city. This means that the majority of the city retains a relatively traditional form.'
• Finish with a conclusion that sums up your points and clearly states the extent to which traditional urban forms are being challenged by new urban forms.

Page 83 — Urban Issues

1 Maximum of 9 marks available. This question is level marked.
HINTS:
• Start by briefly describing some of the social and economic issues that can influence the character of cities, such as economic inequalities, cultural diversity and social segregation.
• For each issue, explain how it might affect a city's character, e.g. 'Economic inequalities within a city can have a range of impacts on the character of a city, for example, the quality of housing and types of businesses will differ between different areas. In addition, people with little or no money may resent those with plenty, possibly leading to tension and even violence between different groups. This can lead to some areas of a city feeling unsafe for residents and visitors.'
• You could bring in examples from specific places you have studied, e.g. 'Some parts of London, such as Notting Hill, have been gentrified by wealthier people. This has forced poorer people out of these areas, changing their character entirely.'
• Finish off with a conclusion, briefly summarising the different ways in which social and economic issues can affect the character of cities.

Page 85 — Urban Climate

1 Maximum of 6 marks available. This question is level marked.
HINTS:
• You need to describe the differences and suggest reasons for them.
• Take your time to study the table and pick out the differences.
• Once you've done that, write about each climate characteristic individually — say what each difference is and explain why the two cities might be different. E.g. 'Annual average rainfall is 100 mm higher in City B than in City A. This could be because City B has more pollution that City A, so there are more condensation nuclei in the air to encourage cloud formation'.
• Include data from the table to support your points. Try to manipulate the data if you can, e.g. 'The average number of days without cloud cover is 50% higher in City A than City B'.

Page 87 — Urban Air Quality

1 One mark for each valid point, up to a maximum of 3 marks. E.g.:
Cities can reduce air pollution by reducing traffic, for example by improving public transport or encouraging walking *[1 mark]*. Improvements to public transport can include introducing bus lanes to make bus journeys faster, cheaper and more efficient *[1 mark]*. There are also larger scale ways of reducing urban air pollution, such as introducing new laws to limit emissions or encouraging the use of cleaner fuels *[1 mark]*. For example, biofuels can directly replace petrol and diesel, and they have lower particulate emissions *[1 mark]*.

Answers

Page 89 — Urban Drainage

1   Maximum of 9 marks available. This question is level marked.

HINTS:

- Start by briefly describing some of the drainage issues faced in cities, such as flooding, water pollution and drought.
- Next, explain briefly what river restoration and conservation are, and some of the methods they use, e.g. replanting of vegetation, creation of wetland areas.
- Explain how river restoration and conservation can help to reduce urban drainage issues, e.g. 'Creating wetlands means that surface runoff from roads enters wetlands rather than being channelled straight to rivers. This increases lag time, which can help to decrease flood risk. Wetlands also help to filter pollutants from water before it enters rivers, so water quality is improved.'
- Outline any reasons why river restoration and conservation may not be successful in reducing urban drainage issues, e.g. 'In some areas, returning a river to its natural state might involve removing structures such as floodwalls. This could significantly increase the risk of flooding in that area.'
- You could use specific examples in your answer, e.g. Enfield in London.
- Finish with a conclusion that sums up your points and clearly states how far you think river restoration and conservation can reduce urban drainage issues.

Page 91 — Urban Waste

1   Maximum of 9 marks available. This question is level marked.

HINTS:

- Start by outlining the different approaches to waste disposal, and stating that each has positive and/or negative environmental impacts.
- Next, discuss the environmental impacts of some of these approaches — focus on both positive and negative impacts. E.g. 'Producing items from recycled material generally uses less energy than creating them from scratch, so it results in lower emissions of greenhouse gases such as CO_2 and has less of an impact on climate. However, recycling also requires separate processing facilities and collections, which can increase emissions. This means that, although recycling still has a lower environmental impact than many other methods of waste disposal, its impacts are not entirely positive.'
- Finish with a brief conclusion, summarising the environmental impacts of each approach you have discussed.

Page 93 — Urban Environmental Issues

1   One mark for each valid point, up to a maximum of 3 marks. E.g.:

Urban dereliction can be reduced by redeveloping abandoned buildings, e.g. disused factories, for other purposes, e.g. luxury flats *[1 mark]*. This attracts new people to the area, who will spend money there, encouraging economic growth and further redevelopment *[1 mark]*. Planners can also create new parks, offices and shopping centres in derelict areas to improve the urban environment and attract more people *[1 mark]*.

Page 95 — Sustainable Urban Development

1   Maximum of 9 marks available. This question is level marked.

HINTS:

- Start by defining urban sustainability and briefly describing some of the characteristics of a sustainable city.
- Next, outline the opportunities cities offer for sustainable development, e.g. 'People are more densely concentrated in cities, so providing services such as clean water, sanitation and public transport is easier and cheaper. This can help to increase social sustainability, because people have a better quality of life, and natural sustainability, because air and water pollution is reduced.'
- Outline some of the challenges to urban sustainability, such as lack of investment, unsuitable infrastructure and rapid population growth.
- You could mention that making cities sustainable is likely to be more difficult in developing countries, because rapid and unplanned growth makes it difficult to provide services or manage environmental impacts.
- You could also bring in examples from your case studies of sustainability strategies that have been used in cities, and how well they have worked.
- Finally, sum up your points and come to a clear conclusion about the extent to which cities can be made sustainable.

Answers

Page 97 — Mumbai — Case Study

1 Maximum of 20 marks available. This question is level marked.
HINTS:
- Begin by defining urbanisation and briefly outlining some of the problems that it can cause, such as air pollution, water pollution and social and economic inequalities.
- Next, outline some of the solutions to these problems, e.g. 'Many cities have attempted to reduce the number of vehicles on the road, for example by improving public transport systems and building cycle lanes.'
- For each solution you mention, discuss how effective it has been — make sure you write about ways in which it may help to solve the problem, and ways in which it won't. E.g. 'Reliable, cheap public transport encourages people to drive less, while cycle lanes encourage them to cycle rather than drive. This helps to reduce traffic congestion and air pollution. However, the cost of implementing new public transport systems may make it difficult to achieve, whilst cycle lanes are not easy to build in cities with narrow roads.'
- You should bring in some specific examples from your case studies of problems that urbanisation has caused, ways that people have tried to resolve these problems, and how effective these solutions have been. For example, you could mention plans to upgrade public transport systems in Mumbai.
- Finish by summing up your points and coming to a clear and balanced conclusion about how far you agree with the statement in the question.

Page 99 — Birmingham — Case Study

1 Maximum of 20 marks available. This question is level marked.
HINTS:
- Start by briefly outlining some of the issues that can affect urban areas — you could mention social, environmental and economic issues.
- Next, discuss some of the ways in which urban issues affect poorer communities more than richer communities. E.g. 'Some people in poorer communities may find it hard to access healthcare facilities, especially if they live in a country with limited free healthcare or if they don't have transport. This would tend to mean that health was poorer and life expectancy lower in poorer areas compared to richer ones.'
- Make any points that contradict the view that poorer communities are more affected by urban issues than richer communities. E.g. 'Some issues, such as flooding, could affect any area of a city. In richer areas, the overall economic impacts of a flood may be greater than in poorer areas.'
- Back up your points with examples from your case studies — you could write about Birmingham, Mumbai or both, e.g. 'In Birmingham, for example, average life expectancy is eight years lower for men living in the poorest communities than in the richest ones, possibly due in part to reduced access to healthcare.'
- Finish with a conclusion that summarises your points and comes to a clear, balanced conclusion about the extent to which you agree that urban issues affect poorer communities more than richer communities.

Topic Six — Changing Places

Page 101 — The Concept of Place

1 One mark for each valid point, up to a maximum of 3 marks. E.g.:
The concept of 'place' involves looking at places as more than locations — geographers look at all the things that come together to make a place what it is *[1 mark]*. This includes all the physical and human characteristics of places *[1 mark]* plus all the things that flow in and out of that place, such as people, money, resources and ideas *[1 mark]*. It also includes people's 'sense of place' — the emotional meanings places have to groups or individuals *[1 mark]*.

Page 103 — The Character of Places

1 One mark for each valid point, up to a maximum of 3 marks. E.g.:
The physical geography of a place refers to the environmental features of a place, such as altitude, aspect, soil type and rock type *[1 mark]*. It can have a direct influence on the character of a place, e.g. rock type may affect the type of landscape that forms *[1 mark]*. It can also affect other factors that influence character, e.g. abundant natural resources in an area may cause it to become characterised by mining *[1 mark]*.

Page 105 — Changing Places — Shifting Flows

1 Maximum of 9 marks available. This question is level marked.
HINTS:
- Start by briefly introducing the place you have studied. You should mention its name and location as well as a short summary of <u>either</u> its demographic and cultural characteristics <u>or</u> its economic characteristics and social inequalities, and how these characteristics have changed over time.
- You should also introduce some of the flows that have affected the place you've studied, such as flows of people, money, resources and ideas.
- Next, explain in detail the flows that have affected one set of characteristics of the place you've studied and the effect they had, e.g. if you're writing about demographic characteristics, you might say 'Flows of people in and out of places can alter their demographic characteristics, such as the age and gender structure of the population as well as the overall population size. For example, flows of younger people out of the town of Uckfield in East Sussex have been caused by high house prices in the area. As a result of these flows, the population now has a high proportion of older people.'
- Do the same for the flows that have affected the other type of characteristics (e.g. cultural).
- Finish with a conclusion that sums up your points and clearly states how the characteristics of the place you've studied have been affected by shifting flows.

Answers

Page 107 — Changing Places

1 Maximum of 9 marks available. This question is level marked.
   <u>HINTS</u>:
   - Start by briefly introducing the place you have studied. You should mention its name and location as well as a short summary of the demographic, cultural, economic and social characteristics that are relevant for answering this question.
   - You should also briefly introduce <u>either</u> the government policies <u>or</u> the decisions of MNCs <u>or</u> the impacts of international institutions that have affected the characteristics of your place, e.g. if you're writing about government policies, you could say 'In 1992 the UK government helped to fund the Hulme City Challenge Partnership, a scheme that was aimed at regenerating this run-down part of the city.'
   - Then you should write in detail about each of the ways your chosen external force has affected the characteristics of your place. You should use examples to back up every point you make, e.g. 'The Hulme City Challenge Partnership rebuilt houses, created a park, refurbished shopping areas, built an arts venue and a business park. This altered the demographic characteristics of the area as the population increased. It also affected the economic and social characteristics of Hulme, as new jobs were created, unemployment was reduced and quality of life increased for some residents.'
   - Finish by summing up your points in a brief conclusion. You need to clearly state the ways in which your chosen external force has affected the characteristics of the place you've studied.

Page 109 — Meanings and Representations of Place

1 One mark for each valid point, up to a maximum of 3 marks. E.g.:
   Quantitative representations of place can be quantified numerically and statistical analyses performed on them *[1 mark]*, for example, statistics or visual representations of statistics such as charts and graphs are quantitative *[1 mark]*. Qualitative representations of place can't be quantified numerically and may be more descriptive or creative *[1 mark]*, for example, art, poetry and photography are all qualitative and can all be used to represent place *[1 mark]*. Quantitative representations are helpful for finding out facts about places, whereas qualitative representations can be more helpful at finding out about sense of place *[1 mark]*.

Page 113 — Place Studies

1 Maximum of 20 marks available. This question is level marked.
   <u>HINTS</u>:
   - Start by introducing the place you have studied, e.g. 'Central Liverpool is located on the River Mersey estuary in north west England, and is the centre of one of the UK's major cities.'
   - Next, you should give details of the past development of the place you've studied, e.g. 'Liverpool was a major port for trading and a centre of manufacturing between the 18th and mid-20th centuries. During this time, the area grew and attracted immigrants from around the world. The docks and factories declined during the 1960s, which led to large scale deprivation. More recently though, Liverpool has attracted a lot of investment for redevelopment and was chosen as the European Capital of Culture in 2008.'
   - Next, you need to use examples to show the extent to which people's lived experience of the place today is affected by its past development, e.g. 'In 2007 a poem called the Liverpool Saga was created to celebrate the 800th birthday of the city. This poem was written by a broad range of people living in the city today, so it reflects a mix of the different lived experiences of Liverpool. One of the lines, "Eight hundred different cultures, eight hundred different tongues" reveals that today Liverpool is a place of many different cultures where many different languages are spoken. This is a result of the large scale immigration to the city from its industrial past, and shows a direct link between the lived experience of the city today, and its past development.'
   - You need to make sure you draw on a mix of quantitative and qualitative sources to show people's lived experience of your place.
   - Finish with a conclusion that sums up your points and clearly states the extent to which people's lived experience of the place you have studied is affected by the past development of that place.

Acknowledgements

Photograph of Dune landscape in Rub al-Khali, Africa on cover: KARIM SAHIB/AFP/Getty Images.

Map of Eden basin on page 18: contains OS data © Crown copyright and database right 2016.

Rainfall data for hydrograph on page 19 © Crown Copyright, the Met Office 2017. Contains public sector information licensed under the Open Government Licence v3.0 - http://www.nationalarchives.gov.uk/doc/open-government-licence/version/3/

River level data for hydrograph on page 19: licensed under the Open Government Licence v3.0. http://www.nationalarchives.gov.uk/doc/open-government-licence/version/3/

*Photographs on **p.24** (Lannacombe Bay) © Philip Halling/ **p.24** (Loch Bracadale) © Richard Dorrell/ **p.25** (Slapton Sands) © Derek Harper/ **p.25** (St Ninian's Isle) © Colin Smith/ **p.32** (wave-cut platforms) © David Pickersgill/ **p.32** (beach near Bridlington) © Christine Johnstone/ **p.32** (sand dunes near Spurn Head) © Hugh Venables/ **p.32** (slumps at Atwick Sands) © Ian S./ **p.32** (aerial photo of Spurn Head) © Chris/ **p.33** (riprap at Withernsea) © Peter Church/ **p.43** (erratic) © Val Vannet/ **p.43** (Striding Edge) © Alan O'Dowd/ **p.44** (Glen Bhaltois) © Marc Calhoun/ **p.47** (terracettes below Morgan's Hill) © Mick Garratt/ **p.48** (Nant Ffrancon) © Meirion/ **p.48** (Devil's Kitchen from Llyn Idwal) © Dudley Smith/ **p.49** (Llyn Ogwen) © John Smith/ **p.49** (Llyn Idwal from below the Devil's Kitchen) © Kenneth Yarham/ **p.49** (cliff erosion) © Eric Jones/ **p.49** (Snowdon Horseshoe, Castell y Gwynt and Glyder Fawr) © Ivan Hall/ **p.77** (London skyline) © Christine Matthews/ **p.92** (Wolfson Research Institute) © Andy Waddington. Licensed for re-use under the Creative Commons Attribution-Share Alike 2.0 Generic Licence. https://creativecommons.org/licenses/by-sa/2.0/*

Landsat imagery on pages 26 and 47 courtesy USGS/NASA Landsat.

Data for graph of global temperature change on page 28: NASA's Goddard Institute for Space Studies (GISS). © NASA/GISS.

Graph of sea level changes on page 28: Figure SPM.9 from IPCC, 2013: Summary for Policymakers. In: Climate Change 2013: The Physical Science Basis. Working Group I Contribution to the Fifth Assessment Report of the Intergovernmental Panel on Climate Change [Stocker,T.F., D.Qin, G.-K. Plattner, M.Tignor, S.K.Allen, J.Boschung, A.Nauels, Y.Xia, V.Bex and P.M. Midgley (eds.)]. Cambridge University Press, Cambridge, UK and New York, USA.

Diagram of Antarctic isotherm on page 37 reproduced from 'Fundamentals of the Physical Environment' by Peter Smithson, Ken Addison and Ken Atkinson, Third Edition, June 2002, Chapter 24, Polar Environments, Fig. 24.2. © 2007, Routledge, member of the Taylor & Francis Group

Map showing global distribution of cold environments at the last glacial maximum on page 37: licensed for re-use under the Creative Commons Attribution-Share Alike 3.0 Generic Licence. https://creativecommons.org/licenses/by-sa/3.0/

Data used in graphs showing changes in glacier length on page 39 © Leclercq, P. W., Oerlemans, J., Basagic, H. J., Bushueva, I., Cook, A. J., and Le Bris, R.: A data set of worldwide glacier length fluctuations, The Cryosphere, 8, 659-672, doi:10.5194/ tc-8-659-2014, 2014. Licensed for re-use under the Creative Commons Attribution 3.0 License.

Image on page 46 (melting pingo and ice wedge): Wikimedia Commons by Emma Pike.

Photograph of solifluction lobes on p.46: © National Oceanic and Atmospheric Administration/Department of Commerce, photographer Dr. John Cloud, NOAA Central Library, Historian.

Maps of Nant Ffrancon and NW Snowdonia on page 48: contain OS data © Crown copyright and database right 2017

Photograph of rollagons on page 53 by Alaska DOT&PF. Licensed for re-use under the Creative Commons Attribution-Share Alike 2.0 Generic Licence. https://creativecommons.org/licenses/by/2.0/

Park Model on page 55: © Chris Park

Waste statistics on page 90 contain data from Hoornweg, Daniel; Bhada-Tata, Perinaz. 2012. What a Waste: A Global Review of Solid Waste Management. Urban development series; knowledge papers no. 15. World Bank, Washington, DC. © World Bank. https://openknowledge.worldbank.org/handle/10986/17388 License: CC BY 3.0 IGO.

Data relating to waste in Singapore on page 91 contains information from Waste Management accessed March 2017 from http://www.nea.gov.sg/energy-waste/waste-management/waste-management which is made available under the terms of the Singapore Open Data Licence version 1.0. https://data.gov.sg/open-data-licence

Data on pages 93, 103, 111, 112 contains ONS data. www.ons.gov.uk licensed under the Open Government Licence v3.0. http://nationalarchives.gov.uk/doc/open-government-licence/version/3/

Population pyramid and total population of Lerwick on page 111: © Crown copyright. Data supplied by National Records of Scotland licensed under the Open Government Licence v3.0. http://www.nationalarchives.gov.uk/doc/open-government-licence/version/3/

Crime rate in Shetland on page 112: Police Scotland.

Map of Helvellyn and Glenridding on page 117: contains OS data © Crown copyright and database right 2017.

Photograph of cattle grazing in Costa Rica on page 118: WILLIAM ERWIN/SCIENCE PHOTO LIBRARY.

Data used to construct graph of urbanisation in Ireland and Botswana on page 118 from The World Bank: World Development Indicators.

Statistics on Hartcliffe and Clifton on page 119: Source: Office for National Statistics licensed under the Open Government Licence v3.0. http://www.nationalarchives.gov.uk/doc/open-government-licence/version/3/

Data used to construct graph of world population on page 122 from World Population Prospects: 2008 Population Database © United Nations, 2009.

Index

Index

Index

Index